INTRODUCTION TO
PHYSICAL STATISTICS

WORKS OF
ROBERT BRUCE LINDSAY

GENERAL PHYSICS
    534 *pages.* 265 *illustrations.* 6 *by* 9. *Cloth.*

PHYSICAL STATISTICS
    306 *pages.* 17 *illustrations.* 5⅞ *by* 9. *Cloth.*

BY ROBERT BRUCE LINDSAY
AND HENRY MARGENAU

FOUNDATIONS OF PHYSICS
    537 *pages.* 29 *illustrations.* 5⅞ *by* 9. *Cloth.*

INTRODUCTION TO
PHYSICAL STATISTICS

BY

ROBERT BRUCE LINDSAY

Hazard Professor of Physics
in Brown University

NEW YORK

JOHN WILEY & SONS, Inc.

London: CHAPMAN & HALL, Limited

1941

PRINTED IN U. S. A.

PREFACE

The growing importance of the statistical method in physics is amply attested by the recent publication of several elaborate treatises emphasizing in their titles the words statistical mechanics. There have also lately appeared a number of other books containing detailed application of statistics to the properties of matter in the solid, liquid, and gaseous states. Most of these, though very useful to the specialist, are likely to appear rather formidable to the student who is just embarking on graduate study and who wishes a thorough but not too lengthy introduction to the method of statistical physics. The author has tried to provide this in the present work, which is intended for readers equipped with an introductory background in theoretical physics.

In this book the attempt has been made to survey as thoroughly as possible the various ways in which statistical reasoning has been used in physics from the classical applications to fluctuation phenomena, kinetic theory, and statistical mechanics to the contemporary quantum mechanical statistics. Emphasis has been laid on methodology. The author has taken the point of view that the greater the number of vantage points from which the subject is examined the deeper will be the student's understanding. For this reason no attempt has been made to provide a strictly unified treatment which would appear to be more logical to many. At the same time, however, particular effort has been exercised to relate the various statistical methods in order that the reader will see their similarities as well as their differences. A glance at the table of contents will show that specific applications have not been neglected, and there are numerous problems to test the reader's grasp of the subject.

It is appropriate for the author to acknowledge in the preface his indebtedness to those who have given help or encouragement. Such acknowledgment is usually confined to professional colleagues or the writings of the masters. Too seldom is attention paid to the contribution of the author's students, whose thorough and patient study of the various stages of organization of the book leads to gradual improvement in the correctness and clarity of presentation. The

v

author feels that he owes a definite debt of gratitude to the graduate students at Brown University who during the past few years have taken the course on which the book has been based. Particular acknowledgment is due to Mr. J. A. Rich for help with the diagrams and the proof.

R. B. L.

June, 1941.

CONTENTS

CHAPTER I

DYNAMICAL AND STATISTICAL THEORIES

CHAPTER II

ELEMENTARY PROBABILITY AND STATISTICS

CHAPTER III

REVIEW OF THERMODYNAMICS

CHAPTER IV

CLASSICAL MAXWELL–BOLTZMANN STATISTICS

CHAPTER VIII

FUNDAMENTALS OF QUANTUM STATISTICS

CHAPTER IX

SPECIFIC HEATS OF GASES AND SOLIDS

CHAPTER X

QUANTUM STATISTICAL THEORY OF ELECTRICAL AND THERMAL PROPERTIES OF METALS

CHAPTER XI

EMISSION OF ELECTRONS FROM SURFACES

CHAPTER I

DYNAMICAL AND STATISTICAL THEORIES

1. THE METHOD OF PHYSICS

Physics is an attempt to describe a certain portion of human experience. From the totality of sense perceptions, the physicist abstracts certain ones for special study and by observation and experiment develops a body of propositions called *physical facts*. He then proceeds to construct on the basis of these facts certain *concepts* which are defined in terms of the more primitive ideas. Such, for example, are the kinematical concepts of mechanics: displacement, velocity, acceleration. These concepts are expressed in symbolic form so that they are amenable to the usual processes of mathematical manipulation. Next, with experience as a guide and usually also with liberal use of the imagination, certain relations, appropriate to a given set of phenomena, are postulated among the concept symbols. These with the concepts themselves form the *hypotheses* of the physical *theory* which is supposed to be the ultimate physical description of the phenomena. From these postulated relations, usually in the form of differential equations, can be derived by mathematical analysis the laboratory equations which are called *physical laws*.

Physical laws are equations containing quantities which have a direct operational significance in the laboratory and to which numbers can be assigned by experiment. Hence these laws are susceptible of experimental test. If they meet this test successfully the theory from which they have been deduced is to that extent successful and a valuable element of physical description. This does not mean, however, that the theory is thereby proved to be *true*. In the first place there may be quite another theory operating with different concepts and different hypotheses which yields the same laws; in the second place the attempt to extend the theory to include just *one* additional bit of experience may fail of verification. It is much safer therefore to say of a physical theory that it is successful or unsuccessful: the successful theory is one which not only implies laws agreeing with already known experience but also *predicts* laws for experiments that have not yet been tried and which leads to complete verification on experiment. Such a theory adds materially to human knowledge, since it suggests experience which presumably no one had previously taken the trouble to acquire.[1]

It is clear that different kinds of physical theories can be constructed. The above remarks suggest that in any comparison of these we should then consider the following elements: (1) the fundamental concepts, (2) the postulated relations or basic hypotheses, and (3) the types of physical laws resulting from (2). On this basis we shall now try to compare two different theoretical structures of importance, viz., the *dynamical* and the *statistical*.

2. THE NATURE OF A DYNAMICAL THEORY

The theory of dynamics or mechanics, as it is often called, has had remarkable success in describing a wide variety of natural phenomena. It is the oldest of physical theories and its concepts, hypotheses, and laws have been so thoroughly studied that they have acquired an air of familiarity not shared by those of any other theory. This does not mean that the structure of dynamical theory is less abstract than that of electromagnetic theory, for example, but merely that we have got so used to thinking in terms of mechanics that we no longer feel the abstractness. Its essential aim is to describe first, all the observed motions of bodies and second, the physical phenomena in which motion is not actually observed, in terms of the motions of invisible bodies. The fundamental dynamical concept is the material particle[2] which is assumed to have position without extension, the property of inertia whose measure is mass, and certain relations with respect to other particles, e.g., gravitation. The concepts of displacement, velocity, and acceleration of a material particle are constructed using the primitive notions of space and time. Certain hypotheses are then introduced, forming the content of what are commonly known as the "laws" of motion, e.g., $\mathbf{F} = ma$. These might better be called the "principles" of mechanical theory, since from them by suitable manipulation the laws, i.e., the laboratory equations containing time and distance, etc., which describe the actual motions of particles, can be derived.

Now classical mechanics, constructed in this way, has been very

---

[1] This statement of the method of physics is a highly compressed treatment which naturally does not pretend to do justice to the profundity of the theme. For a more elaborate statement the reader is referred to Lindsay and Margenau, "Foundations of Physics," Chapter I, John Wiley & Sons, New York, 1936.

[2] Cf., *op. cit.*, Chapter III for an extensive exposition of the fundamentals of mechanics which are here given only in abbreviated form.

successful in dealing with the motion of a single particle in a fixed reference system, of two particles moving subject to their mutual interaction (a much more practical situation, of course, than the highly idealized isolated particle), and of a large number of particles which are rigidly connected so that they exhibit no relative motion (rigid dynamics). Classical mechanics has also proved itself adequate to describe the motion of ideally continuous aggregates of particles such as fluids (hydrodynamics). But it is important to recognize that the general problem of the motion of a large number of discrete particles subject to the action of arbitrary forces cannot be completely solved by classical dynamics. It is true that much can be learned about the motion from the well-known deductions from dynamical principles: the laws of the conservation of mechanical energy and momentum. The complete solution would imply that, given the initial conditions (the initial position and initial velocity of every particle) the position and velocity of every particle are determinable for all time. Even if the solution of the problem could be given it would be useless for a very large number of particles, because of our inability to assign the initial conditions. Suppose, for example, that we are trying to describe the behavior of a gas on the assumption that it consists of a very large number of tiny particles which move under the action of their mutual forces in accordance with the principles of mechanics. It turns out that the number of particles (molecules) per cubic centimeter of the gas has to be so large that it is completely hopeless to try to specify position and velocity for all of them at any one instant. It then appears that the dynamical method suffers here a serious check.

In a situation of this kind the physicist does not give up in despair. He looks around for possible ways out. Two at least would appear to be available. In the first place one could decide to replace the large number of discrete particles by an ideal continuum and apply mechanical principles to this. Unfortunately it appears that while, in following this course, we are able to describe certain properties of the gas, there are other very important ones which elude this mode of attack. Therefore we fix our attention on the alternative procedure, which is simply to forego exact information about individual particles and to allow our questions to concern merely the *average* number of particles which have a certain range of properties at a given instant. When we do this we are departing from strict dynamical theory and are introducing a method which has received the name *statistical*.

3. THE NATURE OF A STATISTICAL THEORY

We have now to try to make clear how a statistical theory differs basically from a dynamical theory in physics. To some persons this may well appear a futile task, for it will be asked, how can one understand a new theoretical point of view until he has studied all its details? The answer is that unless he is given some idea about it and its relations to things otherwise familiar he may not wish to study it at all; at any rate he will not study it with the same appreciation. People have a certain curiosity to know something about what they are getting into when they begin to learn a new discipline. Without laying claim to any particular profundity, in this section we shall go a little way toward satisfying this curiosity.

At first thought it might seem that the difference between a statistical theory and a dynamical theory is not so very great, at any rate in the case we have above described, viz., the motion of a very large number of particles. The fundamental concepts used are those of classical mechanics, i.e., velocity, acceleration, force, mass, energy, etc. Moreover, the principles of mechanics are employed as fundamental assumptions, but the kinds of laws derived are not those of classical dynamical systems, and we have to look closely to find just where the difference lies. In the first place the statistical laws tell us nothing about any particular individual particle; they are entirely concerned with *numbers* of particles which have certain properties, e.g., position in space, velocity, momentum, energy, at a given instant. Moreover they do not even pretend to tell us the precise number of particles in any case, but only an *average* number, from which there will in general be fluctuations. The idea of an average quantity is not foreign to classical dynamics, where we often find it useful to speak about the average velocity of a particle, or the average kinetic energy of a simple harmonic oscillator, for example. In classical dynamics, however, we never speak of the average *number* of particles in a given state; this is a definite criterion distinguishing between the two modes of description, even though the same fundamental concepts occur in both.

Moreover, even though both classical dynamics and statistical physics employ averages their significance is quite different; when in dynamics we employ averages over time it is merely a matter of convenience and not because we cannot compute the precise values of the quantities in question at any instant. One of the fundamental characteristics of mechanical laws is that once the boundary and initial conditions have been inserted, they predict precisely the values of all the variables involved at any instant. Dynamics implies *absolute determinism* for any physical system. This is well illustrated, in celestial mechanics, wherein from a few observations the path of a planet or even a comet can be computed with great accuracy. Now things are quite otherwise in a statistical theory. Here the average is employed because there is no possibility within reason of predicting an exact value. Hence by the very use of such averages, we forego precise determinism. It must be clearly understood that in this renunciation we do not deny that there may be determinism in the system which we are studying, e.g., in a gas, the number of molecules in a given element of volume may actually be uniquely determined as a function of the time. However, the effort to follow through the precise variation with time may be so great as to become unreasonable; it may defeat its own ends by rendering physical description too complicated to be worth while. Rather than be balked by this unhappy situation we decide to get along with average numbers over appropriate periods of time. We do not worry if the actual number at any instant within such a volume interval differs from the average, as long as experimental observations indicate that this difference does not become too large or persist for too long a time.

The reader who has followed the above paragraph closely will undoubtedly be inclined to ask why the statistical theory is effectively any less deterministic than the dynamical theory if we can calculate average numbers precisely and get agreement with experiment. Is not that all that can be expected of a theory? The answer to this question evidently involves the way in which the averages are calculated. As we have emphasized, when we compute the average of a quantity in classical mechanics, we know the value at every instant of time or every point in space as the case may be; the calculation of the average is a mere matter of convenience. In the problems treated by the statistical method we do not know the instantaneous values of the important quantities, and so the question at once arises: how do we propose to calculate their averages? To answer this query fully is indeed the function of a book on physical statistics. However, we can at least say here that the calculation of statistical averages is based fundamentally on the concept of *probability*, a concept which seems to have by no means so clear a meaning as the concepts of mechanics, for example, but of which nevertheless we all feel we have an intuitive grasp. This notion is foreign to dynamical theory, though it enters into every element of experience including the most precise of physical experiments, where it is reflected in our treatment of the variations in the successive measured values of the same quantity, i.e., the theory of errors. To this extent dynamical theory is a highly idealized model since it neglects a very significant feature of experience. On the other hand the human urge to believe in causality has hitherto placed a high premium on the value of a deterministic theory. This is a good illustration of the competition in the construction of concepts which is constantly at work in the human mind in its attempts to describe experience. There are elements in experience which make us feel that determinism is the correct point of view in physics and incline us toward dynamics; there is also much experience which emphasizes the importance of *chance*. This inclines us toward the type of theory which openly employs chance; statistics is a theory of this kind.

There is still another difference between dynamical and statistical theories. This is the distinction between *reversible* and *irreversible* processes. Let us consider a very simple example, namely a particle which moves with constant acceleration a along the x axis. We assume the initial conditions $x = 0$, $\dot{x} = 0$ at $t = 0$ (NOTE: the dot notation is used to indicate differentiation with respect to the time). Suppose the particle reaches the position $x = x_1$ at time $t = t_1$, where $x_1 = at_1^2/2$, in the usual way. Now suppose that at $t = t_1$ the existent velocity $\dot{x}_1 = at_1$ is reversed. What happens? We now have the new initial conditions $x = x_1$, $\dot{x} = -at_1$, whence at the end of a second time interval of magnitude t_1, the distance of the particle from the origin becomes $x = x_1 - at_1^2 + at_1^2/2$. But from $x_1 = at_1^2/2$ it follows that $x = 0$. Also the final velocity at the end of the second time interval is $\dot{x} = -at_1 + at_1 = 0$. This means that the motion of the particle has completely reversed itself. By the mere reversal of the velocity we have brought the particle from the state it had reached at time t_1 back to the original state from which it started. We could have achieved the same result by changing the sign of the time $t = t_1$ and allowing the t parameter to go from $-t_1$ to zero. It is seen that this is mathematically equivalent to reversing the velocity. In any case we have here an example of a reversible motion or process, i.e., one which by suitable manipulation of the parameters can be made to reverse itself and proceed back through all its successive previous states to the initial state, without at the same time changing the state of any other physical system. It is a comparatively simple matter to prove[3] that strictly dynamical systems undergo reversible processes only.

Now let us consider a somewhat different illustration. We suppose that the particle just discussed moves along the x axis under

[3] For a short demonstration see *op. cit.*, p. 195.

the action of a constant force, but that in addition its motion is resisted by a force varying directly as its velocity, or in general of such a character that it always opposes motion; in short, we suppose that a *frictional* force acts on the particle. If now we carry out the same sort of process indicated above, it will be found that the motion does not reverse itself as before; the particle does not return to its original position and velocity after time t_1 if the velocity is reversed at $t = t_1$ when $x = x_1$. In fact a simple calculation (left for the reader to perform) shows that the particle always falls short of reaching its initial position under these conditions. This is an illustration of an irreversible process, or one which can not be annulled simply by reversing some of the parameters of the system in question without disturbing or changing in any way the environment. Thus, in the example just described the only way to get the particle back to its initial state in the time interval t_1 after the reversal of the velocity at $x = x_1$ at time $t = t_1$, will be for some outside influence to compensate for the dissipative effect of the friction.

The distinction between reversible and irreversible processes is of fundamental theoretical significance. Owing to the prevalence of frictional forces, it is clear that irreversible processes are actually the rule in nature. The question then arises: Why do we use the concept of reversible process at all? The answer is that this type of process is associated with the dynamical method of description as the above illustration (first case) has just showed. However, the further question will immediately be asked: Did we not effectively give a dynamical description of the irreversible process also and does this not mean that both reversible and irreversible processes can be described by dynamics? It will be noticed, however, that the solution of the second problem was rather artificial since we assumed a frictional force proportional to the velocity without in any way seeking to understand the nature of the frictional force more closely. Hence although it is true that classical dynamics can handle some kinds of irreversible processes, it is only in a rather formal way and difficulties are encountered as soon as a more thoroughgoing treatment is contemplated. We can put the matter thus: if we leave out of dynamics forces varying as some odd power of the velocity, classical dynamics describes only reversible processes. By formal generalization one can make dynamics describe certain irreversible processes, namely, those in which small frictional dissipation enters. The essential reason for this is that, although friction is always present in natural motions, by suitable manipulation we can make it so small as to have a negligible effect over a period of time which is of interest to us. Thus consider as an example a simple pendulum swinging in air. The simple dynamical theory of the motion describes it as periodic, so that once started the pendulum swings indefinitely with a characteristic frequency and the same amplitude with which it started. Actually it is not observed to do this; each swing is a bit smaller than the previous one and the motion gradually comes to rest. If, however, the motion takes place in a region from which some of the air has been removed, the dissipative effect is observed to be much less and the pendulum takes a much longer time to come to rest. We therefore feel that in the limit of *no* frictional resistance the motion would be completely periodic and hence reversible. Actually even in motion in air if we are content to restrict ourselves to a time interval which does not exceed too many periods of the motion, the dissipation can be neglected and the dynamical treatment is for many purposes satisfactory. It comes down to this: for the sake of what we call *simplicity* we use the dynamical theory with its concomitant reversibility when it leads to approximately correct agreement with experiment, i.e., in which the irreversibility can be neglected in the ideal limit.

Now there are phenomena in nature which appear to be so fundamentally irreversible that in no ideal limit can we consider them as reversible. Such is the *flow of heat*. It is an experimental fact that heat is always observed to flow from a body of higher temperature to one of lower temperature as long as no outside influence is imposed. If this process were reversible it should be possible, without in any way disturbing the state of other bodies but merely by reversing the sign of some parameter connected with the flow, to make the flow proceed in the other direction. Actually there appears no way of doing this: to make heat flow from a low temperature to a higher temperature requires external work (as in a refrigerator). Hence the process is not reversible.

Is there anything inherent in the statistical point of view which renders it particularly fitted for the description of systems undergoing irreversible processes? The answer is yes, for we have seen that the method of statistics uses average distributions of particles with respect to certain properties. It calculates these averages by the use of probabilities and the natural assumption is that those distributions will actually be realized which have the highest probability. Hence there will be a tendency for distributions to change in the direction of increasing probability. This change is evidently a one-way process and by nature irreversible. To be sure, there is involved the curious circumstance that, since we have only proba-

bility considerations to guide us, there will always be a finite probability of any process going either way, e.g., in the conduction of heat,
we cannot rule out as impossible the uncompensated flow of heat from
the cooler to the warmer body. All we are allowed to say is that the
flow in the other direction is overwhelmingly more probable.[4]

4. NON-MECHANICAL STATISTICS

In the previous section we were led to the concept of a statistical
theory through a type of problem which actually employs the fundamental concepts of mechanics but in which the method of dynamics
is unable to give a complete solution. The type of statistical theory
which uses mechanical concepts is very important for physics but it
must be pointed out that it is by no means the only useful kind of
application of statistics in physics. There are some physical phenomena in which the concepts of mechanics seem to play no role at
all. An example is the phenomenon of *radioactive decay* which appears
to be best described by saying that in a special, simple case of disintegration the number of radioactive atoms disintegrating per unit time
is directly proportional to the number present. No mechanism is
provided to govern the disintegration and the treatment is purely
statistical, leading to the well-known equation

$$N = N_0 e^{-\lambda t} \tag{1}$$

giving the number of atoms undisintegrated after time t if N_0 is the
original number present. It is to be observed that nothing remotely
connects this formula with dynamics. It merely associates a *number*
with the time and does so on a probability basis, i.e., the number is
an *average*. We may well expect fluctuations from it when the experiment which it describes is repeated again and again. We must make
one more important observation: the number N must be a large
number if the formula is to have much meaning. This, of course, is
universally true of statistical formulas: they lose their significance
if the numbers entering into them are too small.

It is then clear that whether we begin with the assumption (*a*) that
all physical phenomena are ultimately describable in terms of mechanical concepts or (*b*) that some physical phenomena are not
explicable in this way, we are led to the desirability of using statistical
reasoning in physics. It is the plan of this book to indicate how this
can be done and to give many illustrations of the actual process.

---

[4] For further general discussion, *op. cit.*, pp. 196 ff., may be consulted.

PROBLEMS AND QUESTIONS

1. Prove that when a force varying directly with the velocity acts on a particle subject otherwise to a constant force, irreversible motion results.

2. Make a list of irreversible processes in physics and indicate which of them can be replaced effectively by ideal reversible processes. Discuss some of these processes in detail.

3. Prove by the use of Hamilton's principle (cf. eq. 8 of Chapter VI) that all conservative dynamical systems undergo reversible processes only.

4. A particle falls under the influence of gravity through a medium which resists its motion by a force varying directly as the velocity. Show that the velocity of the particle approaches a limiting value and comment on the connection between this and the irreversibility of the motion.

5. Set up the differential equation whose solution is eq. (1) of this chapter. Give two physical interpretations of the constant λ. From the fact that N and N_0 in eq. (1) must be integers, what mathematical difficulty do you find associated with the formula? Should a physicist be greatly disturbed over this difficulty? Why?

CHAPTER II

ELEMENTARY PROBABILITY AND STATISTICS

1. A SIMPLE PROBLEM IN PHYSICAL STATISTICS

We begin our study with a definite physical problem which has some interest in itself and yet is simple enough to illustrate clearly the fundamental statistical methods we intend to develop.

Consider a single material particle which is restricted to move along a straight line, say the x axis. Suppose that in time T it makes n displacements each of length l, where $n \gg 1$. These displacements can be either in the positive or negative x direction. In fact we shall assume that a positive displacement is just as likely or probable as a negative displacement. Let us further suppose that the number of positive displacements in time T is n_1 and the number of negative displacements n_2, so that $n_1 + n_2 = n$. The distance of the particle from its starting point at time T is then

$$L = l(n_1 - n_2). \tag{1}$$

Now if we knew all the forces acting on the particle we should, of course, be able to calculate by the principles of mechanics the exact value of L. However, we are here assuming that we do not know the forces and therefore cannot use mechanics. The best we can do is to try to calculate an *average* value of L. To see the meaning of this, imagine that it is possible to carry out an experiment and observe L directly. Further suppose that the experiment can be repeated many times, very likely with differences in the values of L obtained. We could then find an average L by direct arithmetical means. However, life is too short to spend our time on such experiments. What we should like to do is to *calculate* an average L with the hope that it will agree well enough with that experimentally observed to serve as the basis for further theoretical predictions about the behavior of the particle.

As stated in Chapter I, in order to calculate an average when we do not know the detailed time-course of the phenomenon, we must have and use some probability values. This means that we must be able to compute the probability associated with each value of L.

2. ELEMENTARY PROBABILITY

It is not practicable in this book to explore all the problems and controversies associated with the definition of probability. It is obviously a concept difficult to define logically so as to be proof against all objections that can be brought against it. Fortunately for the present purpose we can be content with the simple "frequency" viewpoint, which is essentially that of v. Mises.[1] If we consider once more the n displacements of the particle (Sec. 1) in time T, an important concept is the total number of ways in which the n displacements can be divided into two groups, i.e., positive and negative, without any restriction on the number in each group. If there were only *one* displacement it could take place in either of *two* ways, viz., either positive or negative. If there were *two* displacements there would be *four* ways of performing them, as indicated in the following table

| First displacement | + | + | − | − |
| Second displacement | + | − | + | − |

For n displacements the number of ways in question is 2^n. This is a mere matter of counting: there are two ways of performing the first displacement, two ways for the second, $\cdots$, two ways for the nth. They are all assumed to be independent of each other, i.e., the fact that the first happens to be positive or negative entails no restriction on any of the subsequent ones. Hence the total number of ways of grouping the displacements is $2 \cdot 2 \cdot 2 \cdots$ to n factors or 2^n. Now of all these ways there will be a certain number corresponding to n_1 positive displacements and n_2 negative displacements (where $n = n_1 + n_2$). This number is very readily obtained. We can choose the first positive displacement in n ways, the second in $(n - 1)$ ways, the third in $(n - 2)$ ways, $\cdots$ and finally the n_1th in $(n - n_1 + 1)$ ways. Since these are all independent the total number of ways desired would appear to be $n(n - 1) \cdots (n - n_1 + 1)$. But many of these correspond to mere rearrangement of the n_1 positive displacements. We are not interested in the order in which the displacements occur but merely in their number and must therefore divide the above by the number of ways in which n_1 displacements can be rearranged among themselves, namely, $n_1!$. Therefore the total number

---

[1] R. v. Mises, "Wahrscheinlichkeitsrechnung," Leipzig, 1931. For a brief review of this point of view, consult "Foundations of Physics," pp. 159 ff.

of ways of dividing the n displacements into n_1 positive and n_2 negative without regard to order is

$$\binom{n}{n_1} = \frac{n(n-1)\cdots(n-n_1+1)}{n_1!}. \tag{2}$$

By multiplying numerator and denominator by $n_2!$ we can bring this into the more symmetrical form

$$\binom{n}{n_1} = \frac{n!}{n_1!\,n_2!}. \tag{2'}$$

The situation then is this: Out of 2^n ways of grouping n displacements into the two classes, positive and negative, there are $\binom{n}{n_1}$ ways for which n_1 are positive and $n - n_1 = n_2$ are negative without regard for order. The relative frequency of occurrence of the n_1, n_2 combination is therefore given by the ratio $\binom{n}{n_1}/2^n$, and we shall call this the *probability* P_{n_1} of the occurrence of such a combination. Thus

$$P_{n_1} = \frac{1}{2^n} \cdot \binom{n}{n_1} = \frac{1}{2^n} \cdot \frac{n!}{n_1!\,n_2!}. \tag{3}$$

In our problem this is the probability connected with the value $L = l(n_1 - n_2)$ for the final displacement of the particle from its initial position after time T.

The reader familiar with v. Mises' notation will see that we are assuming that the total number of ways of grouping the n displacements into the two groups forms a so-called *probability aggregate*. It is unnecessary, however, to discuss the fundamental nature of such an aggregate. We note only that the quantity P_{n_1} in (3) is always a proper fraction and that

$$\sum_{n_1=0}^{n} P_{n_1} = 1. \tag{4}$$

3. CALCULATION OF AVERAGES

We are now ready to use the results of Sec. 2 in the calculation of the average value of L. To obtain this we have merely to multiply the value of L corresponding to a particular n_1, n_2 combination by the probability associated with this combination and to sum the products so obtained over all values of n_1, namely from 0 to n. If we denote the average of L by $\bar{L}$, we have then

$$\bar{L} = \sum_{n_1=0}^{n} L_{n_1} P_{n_1} = \frac{l}{2^n} \Sigma(n_1 - n_2) \binom{n}{n_1}. \tag{5}$$

The problem now is to evaluate (5). Expanding the sum gives

$$\left(n_1 = n - n_2\right) \qquad \Sigma(n_1 - n_2)\binom{n}{n_1} = 2\,\Sigma n_1 \binom{n}{n_1} - n \cdot 2^n. \tag{6}$$

The computation of $\Sigma n_1 \binom{n}{n_1}$ is based on the fact that the quantities $\binom{n}{n_1}$ are actually the coefficients in the binomial expansion. From elementary algebra

$$(1 + x)^n = 1 + \binom{n}{1}x + \binom{n}{2}x^2 + \cdots + \binom{n}{n_1}x^{n_1} + \cdots + x^n$$

$$= \sum_{n_1=0}^{n} \binom{n}{n_1}x^{n_1}. \qquad x=1 \quad (1+x)^n = 2^n = \binom{n}{n_1} \tag{7}$$

If we differentiate both sides of this identity with respect to x we get

$$n\,(1 + x)^{n-1} = \sum_{n_1=0}^{n} n_1 \binom{n}{n_1} x^{n_1-1}. \tag{7'}$$

Since x is arbitrary we can set it equal to unity and have

$$\sum_{n_1=0}^{n} n_1 \binom{n}{n_1} = n \cdot 2^{n-1}, \tag{8}$$

which in connection with (5) and (6) at once leads to

$$\bar{L} = 0. \tag{9}$$

This is a not unexpected result. It means simply that on the average the number of positive displacements n_1 equals the number of negative displacements n_2 which is, of course, inherent in the initial assumption that a positive displacement is just as likely as a negative one, so that indeed we must expect $\bar{n}_1 = n/2$. Mathematically speaking, this result is trivial. We have presented the analysis mainly because of its future utility.

There will still be some interest in an average which gives some information about the *absolute* value of L.   Let us average L^2 instead of L.   Thus from (1)

$$\overline{L^2} = \frac{l^2}{2^n} \Sigma (2n_1 - n)^2 \binom{n}{n_1} = \frac{4l^2}{2^n} \Sigma n_1^2 \binom{n}{n_1} - \frac{4l^2 n}{2^n} \Sigma n_1 \binom{n}{n_1}$$

$$+ \frac{l^2 n^2}{2^n} \Sigma \binom{n}{n_1}. \qquad (10)$$

Differentiation of (7′) with respect to x yields

$$n(n-1)(1+x)^{n-2} = \Sigma n_1 (n_1 - 1)\binom{n}{n_1} x^{n_1-2},$$

whence, with $x = 1$ as before,

$$n(n-1)2^{n-2} = \Sigma n_1^2 \binom{n}{n_1} - n \cdot 2^{n-1}.$$

Then

$$\frac{4l^2}{2^n} \Sigma n_1^2 \binom{n}{n_1} = l^2 n(n+1).$$

The other terms in (10) are already known.   Hence substitution yields

$$\overline{L^2} = nl^2. \qquad (11)$$

The square root of $\overline{L^2}$, which we may call the *root-mean-square* value of L, will serve as a kind of average of L without regard to its sign. Thus

$$\sqrt{\overline{L^2}} = \sqrt{n}\, l. \qquad (12)$$

There is another interpretation of this result.   Let us compute the mean square deviation of L from its average value.   This is called in statistical parlance the *dispersion* and usually denoted by σ^2.   We then get the important general relation

$$\sigma^2 = \overline{(L - \overline{L})^2} = \overline{L^2} - 2\overline{L}^2 + \overline{L}^2 = \overline{L^2} - \overline{L}^2. \qquad (13)$$

In the special case under consideration $\overline{L} = 0$, and therefore $\sigma^2 = \overline{L^2}$. Here the mean-square value of L is simply equal to the mean-square deviation of L from its average.   The square root of σ^2, or root-mean-square deviation from the average, is usually known as the *standard deviation*.   In our problem the standard deviation is the root-mean-square of L itself.

The concepts of mean or average value, dispersion and standard deviation, are so important for statistical reasoning that we may well pause a little to discuss them further.   The idea of average, indeed, has probably been discussed enough to be reasonably clear.   If we were to make several repetitions of the experiment of observing the particle after an interval T, we should expect that some of the displacements from the origin would be positive, others negative, but the average close to zero. We have no reason to expect the average to be exactly zero, but if we found on repeated trials that the average failed to stay close to zero, we should suspect that we were overlooking some important feature of the problem and that our statistical reasoning was not applicable or at any rate not applicable in the simple form here assumed. In the standard deviation we have an additional test. The successive tries will yield values of L different from $\bar{L}$, i.e., we must expect deviations or fluctuations from the mean. However, we have just shown we can calculate an average value for these fluctuations, viz., $\sqrt{nl}$ in our problem. We should expect that the observed value of this deviation for a great many trials would not differ markedly from $\sqrt{nl}$. If it did we might suspect that something was being neglected.

Now in most applications of statistics in physics we do not and indeed cannot actually proceed to verify our fundamental assumptions quite as directly as all this. Rather we assume at the outset that the statistical method is the one appropriate for the problem and assign probabilities in what appears to be the most plausible manner. From these we calculate averages and what is more important, *relations* among these averages and parameters which by the nature of the case have fixed values. These relations are the laws (in the sense of Chapter I) which should describe the phenomena in question. We then proceed to identify the average values with the actual results of experiment and hope to find that the statistical laws we have derived really do provide an accurate description.

The fluctuations mentioned above are not to be dismissed as unimportant, for at times the theory may predict rather large ones and then experiment should certainly reveal them if the theory is applicable.

4. LAPLACE'S FORMULA

The formula (3) for the probability of the occurrence of n_1 positive displacements with n_2 negative ones in a total of $n = n_1 + n_2$ (usually called Newton's formula) is not convenient for mathematical manipulation since it contains the important number n_1 and consequently L in the form of the factorial. There is advantage in expressing the probability explicitly as an analytic function of L. This has been done in an approximation formula associated with the name of Laplace.

Let us express $\binom{n}{n_1}$ in terms of L. From $L = (n_1 - n_2)l$ and $n_1 + n_2 = n$ we have at once $n_1 = (n + L/l)/2$ and $n_2 = (n - L/l)/2$. For simplicity let $L/2l = x$. Then we can write

$$\binom{n}{n_1} = \frac{n!}{(n/2 + x)!\,(n/2 - x)!} = \frac{n!\,[(n/2)\,!]^2}{(n/2 + x)!\,(n/2 - x)!\,[(n/2)\,!]^2}$$

$$= \frac{n!\,n/2 \cdot (n/2 - 1) \cdots (n/2 - x + 1)}{[(n/2)\,!]^2 \cdot (n/2 + x) \cdot (n/2 + x - 1) \cdots (n/2 + 1)}. \qquad (14)$$

The form (14) assumes tacitly that x is positive. The form will change if x is negative but the reader can show that the same ultimate result is obtained. It is assumed, of course, that n is a very large number compared with x. Multiply both numerator and denominator by $(2/n)^x$ and get

$$\binom{n}{n_1} = \frac{n!}{[(n/2)\,!]^2} \cdot \frac{(1 - 2/n) \cdot (1 - 4/n) \cdots (1 - (2x - 2)/n)}{(1 + 2/n) \cdot (1 + 4/n) \cdots (1 + 2x/n)}. \qquad (15)$$

Under the assumption just made (15) can be written to a very close approximation

$$\binom{n}{n_1} \doteq \frac{n!}{[(n/2)\,!]^2} \cdot \frac{e^{-1/n \cdot (2+4+6+\cdots+2x-2)}}{e^{1/n \cdot (2+4+6+\cdots+2x)}}. \qquad (16)$$

Making use of the arithmetical progression formula $2 + 4 + 6 + \cdots + 2x = x^2 + x$, etc., we can finally write $\binom{n}{n_1}$ in the form

$$\binom{n}{n_1} \doteq \frac{n!}{[(n/2)\,!]^2}\, e^{-2x^2/n} = \frac{n!}{[(n/2)\,!]^2}\, e^{-L^2/2nl^2}, \qquad (17)$$

in which L is now released from the bondage of the factorial and appears in explicit form in the exponential. Equation (17) is commonly termed Laplace's formula. The function e^{-ax^2} has long been known as the Gauss probability or error function. It has the well-known form indicated in the accompanying Fig. 2·1, where we have plotted $\binom{n}{n_1}$ as a function of x. Strictly speaking Laplace's formula represents $\binom{n}{n_1}$ accurately only for $x \ll n/2$ and its value for larger values of x

might appear highly questionable. Fortunately we are usually interested in such large values of n, that for large x the value of the ordinate is very small indeed compared with its value at $x = 0$, and the *percentage* error involved in the use of the analytical formula in place of Newton's factorial formula becomes very small. This enables us to use Laplace's formula in the evaluation of averages, for which its form renders it particularly suitable. The error function is an *even* function, i.e., the value for given x is the same as for $-x$, expressing the fact that a given positive value of L is equally probable with $-L$. Moreover the maximum value occurs for $x = 0$ or $L = 0$, indicating maximum probability for the average value.

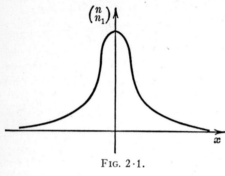

FIG. 2·1.

5. EVALUATION OF THE COEFFICIENT IN LAPLACE'S FORMULA. STIRLING'S FORMULA

Practical use of Laplace's formula (17) can be made only if the factorial coefficient $n!/[(n/2)!]^2$ is evaluated in terms of a simple function of n. This involves essentially the development of a formula for $n!$. Such a one is Stirling's formula. There are several ways of deriving this presented in books on advanced calculus. We shall give a brief derivation here as an excuse for introducing the gamma function, which will be of considerable use to us later. Thus by definition for any real positive n and z (we are here contented with real variables)

$$\Gamma(n) = \int_0^\infty z^{n-1}e^{-z}dz, \tag{18}$$

whence a partial integration gives $\Gamma(n) = (1/n)\int_0^\infty z^n e^{-z}dz$, so that $n\Gamma(n) = \Gamma(n+1)$. But since $\Gamma(1) = 1$ by direct integration, we have for integral values of n

$$\Gamma(n+1) = n!, \tag{19}$$

so that

$$n! = \int_0^\infty z^n e^{-z}dz. \tag{19'}$$

If we make the substitution $z = n + \sqrt{n}u$, taking advantage of the fact that for $z = n$ or $u = 0$ the integrand in (19') attains its maximum value,

$$n! = \sqrt{n}e^{-n}\int_{-\sqrt{n}}^{\infty} e^{n\log(n+\sqrt{n}u)-\sqrt{n}u}\, du. \qquad (20)$$

We can now write $\log(n + \sqrt{n}u) = \log n + \log(1 + \sqrt{1/n}u)$ and expand the second term in a Maclaurin series, getting $\log(1 + \sqrt{1/n}u) \doteq \sqrt{1/n}u - u^2/2n$ to terms of the second order which are sufficient for our purpose since n is assumed to be large. Substitution into (20) then yields

$$n! \doteq \sqrt{n}e^{-n}n^n\int_{-\sqrt{n}}^{\infty} e^{-u^2/2}\, du. \qquad (21)$$

Now the integral

$$\sqrt{2/\pi}\int_{x}^{\infty} e^{-u^2/2}\, du = \Phi(x) \qquad (22)$$

is known as the error function and plays an important role in the applications to follow. The particular case when $x = 0$ is important. We have [2]

$$\Phi(0) = \sqrt{2/\pi}\int_{0}^{\infty} e^{-u^2/2}\, du = 1. \qquad (23)$$

Consequently (21) becomes

$$n! \doteq \sqrt{n}e^{-n}n^n[\sqrt{2\pi} - \sqrt{\pi/2}\,\Phi(\sqrt{n})]. \qquad (24)$$

But as x increases indefinitely $\Phi(x) \to 0$. Hence, since n is assumed to be large we are justified in neglecting $\sqrt{\pi/2}\,\Phi(\sqrt{n})$ compared with $\sqrt{2\pi}$. This yields the approximation

$$n! \doteq \sqrt{2\pi n}\left(\frac{n}{e}\right)^n. \qquad (25)$$

The demonstration is not intended to be taken as mathematically rigorous. Stirling's formula is, however, a very useful and surprisingly accurate one, with a very small percentage error even for n as small as 10. The absolute error grows with n, but this is of little consequence in most physical applications.

We are now ready to apply the expression (25) to Laplace's formula (17). The result is the approximate formula

$$\binom{n}{n_1} \doteq \frac{2^{n+1}}{\sqrt{2\pi n}}e^{-L^2/2nl^2}. \qquad (26)$$

[2] Cf., for example, F. S. Woods, "Advanced Calculus," p. 153, Ginn and Company, 1934, or any similar book on the subject.

This at once shows that $\binom{n}{n_1}$ is a maximum for $n_1 = n_2 = n/2$ or $L = 0$ and decreases more or less rapidly as L increases.

It is now desirable to associate a probability not with a single definite value of n_1 or L but a finite (though small) range of values of L. We shall agree to define the probability associated with the interval L to $L + dL$ as

$$P_L d\left(\frac{L}{2l}\right) = \frac{2}{\sqrt{2\pi n}} e^{-L^2/2nl^2} \cdot d\left(\frac{L}{2l}\right). \qquad (27)$$

Since the probability is a pure number with no physical dimensions we use $d(L/2l)$ instead of dL to denote the interval. Moreover $L/2l = x$ measures the deviation of n_1 and n_2 from their mean values. In the expression (27) P_L appears as the probability associated with *unit* interval of $L/2l$ in the neighborhood of $L/2l$. The form of (27) is governed by one other criterion: if we integrate both sides with respect to the independent variable $L/2l$ and allow L to take on the limiting values $-nl$ and $+nl$ we expect to obtain the value unity since it is certain that L will be somewhere in the interval from $-nl$ to $+nl$. We thus demand that

$$\int_{-n/2}^{+n/2} P_L d\left(\frac{L}{2l}\right) = 1, \qquad (28)$$

where the limits have been changed to those of x. From (22) and (23) there results

$$\int_0^{n/2} P_L d\left(\frac{L}{2l}\right) = \tfrac{1}{2}[1 - \Phi(\sqrt{n/2})], \qquad (29)$$

and since from the even character of the integrand, the integral in (28) is double that in (29), we conclude that as n becomes very great, (28) is true if P_L is given by (27).

Equation (27) is usually known as the *normal* or *Gaussian* distribution law. It has already been emphasized that it is a good representation of the Newtonian algebraic distribution law (3) only in the range where $L/l < n$. This does not limit its usefulness as much as might be supposed, since in the region where L is large, the large exponent in the exponential function makes P_L vanishingly small in any case. This fact renders the normal distribution law very useful in the calculation of averages.

6. USE OF THE NORMAL DISTRIBUTION LAW IN THE CALCULATION OF AVERAGES

The advantage of the normal distribution (27) is that it corresponds to a continuous variation in L and therefore reduces the averaging process to a mere matter of integration.   An objection may be made that the actual distribution is *not* continuous, for L makes only discrete steps.   Nevertheless, if n is very large the difference from step to step becomes a very small fraction of the maximum L, and the variable $L/2l = x$ can be considered continuous to a sufficiently good approximation.   Indeed it is not to be expected that the normal distribution will apply to all statistical problems in physics.   We shall later meet with some in which it is an extremely poor approximation. Nevertheless here, where the probabilities of positive and negative displacements are equal, if $x \ll n$, the value of the distribution cannot be doubted.   We shall see indeed that it gives the same values of $\bar{x}$ and σ^2 as were obtained above with the algebraic formula.

Thus for the average x ($= L/2l$), the usual way of defining an average for a continuous distribution gives

$$\bar{x} = \int_{-\infty}^{+\infty} x P_L(x)dx = \frac{2}{\sqrt{2\pi n}} \int_{-\infty}^{\infty} x e^{-2x^2/n}\, dx = 0, \qquad (30)$$

where the result of the integration follows at once from the fact that $xe^{-2x^2/n}$ is an *odd* function of x.   The limits of the integration are from $-\infty$ to $+\infty$, whereas strictly speaking x is limited to the range $-n/2$ to $+n/2$.   But if n is very large the introduction of the infinite limits involves no greater error than is already present in the choice of $P_L(x)$.   We shall hereafter consistently use the infinite limits for the sake of mathematical simplicity.

The average value of the magnitude of x, i.e., $\overline{|x|}$, is

$$\overline{|x|} = \frac{4}{\sqrt{2\pi n}} \int_0^{\infty} x e^{-2x^2/n}dx = \frac{1}{\sqrt{2\pi}} \sqrt{n} = 0.399 \sqrt{n}. \qquad (31)$$

This gives

$$\overline{|L|} = 0.798 \sqrt{n}l. \qquad (31')$$

In similar fashion

$$\overline{x^2} = \frac{4}{\sqrt{2\pi n}} \int_0^{\infty} x^2 e^{-2x^2/n}\, dx = \frac{n}{4}. \qquad (32)$$

This result is in agreement with the one obtained by purely algebraic means in eq. (10). For $\overline{L^2} = 4l^2\overline{x^2} = nl^2$, leading to $\sqrt{\overline{L^2}} = l\sqrt{n}$ or

$$\sqrt{\overline{x^2}} = 0.500\sqrt{n},\tag{33}$$

which is also a measure of the standard deviation of the distribution as a function of x. It is of interest to note that whereas the values of $\overline{|x|}$ and $\sqrt{\overline{x^2}}$ actually differ in value by about 20 per cent, nevertheless they are of the same order of magnitude. If they had proved to be of quite different orders of magnitude, we might well have had our doubts about the value of the distribution law. It is natural to inquire about the averages of higher order, e.g., $\sqrt[4]{\overline{x^4}}$. We see at once that the odd power averages all vanish for the same reason that $\bar{x} = 0$. The reader may show that for k even

$$\sqrt[k]{\overline{x^k}} = [1 \cdot 3 \cdot 5 \cdots (k-1)]^{1/k} \frac{\sqrt{n}}{2}.\tag{34}$$

The significance of this result is that all the averages are multiples of $\sqrt{n}$ with coefficients slowly increasing with k. The root-mean-square average is, of course, the most useful one in statistical problems.

There is, to be sure, another type of average somewhat different from those just considered. This is the arbitrarily termed "probable" average. It is the value of x, usually denoted by x_P, such that there are just as many cases in which x exceeds this in absolute value as there are cases in which x is less than this in absolute value. This is equivalent to saying that the ordinate for $|x_P|$ divides the area under the probability curve (Fig. 2·1) to the right of the origin into two parts. This area has however the numerical value $\frac{1}{2}$. Consequently

$$\frac{2}{\sqrt{2\pi n}} \int_0^{x_P} e^{-2x^2/n}\, dx = \frac{1}{4}.$$

By consulting the table of values of the probability function $\Phi(x)$, we find that this requirement can be uniquely satisfied by

$$x_P = 0.338\sqrt{n},\tag{35}$$

approximately. We note the agreement in order of magnitude with $\overline{|x|}$ and $\sqrt{\overline{x^2}}$. Placed in order, $x_P < \overline{|x|} < \sqrt{\overline{x^2}}$.

An important measure of the significance of these average values is found in the probability that the value of the deviation x shall not exceed them. The probability that x shall not exceed the value x_0 in absolute magnitude will be written

$$P(x_0) = \frac{4}{\sqrt{2\pi n}} \int_0^{x_0} e^{-2x^2/n}\, dx.\tag{36}$$

For $x_0 = x_P$, $P(x_P) = \frac{1}{2}$ by definition. More generally, from the definition of the error function $\Phi(x)$ in eq. (22),

$$P(x_0) = 1 - \Phi\left(\frac{2x_0}{\sqrt{n}}\right). \tag{37}$$

Thus $P(\overline{|x|}) = 1 - \Phi(0.798) = 0.576$, while $P(\sqrt{\overline{x^2}}) = 1 - \Phi(1) = 0.683$. We can express this as follows: On the average there are 576 chances in 1,000 that a deviation or fluctuation will turn up which is equal to or less than, i.e., not exceeding $\overline{|x|}$, while there are 683 chances in 1,000 that the deviation x shall not exceed $\sqrt{\overline{x^2}}$. There are 500 chances in 1,000 that x shall not be greater than x_P. The probability rises with the magnitude of the average.

7. UNEQUAL A PRIORI PROBABILITIES

The physical problem so far treated in this chapter is a rather idealized one, though a somewhat more general case of it occurs in the so-called Brownian movement of small colloidal particles suspended in a liquid or a gas. This we shall discuss later in some detail. One of the fundamental idealizations in the problem is the assumption that a *positive* displacement of length l is just as likely as a *negative* displacement. There are few problems in physical statistics in which a simple assumption of this kind can be made with any success. Therefore, although the mathematical developments we have carried out are fundamental, they are not all immediately applicable to actual physical situations. It should indeed be mentioned that interesting illustrations of the formulas of the preceding sections may be found in the simple physical experiment of coin tossing. This can be made formally analogous to the physical problem of Sec. 1 merely by associating heads with a positive displacement of the particle and tails with a negative displacement. The problems at the end of this chapter show how well our theoretical expressions agree with experience of this kind.

Now, however, a generalization is in order. We shall assume that the two types of displacement are not equally likely but that the *a priori* probability of a positive displacement is p/q times that of a negative displacement, where p and q are positive proper fractions with the property that $p + q = 1$. The term *a priori* demands careful consideration. Two possibilities are at hand: (a) we may have observed by direct experiment that the fraction p/q represents the relative frequency. In most physical problems this course is not open and hence we must use the other possibility: (b) assume the ratio from the best information we have about the system in question.

The problem of the preceding sections corresponds to $p = q = \frac{1}{2}$. We now desire to derive the more general formulas. Again consider n displacements divided into two groups, i.e., n_1 positive and n_2 negative, with $n_1 + n_2 = n$. If the probability of a positive displacement is p, the probability of n_1 positive displacements independent of any negative displacements will be p^{n_1}. The negative displacements behave similarly. Hence the probability of a combination of n_1 positive displacements with n_2 negative displacements, if there were only one way of realizing it, would clearly be $p^{n_1}q^{n_2}$. However, we have already seen that there are $\binom{n}{n_1}$ ways of realizing this distribution. Consequently the actual probability corresponding to this combination is

$$P_{n_1} = \binom{n}{n_1} p^{n_1}q^{n_2}. \tag{38}$$

The calculation of the average displacement $\overline{L}$ in this case proceeds thus:

$$\overline{L} = \sum_{n_1=0}^{n} L_{n_1} P_{n_1}$$

$$= 2l \, \Sigma n_1 \binom{n}{n_1} p^{n_1}q^{n_2} - nl \, \Sigma \binom{n}{n_1} p^{n_1}q^{n_2}. \tag{39}$$

Since $\Sigma P_{n_1} = 1$ the second term in (39) reduces to nl. Now write

$$(q + px)^n = \sum_{n_1=0}^{n} \binom{n}{n_1} p^{n_1}q^{n_2}x^{n_1}. \tag{40}$$

By differentiating both sides with respect to x, we get (after letting the parameter $x = 1$)

$$np = \sum_{n_1=0}^{n} n_1 \binom{n}{n_1} p^{n_1}q^{n_2}. \tag{41}$$

Therefore substitution into (39) gives

$$\overline{L} = n(p - q)l. \tag{42}$$

We could indeed have computed n_1 and n_2 directly and have found by the above method $\overline{n_1} = np$ and $\overline{n_2} = nq$, so that $\overline{L} = (\overline{n_1} - \overline{n_2})l = n(p - q)l$. We see that the general result (42) agrees with the special formula (9) when $p = q = \frac{1}{2}$, giving $\overline{L} = 0$. However, for $p \neq q$,

$\overline{L} \neq 0$. In particular, for $p \gg q$, we get approximately $\overline{L} = npl$ or practically nl.

The calculation of the mean-square displacement $\overline{L^2}$ follows in similar fashion with the result

$$\overline{L^2} = nl^2[4pq + n(p - q)^2]. \qquad (43)$$

In the special case where $p = q = \frac{1}{2}$, this reduces to the previously obtained value (11). More interesting perhaps is the dispersion $\sigma^2 = \overline{L^2} - \overline{L}^2$. This becomes

$$\sigma^2 = 4npql^2. \qquad (44)$$

The corresponding dispersion in $x = L/2l$ is clearly

$$\sigma_x^2 = npq, \qquad (45)$$

with the standard deviation

$$\sigma_x = \sqrt{npq}. \qquad (46)$$

8. GENERALIZED LAPLACE'S FORMULA

We now wish to find the more general Gaussian distribution formula for the case where $p \neq q$. For this we shall express P in terms of the deviation of n_1 from its average np. This deviation will be denoted by u, so that $n_1 = np + u$, and $n_2 = nq - u$. The problem is then to obtain an expression for (38), viz.,

$$P = \frac{n!}{(np + u)! \, (nq - u)!} \cdot p^{np+u} q^{nq-u}, \qquad (47)$$

in which the quantity u is freed from the bondage of the factorial. For the sake of variety we proceed somewhat differently than in Sec. 4. Taking the logarithm of P, we obtain

$$\log P = \log n! - \log(np + u)! - \log(nq - u)!$$
$$+ (np + u) \log p + (nq - u) \log q. \qquad (48)$$

Next we suppose that the factorials are all large enough so that we can apply Stirling's formula in the form (cf. eq. 25).

$$\log n! = n \log n - n + \tfrac{1}{2} \log 2\pi n. \qquad (49)$$

We also take advantage of the expansion for the $\log (1 + x)$ where $x \ll 1$ (satisfied, e.g., by u/nq and u/np), viz.,

$$\log (1 + x) = x - \tfrac{1}{2}x^2 + \cdots. \qquad (50)$$

The expansion of (48) using (49) and (50) though a little lengthy is perfectly straightforward and need not be set down here in full. After collection of terms we get

$$\log P = -\frac{u^2}{2npq} + \log \frac{1}{\sqrt{2\pi npq}} + \frac{u(p-q)}{2npq} + \frac{1}{4}\frac{u^2}{n^2p^2} + \frac{1}{4}\frac{u^2}{n^2q^2},$$

neglecting powers of u higher than the second. Examination discloses that the first term on the right is of greater order of magnitude than the third, fourth, and fifth. Consequently if we wish to keep only the highest order term in u, the result will be

$$P = \frac{1}{\sqrt{2\pi npq}} e^{-u^2/2npq}. \tag{51}$$

This is the generalized form of Laplace's formula. It represents the normal or Gaussian distribution for the deviation of n_1 and n_2 from their average values, np and nq, respectively. For $p = q = \frac{1}{2}$, (51) naturally reduces to (27). It must be emphasized that (51) holds only for u small compared with np and nq.

9. VOLUME DISTRIBUTION OF GAS MOLECULES. FLUCTUATIONS

It will now be of interest to apply the analysis developed in the preceding sections to a somewhat more practical problem than that discussed in Sec. 1. We shall consider an ideal gas, which we shall assume to be composed of molecules in accordance with the elementary kinetic theory. In a volume V of gas, in a closed space containing N identical and indistinguishable molecules, the molecules will be moving about with varying velocities colliding frequently with each other and the walls of the containing vessel. If some one were to ask how many molecules there will be in a subvolume of V, say V_1, we should have to admit that in all probability the precise number will change from instant to instant and all we can hope to do is to assign an *average* value to the number N_1. How can this average be calculated? Let us proceed in the simplest possible fashion by assigning the value V_1/V to the probability that a given molecule shall be in the subvolume V_1. This leads to certainty that the molecule shall lie in V, i.e., unit probability, while the probability decreases as the size of V_1 decreases relatively to V. Obviously there is no proof of this choice; it is only an assumption, but certainly a reasonable one. Similarly the probability that the molecule shall not be in V_1 but in $V_2 = V - V_1$, is V_2/V. If we denote the probability V_1/V by p and the probability V_2/V by q (with $p + q = 1$) we should be able to apply the considerations of Secs. 7 and 8. In particular the probability that N_1 molecules shall be in V_1 and N_2 molecules in V_2 (with $N_1 + N_2 = N$) will be simply

$$P_{N_1} = \frac{N!}{N_1!N_2!} p^{N_1} q^{N_2}. \tag{52}$$

Applying Sec. 7, the average values of N_1 and N_2 become

$$\overline{N}_1 = Np, \quad \overline{N}_2 = Nq. \tag{53}$$

Clearly there will be fluctuations from these average values. If neither Np nor Nq is too small, i.e., if the subvolumes are not too small nor the gas too rare, we can immediately compute from Laplace's formula the probability of a fluctuation $u = N_1 - Np$. It is indeed given by (51) with N in place of n. This enables us to compute, for example, the probability that the fluctuation will equal or exceed a certain amount. Let us take an actual case, namely, $V = 1$ cm^3, $V_1 = 10^{-3}$ cm^3, with $N = 2.7 \times 10^{19}$, the number of molecules per cm^3 in an enclosed gas under standard conditions. Then $p = 10^{-3}$ and $\overline{N}_1 = 2.7 \times 10^{16}$. Let us compute the probability that $u/\overline{N}_1$ shall equal or exceed 10^{-3} in absolute value, or 0.1 per cent. This will be given to close approximation by

$$P = \frac{2}{\sqrt{2\pi Npq}} \int_{10^{-3}\overline{N}_1}^{\infty} e^{-u^2/2Npq} du$$

with $N = 2.7 \times 10^{19}$, $p = 10^{-3}$, $q = 1 - 10^{-3}$, $\overline{N}_1 = 2.7 \times 10^{16}$. To evaluate we change variables so that $u^2/2Npq = v^2/2$ or $u = v\sqrt{Npq}$, whence

$$P = \sqrt{\frac{2}{\pi}} \int_{10^{-3}\overline{N}_1/\sqrt{Npq}}^{\infty} e^{-v^2/2} dv = \Phi(\sqrt{2.7 \times 10^{10}}).$$

For $x \gg 1$, we have $\Phi(x) = \sqrt{2/\pi} \cdot e^{-x^2/2}/x \cdot (1 - 1/x^2 \cdots)$. Consequently P here becomes approximately

$$\sqrt{\frac{2}{\pi}} \cdot \frac{e^{-1.35 \times 10^{10}}}{\sqrt{2.7 \times 10^5}}.$$

This indicates that a fluctuation equal to or greater than the one indicated is very rare indeed.

Another way of viewing the same problem is to calculate the standard deviation of N_1. From eq. (46) this is given by

$$\sigma = \sqrt{Npq}. \tag{54}$$

In the present example, $\sigma = 1.64 \times 10^8$, approximately. This is large in actual value but not in comparison with $\bar{N}_1$. Of greater significance than σ is the fractional or relative standard deviation, $\sigma/\bar{N}_1$. In the present case this is only $1.64 \times 10^8/2.7 \times 10^{16} \sim 10^{-8}$ or 10^{-6} per cent. The chance of finding such a small relative standard deviation by detecting density fluctuations experimentally would appear to be negligible. It might be supposed that if we could take a *small* enough subvolume the chance of detection would be greater. Thus if $V_1 = 10^{-8} \text{ cm}^3$, $p = 10^{-8}$, $\bar{N}_1 = 2.7 \times 10^{11}$, $\sigma \sim 5 \times 10^5$ and $\sigma/\bar{N}_1 \sim 2 \times 10^{-6}$, which is some two hundred times larger than the former value though still small. As one looks around for possible means of detecting such a density fluctuation in such a small volume, one inevitably thinks of the effect of density change on the index of refraction of light.

The dependence of the index of refraction of a gas on the density may be written rather accurately in the form

$$\mu = 1 + \alpha\rho, \tag{55}$$

in which ρ is the density and α is a constant over a considerable range of variation. From this we immediately conclude that

$$\frac{\Delta\mu}{\mu} = \frac{\alpha\Delta\rho}{1 + \alpha\rho} \sim \alpha\Delta\rho, \tag{56}$$

since $\alpha\rho \ll 1$ for gases. Thus for air the *average* $\mu = 1.00029$ approximately for standard conditions, i.e., $\alpha\rho_0 = 0.00029$. Hence

$$\frac{\Delta\mu}{\mu} = 0.00029 \frac{\Delta\rho}{\rho_0}. \tag{57}$$

Suppose now we consider as our fundamental volume a cubic wavelength of the yellow light from sodium vapor, viz., that with an approximate wavelength of 6×10^{-5} cm. Then $V_1 \sim 2 \times 10^{-13} \text{ cm}^3$, $\bar{N}_1 \sim 5 \times 10^6$ and $\sigma \sim 2 \times 10^3$ with $\sigma/\bar{N}_1 \sim 5 \times 10^{-4} \, \Delta\rho/\rho_0$, from the definition of density. Consequently in this case

$$\frac{\Delta\mu}{\mu} \sim 1.5 \times 10^{-7}.$$

In other words there should be a fluctuation of about one unit in the seventh decimal place of the average index of refraction of air for visible light. This is scarcely large enough for experimental detection. For light of shorter wavelength the fluctuation is somewhat increased but is still very small. It has been shown by Smoluchowski [3] and others that for real gases near the critical temperature the above simple fluctuation theory (based on an ideal gas) is inadequate. Smoluchowski showed that for real gases the expression for $\sigma/\overline{N}_1$ given above is not correct. Actually analysis shows that the more nearly correct result is

$$(\sigma/\overline{N}_1)^2 = \frac{RT}{\overline{N}_1 V^2 \left| \partial p/\partial V \right|}.$$

For an ideal gas $\dfrac{\partial p}{\partial V} = RT/V^2$ and $(\sigma/\overline{N}_1)^2$ reduces to $1/\overline{N}_1$ or σ^2 becomes $\overline{N}_1$, which is the approximate result given in our work by (54). On the other hand for a real gas near the critical point where $\left| \dfrac{\partial p}{\partial V} \right|$ is very small the value of $(\sigma/\overline{N}_1)^2$ can become very much larger than (54) would predict. Actually such gases at the critical point when illuminated show an opalescence which has been attributed to the density fluctuation.

The blue color of the sky has also been explained by density fluctuations like those considered here. We shall return to the problem in a somewhat different form when we encounter the Brownian motion.

10. THE SHOT EFFECT AS A FLUCTUATION PHENOMENON

Another interesting illustration of fluctuation phenomena in physics is provided by the so-called shot effect. This explains the continual background of noise in a loud speaker actuated by the thermionic current in a vacuum tube in terms of the random emission of electrons from the cathode of the tube. This chance emission produces current fluctuations in the tube circuit. If we assume that the electron emission is completely unordered in the sense that the motion of each electron from the cathode is independent of that of any other, our statistical formulas should apply.

Let us assume that over a very long time T the number of electrons emitted by the cathode is N, whence the expected average number per second is N/T. Actually the number N_t in time intervals of the magnitude t ($\ll T$) will fluctuate from the expected average Nt/T. The fluctuation is given by

$$u_t = N_t - \frac{Nt}{T}. \tag{58}$$

---

[3] M. v. Smoluchowski, *Ann. der phys.* **25**, 205 (1908).

The foregoing theory then indicates that the standard deviation of the distribution is

$$\sigma = \sqrt{\frac{Nt}{T}(1 - t/T)} \sim \sqrt{\frac{Nt}{T}}, \tag{59}$$

and the average relative fluctuation is

$$\frac{\sigma}{Nt/T} \sim \frac{1}{\sqrt{Nt/T}}. \tag{60}$$

B. Rajewsky [4] has been able to check this result by measuring the mean-square fluctuation in the tube-circuit current. Thus the average current over time T is

$$I_0 = \frac{eN}{T},$$

while the actual current during any interval t is

$$I_t = \frac{eN_t}{t}.$$

Hence the current fluctuation is

$$\Delta I = I_t - I_0 = \frac{eu_t}{t}.$$

The mean-square current fluctuation is

$$\overline{\Delta I^2} = \frac{e^2}{t^2} \cdot \overline{u_t^2} \sim \frac{e^2}{t^2} \cdot \frac{Nt}{T} = \frac{I_0 e}{t} \tag{61}$$

In Rajewsky's experiment he studied the emission of electrons from a special form of photocell constructed after the fashion of a Geiger-Müller counter. This allowed the counting of single electrons. In one particular case, for example, he counted 1,272 electrons in a period of 30 minutes. In our notation then $T = 30$ minutes and $N = 1,272$. This corresponds to an expected average of 42.4 electrons per minute. He observed the fluctuations from this figure over 2-, 6-, 10-, and 20-minute intervals with results as follows

t IN MINUTES	$1/\sqrt{Nt/T}$, OBS.	$1/\sqrt{Nt/T}$, CALC.
2	0.179	0.109
6	0.061	0.063
10	0.042	0.048
20	0.019	0.034

The agreement in order of magnitude may be considered good enough

[4] *Physik. Z.* **32**, 121 (1931).

to support the thesis that the shot effect comes within the realm of our simple statistical theory.

Allied to the fluctuation problem just considered is the fluctuation in electric charge which must continually take place in all bodies which according to the atomic theory of the structure of matter are assumed to consist of positively and negatively charged particles. Let us suppose that a given volume of matter consists of N_1 particles with charge $+e$ and N_2 particles with charge $-e$. If the material is electrically neutral we expect on the average that $N_1 = N_2$. However, with large N_1 and N_2 fluctuations are to be expected. Assume for simplicity that the charged particles are free and do not exert any influence on each other. The excess of positive over negative charge is

$$\delta = e(N_1 - N_2).$$

The analogy between this and eq. (1) of this chapter should be sufficiently clear. If $N_1 + N_2 = N$, the root-mean-square value of δ will be (cf. eq. 12)

$$\sqrt{\overline{\delta^2}} = e\sqrt{N},$$

which is a measure of the average fluctuation from complete electrical neutrality. The neglect of the electrical interaction between the charged particles makes this result too large and of questionable utility. Nevertheless it is conceivable that such fluctuations may some day be observed with sufficiently sensitive apparatus.

11. RADIOACTIVE EMISSION AS A FLUCTUATION PHENOMENON

In Sec. 4, Chapter I, we commented on the phenomenon of radioactive decay as describable in statistical terms. If this is so, we ought to be able to apply the reasoning of Sec. 7 to the emission of α particles from radioactive substances. The following description of an early experiment by Rutherford will bring out the essential features.

Using the scintillation method in which the flash produced by the impact of an α particle on a fluorescent screen is used to count the number of such particles emitted by a radioactive substance in a given interval of time, Rutherford in a certain experiment counted 10,097 particles emitted over a period of 326 minutes. For convenience he divided this period into 2,608 subintervals of $\frac{1}{8}$ minute each and noted the number of particles emitted in each subinterval. The results of the count are given in the following table.

Number of subintervals	57	203	383	525	532	408	273	139
Number of scintillations	0	1	2	3	4	5	6	7

Number of subintervals	45	27	10	4	0	1	1
Number of scintillations	8	9	10	11	12	13	14

This means that, e.g., there were 525 subintervals in which 3 scintillations were observed, while there were only 4 subintervals in which 11 scintillations appeared. Now if this is really a statistical distribution, the calculated standard deviation should agree with the observed standard deviation. The former is simply (cf. 54)

$$\sigma = \sqrt{Npq},$$

where here $N = 10,097$ and $N_1 = Np = 10,097/2,608 = 3.87 =$ average number of scintillations per $\frac{1}{8}$ minute subinterval. Hence $p = 1/2,608$, $q \sim 1$ and

$$\sigma = \sqrt{3.87}.$$

If now we compute the actually observed standard deviation, we have

$$\sigma^2_{obs} = \frac{57(3.87 - 0)^2 + 203(3.87 - 1)^2 + \cdots + 1(3.87 - 14)^2}{2608}$$

and get

$$\sigma_{obs} = \sqrt{3.70}.$$

The agreement between σ_{obs} and σ (about 5 per cent discrepancy) may be considered close enough to justify the use of statistical analysis in treating the problem.[5] Of course this does not mean that we have a right automatically to use the Laplace formula or normal distribution law to describe the distribution in detail; if the Laplace formula were to be found not to apply, there would not necessarily be a contradiction. As a matter of fact, if we examine the assumptions on which the Laplace formula is based we see that it can be expected to hold only if neither Np nor Nq is too close to unity. The implication is that neither p nor q is very small. Here, however, p clearly violates this condition. Another type of approximation for Newton's formula (38) is then clearly called for.

12. POISSON'S FORMULA

If in the expression (38) we substitute $\bar{n}_1 = np = c$, where c is a number of order unity we get

$$P_{n_1} = \binom{n}{n_1}\left(\frac{c}{n}\right)^{n_1}\left(1 - \frac{c}{n}\right)^{n - n_1}. \tag{62}$$

This can be written in the form

$$P_{n_1} = 1\left(1 - \frac{1}{n}\right)\left(1 - \frac{2}{n}\right) \cdots \left(1 - \frac{n_1 - 1}{n}\right) \cdot \frac{(1 - c/n)^n c^{n_1}}{(1 - c/n)^{n_1} n_1!}. \tag{63}$$

[5] For more recent precision observations on radioactive decay, reference should be made to L. F. Curtiss, *Bureau of Standards Journal of Research*, **8**, 339 (1932).

Now let it be assumed that $n_1 \ll n$. Hence each of the parenthetical expressions like $\left(1 - \dfrac{n_1 - 1}{n}\right)$ is approximately unity and the same is true of $(1 - c/n)^{n_1}$. As we recall further that $\lim\limits_{n \to \infty} (1 - c/n)^n = e^{-c}$ and note that n_1 is, of course, finite, we have in the limit as $n \to \infty$

$$P(n_1) \to \frac{e^{-c}c^{n_1}}{n_1 !} = \frac{e^{-np}(np)^{n_1}}{n_1 !}. \tag{64}$$

This is called Poisson's formula. It is applicable as long as n_1 is small compared with n. When plotted the Poisson formula gives rise to a skew curve as distinct from the symmetrical normal curve of the Laplace distribution formula.[6] However as np gets larger the skew curve approaches the symmetrical one. The reader may show that the distribution expressed by (64) represents rather closely that observed in the radioactive emission experiment discussed in Sec. 11. For comparison the corresponding normal distribution should also be computed.

13. THE THEORY OF ERRORS

A review of the elementary applications of probability and statistics to physics would scarcely be complete without a reference to the theory of errors which is fundamental for the estimation of the validity of all physical measurements.

In the performance of any quantitative experiment the aim is to secure maximum significance of the result by reducing to a minimum all extraneous disturbing influences. Thus in the experimental study of the relation between the pressure and volume of a gas at constant temperature it is essential that the temperature remain really constant throughout a whole series of observations of pressure and volume. This is a problem demanding precise experimental technique. The great progress in accurate measurement has come from the development of such technique. When all precautions have been taken, however, it still remains true in every measurement that the apparently precise repetition of a particular operation under apparently identical conditions will rarely yield the same numerical result. What numerical value is then to be chosen to represent the quantity being measured? It is the task of the theory of errors to answer this question.

[6] For a figure showing the relation between the Poisson formula and that of Gauss (Fig. 2·1), cf. T. C. Fry, "Probability and Its Engineering Uses," p. 239, D. Van Nostrand, 1928.

Let the quantity being measured be denoted by z and let a set of measurements of z under presumably carefully controlled experimental conditions be $z_1, z_2, \cdots z_n$. It is customary to ascribe the differences among the z's to *accidental* errors as distinct from systematic errors which can be guarded against or accounted for by proper manipulation of the measuring apparatus. From the set of n values it is necessary somehow to produce a value which shall stand as the final "correct" or acceptable one. It is most natural to assume that this will be some kind of *average* of the z's. The simplest type of average is the arithmetical mean, i.e.,

$$\bar{z} = \frac{z_1 + z_2 + \cdots + z_n}{n}. \tag{65}$$

Let us for the moment adopt this as the acceptable value of the measured quantity. The quantities

$$\Delta_i = z_i - \bar{z} \tag{66}$$

then represent the fluctuations or deviations from the mean of the various measured values. It is an observed fact that if in any carefully performed experiment we plot as ordinate the number of values as a function of the deviation from the mean, a frequency curve is obtained which, although it differs in detail for different experiments, nevertheless always possesses certain definite general characteristics. Strictly speaking, of course, the deviation from the mean is not a continuous set of values. What we do is to divide the total range of deviation into a set of equal intervals, i.e., from 0 to $+a$, from $+a$ to $+2a$, etc. In the middle of each interval is plotted the number of measurements for which the deviation falls in this interval. If a smooth curve is passed through the resulting points as n is made sufficiently large, the result generally resembles the Gauss probability curve in Fig. 2·1 in the following respects: (a) there are many more values for which the magnitude of the deviation Δ is small than there are for which the magnitude of the deviation is large; (b) the number of values for any particular positive deviation interval tends to approximate the number of values for the corresponding negative deviation interval. Thus there always tends to be a maximum in the curve near $\Delta = 0$ though, of course, there may also be subsidiary but lower maxima.

If there were no accidental errors involved in the measurement we should expect the same value z to result from every observation. The differences among the z's may therefore be called errors and the frequency curve above described may be called an error curve in which the ordinate gives the number of cases in which the error lies within a particular interval, say from Δ to $\Delta + d\Delta$. By division with n, the ordinate may further represent the probability of an error lying within the given interval. The "normal" or Gaussian error curve is then represented by the equation

$$P(\Delta)d\Delta \;=\; \frac{h}{\sqrt{\pi}}\, e^{-h^2\Delta^2} d\Delta, \qquad (67)$$

where $P(\Delta)d\Delta$ is the probability that the error of an observation shall lie in the interval Δ, $\Delta + d\Delta$. The quantity h is called the "measure of precision." Its value depends on the spread of the measurements.

An important task of the theory of errors is to show under what conditions the expression (67) is justified. Many derivations of the normal law have been given based on a variety of fundamental hypotheses on the nature of accidental errors.[7] We shall not repeat any of these here but shall only show the intimate connection between the normal law and the arithmetical mean. This will indeed involve the demonstration that the assumption that the most probable value of a measured quantity is the arithmetical mean, leads directly to the normal law.

Let us suppose that the probability that the error in a measured quantity shall lie in the interval Δ, $\Delta + d\Delta$ is $f(\Delta)d\Delta$, where $f(\Delta)$ is the error function whose form we are seeking. If the n observed values of the quantity in question are $z_1, z_2, \cdots z_n$, respectively, and z is assumed to be the actual "correct" value, the errors in the various measurements are

$$\Delta_1 = z_1 - z, \quad \Delta_2 = z_2 - z, \;\cdots\; \Delta_n = z_n - z. \qquad (68)$$

The probability that an error shall lie in an arbitrarily small but definitely assigned region in the neighborhood of Δ_i is

$$Kf(\Delta_i),$$

where K is a constant representing the size of the region. It is strictly the value of $d\Delta_i$, but we are practically agreeing to take all $d\Delta_i$ of the same size and call their magnitude K. The probability that in the set of n measurements we shall make the n errors Δ_i will then be

$$P \;=\; K^n \prod_i f(\Delta_i). \qquad (69)$$

[7] For one such derivation, cf. Lindsay and Margenau, "Foundations of Physics," pp. 181 ff.

Since z has been assumed to be the "correct" value, the only meaning we can give to this statement is that P shall be a maximum for z. The condition for this is, however,

$$\sum_{i=1}^{n} \frac{1}{f(\Delta_i)} \frac{df(\Delta_i)}{d\Delta_i} \frac{d\Delta_i}{dz} = 0. \tag{70}$$

From (68) we have

$$\frac{d\Delta_i}{dz} = -1, \quad \text{for all } z. \tag{71}$$

Hence the maximizing condition is

$$\sum_{i=1}^{n} \frac{1}{f(\Delta_i)} \frac{df(\Delta_i)}{d\Delta_i} = 0. \tag{72}$$

Let us now assume that z is the arithmetical mean. The condition (72) is then subject to the auxiliary condition

$$\sum_{i=1}^{n} \Delta_i = 0. \tag{73}$$

By the method of Lagrange's multipliers (described and used in Sec. 2 of Chapter IV) we can now express the conditions (72) and (73) in the form

$$\sum_{i=1}^{n} \left(\frac{1}{\Delta_i f(\Delta_i)} \frac{df(\Delta_i)}{d\Delta_i} + \lambda \right) \Delta_i = 0, \tag{74}$$

where λ is an undetermined multiplier. In order to satisfy this condition we have to set, for all i

$$\frac{df(\Delta_i)}{d\Delta_i} = -\lambda \Delta_i f(\Delta_i). \tag{75}$$

The solution of this set of differential equations is

$$f(\Delta_i) = Ce^{-\lambda \Delta_i^2/2}. \tag{76}$$

By employing the condition that P shall be a maximum and not a minimum it can be established that λ is positive. Equation (76) is equivalent to the normal error law. It only remains to evaluate C. Since all errors must lie between $-\infty$ and $+\infty$, we must have

$$\int_{-\infty}^{+\infty} f(\Delta)d\Delta = C \int_{-\infty}^{+\infty} e^{-\lambda \Delta^2/2} d\Delta = 1. \tag{77}$$

This fixes

$$C = \sqrt{\frac{\lambda}{2\pi}}.$$ (78)

If we let $\lambda/2 = h^2$, we have

$$f(\Delta) = \frac{h}{\sqrt{\pi}} e^{-h^2\Delta^2},$$ (79)

which is equivalent to (67).

The arithmetical mean has another important property. Let us form the so-called "residuals" by subtracting $\bar{z}$ from each measured value. Thus we have the set of quantities

$$r_i = z_i - \bar{z}.$$

Now note that if we formed similar quantities for any *other* value, say z, we should have

$$\sum_{i=1}^{n} (z_i - z)^2 = \sum_{i=1}^{n} r_i^2 + n(z - \bar{z})^2.$$ (80)

When $z = \bar{z}$, the sum of the squares of the residuals is least. This is the basis of the so-called method of least squares.

The significance of the parameter h^2 in the normal error law becomes greater when we inquire as to the *average* error in a set of measurements of a single quantity. There are various ways of defining such an average, just as we found many ways of defining average deviation in the earlier sections of this chapter. Perhaps the most valuable average is the mean square average error. This is defined as

$$\overline{\Delta^2} = \frac{h}{\sqrt{\pi}} \int_{-\infty}^{+\infty} \Delta^2 e^{-h^2\Delta^2} d\Delta.$$

The evaluation of the integral (cf. eq. 32) gives

$$\overline{\Delta^2} = \frac{1}{2h^2}.$$ (81)

The root-mean-square average error is then

$$\sqrt{\overline{\Delta^2}} = \frac{1}{\sqrt{2}h}.$$ (82)

This serves to reinforce the meaning of h as a measure of precision, since the larger h is, the smaller is the root-mean-square error in a series of measurements of a quantity.

The question now arises: Can we give an estimate of the error involved in the arithmetical mean itself? We can interpret (69) as the probability that any particular value z shall be the "correct" value from the set of measurements $z_1 \cdots z_n$. This probability can be written

$$P(z) = \frac{K^n h^n}{\pi^{n/2}} e^{-h^2 \Sigma (z_i - z)^2}. \tag{83}$$

But from (80), this can be put into the form

$$P(z) = \frac{K^n h^n}{\pi^{n/2}} e^{-h^2 [\Sigma r_i^2 + n(z - \bar{z})^2]}. \tag{84}$$

We can include $e^{-h^2 \Sigma r_i^2}$ with the multiplicative constant and write

$$P(z) = C e^{-nh^2 (z - \bar{z})^2}. \tag{85}$$

C is evaluated in the usual fashion, i.e.,

$$C \int_{-\infty}^{+\infty} e^{-nh^2 (z - \bar{z})^2} dz = 1, \tag{86}$$

whence

$$C = h \sqrt{\frac{n}{\pi}}. \tag{87}$$

The probability associated with the arithmetical mean is therefore from (85)

$$P(\bar{z}) = \sqrt{\frac{n}{\pi}} h. \tag{88}$$

This means that the probability that the arithmetical mean shall represent the "correct" value for a quantity grows with the square root of the number of observations of the quantity. We can go further and express the mean-square error associated with the arithmetical mean z in the form

$$\int_{-\infty}^{+\infty} (z - \bar{z})^2 P(z) dz = \frac{1}{2nh^2}. \tag{89}$$

The root-mean-square error associated with the arithmetical mean is thus

$$\frac{1}{\sqrt{2}h} \cdot \frac{1}{\sqrt{n}}. \tag{90}$$

Since we have already seen that the root-mean-square error associated with any one of the measured values is $\dfrac{1}{\sqrt{2}h}$ (eq. 82) it follows that the arithmetical mean is $\sqrt{n}$ times as accurate as any one of the measured values.

The statistical theory of errors is now a very large subject to which we cannot begin to do justice in the above brief survey which has confined itself exclusively to the normal law and has disregarded other types of error distributions found in practice. A good review of the whole field will be found in the article by W. E. Deming and R. T. Birge, "On the Statistical Theory of Errors," in *Reviews of Modern Physics*, **6**, 119 (1934).

PROBLEMS

1. Compare Stirling's formula for the integers 1 to 10 inclusive with the exact values of $n!$. Compute the absolute and percentage errors involved in the use of the formula. Do the same for log $n!$ and in addition find the percentage error (for the range of n above specified) involved in using simply log $n! = n$ log $n-n$, i.e., neglecting log $\sqrt{2\pi n}$.

2. In connection with the higher order average deviations from the mean in a distribution of n objects, prove that when k is even

$$\sqrt[k]{\overline{x^k}} = [1.3.5 \cdots (k-1)]^{1/k} \cdot \frac{\sqrt{n}}{2}.$$

3. Use Stirling's formula directly to transform Newton's formula to Laplace's formula, i.e., eq. (17).

4. In a coin-tossing experiment 10 coins (U. S. one cent pieces) were tossed 1,100 times and the distribution of heads and tails noted after each toss. The results of this and another similar series of tosses are presented in the following table. For the interpretation of the table it may be remarked, for example, that there were in the first series 198 tosses giving 6 heads and 4 tails and 207 such tosses in the second series. Compute the expected distribution from the algebraic formula (2'). Then

Heads	Tails	Series 1	Series 2
10	0	0	0
9	1	8	11
8	2	53	45
7	3	125	134
6	4	198	207
5	5	291	274
4	6	237	233
3	7	123	136
2	8	53	51
1	9	11	7
0	10	1	2
	Total	1,100	1,100

calculate the average deviation from the expected mean (without regard to sign) as well as the standard and probable deviations. Compare these with the actually observed deviations in the two series of experiments. Comment on the results.

Noting that in the first series the total number of heads was 5,448 and the total tails 5,552, whereas the expected mean would be 5,500 of each, calculate the probability (eq. 36) of a deviation as large as that observed. Do the same for the second series and then for the results of both series taken together. Draw from this whatever conclusions you deem reasonable and plausible.

5. In Problem 4, plot (1) the expected distribution from the algebraic formula for $\binom{n}{n_1}$, (2) the expected distribution from Laplace's approximation (26), and (3) the actual distribution. Do this for both series.

6. Carry out the analysis leading to the generalized Laplace's formula (eq. 51).

7. Apply Smoluchowski's expression for $\sigma \sqrt{N_1}$ to the case of carbon dioxide at $31.89°$ C (cf. Int. Crit. Tables for data). Do the same for $100°$ C. Compare the result in each case with that obtained from the simple formula (54).

8. Use Rajewsky's observed results on the shot effect to obtain the root-mean-square current fluctuation in his experiment. Could this scheme be used as a method of determining the charge on the electron?

9. Plot the radioactive emission data of Sec. 11 as well as the corresponding Laplacian and Poisson distribution formulas and compare the experimental and theoretical distribution in each case.

10. The median of a set of measured values is that value such that there are as many greater than it as there are less than it. Find the law of errors corresponding to the assumption that the median is the most probable value of the measured quantity.

CHAPTER III

REVIEW OF THERMODYNAMICS

1. FUNDAMENTAL CONCEPTS

In Chapter I we stressed the difficulties associated with the classical dynamical method of describing physical systems containing a large number of constituent particles. The alternative, the statistical point of view, is the one which will be followed out in detail in this book. It is well to recall, however, that there is a well-known dynamical method of describing the behavior of physical systems, particularly with relation to heat. This is thermodynamics. It has been remarkably successful in correlating a vast amount of empirical data concerning the thermal changes of bodies. Its program has been accomplished without postulating a molecular constitution for physical objects; hence it has avoided the above-mentioned obstacles in the path of the precise application of dynamics to systems of many degrees of freedom. Since the object of much statistical reasoning in physics is to provide a basic theory in terms of which the facts of thermodynamics find a rational explanation, it is desirable at this place to review the fundamental concepts of this subject.

Thermodynamics is a discipline which endeavors to describe the behavior of large scale bodies, particularly with reference to their thermal changes, by the use of dynamical concepts. As has already been emphasized, however, the method of attack is quite different from that of classical mechanics. Instead of visualizing a body as a system composed of a large number of material particles, whose motion is sufficient to account for its behavior, we consider the body as a whole, i.e., *macroscopically*. In particular its state is no longer defined in terms of component particles but rather in terms of large scale quantities, operationally defined. These are volume, pressure, and temperature, which are termed the fundamental state variables. Only two of these are independent, since for every body there exists a so-called "equation of state" (cf. Sec. 3) connecting them. Thermodynamics does not pretend to relate pressure, volume, and temperature for all conditions of bodies, but only those in which the system if left to itself will remain unchanged, i.e., what we shall call *states of equilibrium*.

41

Whenever the same state of equilibrium is reproduced the state variables return to their previous values. In other words, they depend on the state alone and not on how the system got into the state.

All thermodynamic changes of state are called *processes*. They may be reversible or irreversible. A process is reversible when by an infinitesimally small change in the parameters controlling the state, the system may be made to pass in either direction through a sequence of states, without any net change in the surrounding environment. All other processes are irreversible (cf. Sec. 3, Chapter I). A process that carries a system through a sequence of states back to the initial state is called a *cyclic* process. The Carnot cycle is a familiar illustration.

Thermodynamics employs other concepts besides state variables. Thus in a cyclic process, a certain quantity of *heat* may be absorbed and a certain quantity of *work* done by the system. After the system has come back to its original state these quantities do not return to their original value; in fact there is no meaning to this statement. Quantity of heat absorbed or given up by a system is not a state variable; neither is quantity of work done by or on the system. Both these quantities depend vitally on *how* the system goes from its initial to its final state. It is clear that for a thermodynamical variable to be a state variable it must be expressible in terms of the fundamental variables of state in such a way that any small change in it is a perfect differential of the corresponding changes in the state variables.

2. THE TWO LAWS OF THERMODYNAMICS

With these preliminaries out of the way we shall now recall that the theoretical basis of thermodynamics consists of two principles, called the first and second laws. The first law of thermodynamics comprises the assumptions that heat is a form of energy and that in any thermodynamic process there is conservation of energy. This can be written in symbolic form by the introduction of a new thermodynamic state variable, the total internal energy of the system, which we shall denote by E. The principle says that if a quantity of heat ΔQ is added to a system and a quantity of work ΔW is done by it, the associated change in the internal energy ΔE is given by

$$\Delta E = \Delta Q - \Delta W. \qquad (1)$$

We have already emphasized that Q and W are not variables of state or state functions. However, it is part of the content of the first law that E is a state variable. In other words, if a system is allowed to undergo a series of thermodynamic cyclic processes from a definite initial state back to this same state, although ΔQ and ΔW may be quite different for the different processes, experiment indicates that $\Delta Q - \Delta W$ is zero for all the processes, thus suggesting that ΔE is always zero for a cyclic process and therefore that E is a state variable. This experimental suggestion is erected into a definite postulate. We therefore use dE to denote a change in E, implying that it is a perfect differential of the fundamental state variables, while we shall continue to use ΔQ and ΔW to bring out that these are not perfect differentials. It is scarcely necessary to emphasize that in (1) all quantities are expressed in energy units by the use of the mechanical equivalent of heat, approximately 4.2 joules per calorie.

The first law is too general to serve by itself as the single basis of thermodynamics. It is necessary to supplement it by another principle whose purpose is to express the *direction* in which thermodynamic processes take place. We have already commented in Chapter I on the irreversible nature of many natural processes, particularly those in which heat transformations are concerned. The principle (1), however, will apply just as well to reversible as irreversible processes. We need therefore a state variable which changes only in one direction, i.e., either never increases or never decreases. Such a quantity is found in the *entropy* which is defined by its differential, i.e.,

$$dS = \Delta Q/T. \tag{2}$$

In this definition it is understood that ΔQ is the change in heat energy in a *reversible* process. The function S defined in this way is a state variable, though Q is not. This can be shown by the generalization [1] to the case of any reversible cycle of the fact that if in any Carnot cycle heat ΔQ_1 is taken in at temperature T_1 and heat ΔQ_2 is given out at temperature T_2, we have

$$\frac{\Delta Q_1}{T_1} - \frac{\Delta Q_2}{T_2} = 0. \tag{3}$$

In order to state the second law of thermodynamics we need one more concept, that of a *closed* system. This means a system which has no interaction with its environment, i.e., it cannot gain energy from nor lose energy to its surroundings. With this and the foregoing in mind we can state the second law in the form: *the entropy of a closed system never decreases.* It may not change (as in a reversible cycle) but if it does change, it must increase, and this is always true for

---

[1] See, for example, Leigh Page, "*Introduction to Theoretical Physics,*" (second edition), p. 289. D. Van Nostrand Co., New York, 1935.

irreversible processes. In the latter case it is not possible to calculate the change in entropy from (2): it is necessary to replace the irreversible process by a reversible one which has the same initial and final states. Then (2) can be applied. The reader will recall several conventional ways of stating the second law, e.g., that it is impossible for a self-acting engine continuously to convey heat from a body of lower temperature to one of higher temperature. All such statements may be shown to be logically equivalent to the one we have given above.

The entropy may be used to give an alternative formulation of the first law (1). Thus

$$dE = TdS - \Delta W. \tag{4}$$

As we have already emphasized, the work ΔW depends on the nature of the process. However, it may be thought of as owing to the change in certain parameters $\xi_1 \cdots \xi_n$ which express the dependence of the system on its external surroundings. If the change in ξ_j is associated with a generalized force F_j, the work done in the change $d\xi_j$ is $F_j \, d\xi_j$ and we can write (4) in the form

$$dE = TdS - \sum_{j=1}^{n} F_j \, d\xi_j. \tag{5}$$

It must be pointed out that eq. (5) does not refer to a closed system since it contemplates interaction of the system and its environment. Hence in (5) dS need not be zero or positive as is required by the second law for a closed system.

It cannot be too strongly emphasized that the changes symbolized in (5) are those that take place between *equilibrium* states. Nevertheless since E and S are state variables, eq. (5) will apply even when the change from one equilibrium state to another takes place irreversibly, i.e., through a series of non-equilibrium states. Can we talk about the entropy of a system when it is not in an equilibrium state? Certainly we cannot compute it by eq. (2), since that applies only to a reversible process and a closed system cannot reach a non-equilibrium state by a reversible process. It can, however, reach an equilibrium state from a non-equilibrium state by means of an irreversible process in which the entropy will increase. Hence we can say that the entropy of a closed system in a non-equilibrium state is less than its value in the equilibrium state toward which it proceeds. This is the basis of the statement of the second law in the form: the entropy of a closed system tends to a maximum value or the entropy in an equilibrium state is a maximum with respect to its value for all non-equilibrium states from which the given equilibrium state can be reached by irreversible processes. Naturally the closed system, if in an equilibrium state, will not proceed by an irreversible process to a non-equilibrium state; this is inherent in the definitions of equilibrium state and irreversible process.

3. FREE ENERGY AND OTHER THERMODYNAMIC FUNCTIONS

From the entropy, internal energy, volume, pressure, and temperature other state variables can be formed. The most important of these are the following:

(a) Helmholtz free energy (or Gibbs' Ψ function)

$$\Psi = E - TS. \tag{6}$$

In future applications, when we speak of "free energy" it will be this function which is meant.

(b) Enthalpy (or Gibbs' X function)

$$X = E + pV. \tag{7}$$

(c) Gibbs free energy (or Gibbs' Z function)

$$Z = E + pV - TS = X - TS = \Psi + pV. \tag{8}$$

For the statistical interpretation of thermodynamics the Helmholtz free energy is the most important, though for most applications of thermodynamics, the Z function is more significant. As eq. (8) indicates, Z and Ψ are closely related.

From (6) we have

$$d\Psi = dE - TdS - SdT. \tag{9}$$

But (5) can be used to transform this to

$$d\Psi = - SdT - \sum_j F_j \, d\xi_j. \tag{10}$$

For an isothermal process ($dT = 0$) eq. (10) says that there is a decrease in free energy equal to the external work done by the system. If the only way in which the system can do work on its surroundings is to change its volume against external pressure p and if this process is isothermal, we have $\Sigma F_j \, d\xi_j = p dV$ and hence (10) becomes

$$d\Psi = - p dV, \tag{11}$$

or

$$p = - \left(\frac{\partial \Psi}{\partial V}\right)_T. \tag{12}$$

This important relation is called the *equation of state* of the system. If Ψ can be found as a function of V and T, it enables us to connect p, V, and T for the system. As an illustration, we shall later see that a statistical analysis yields for the free energy of an ideal gas of N particles occupying volume V at temperature T

$$\Psi = -\, NkT \log V + K, \tag{13}$$

where k is the so-called Boltzmann gas constant ($k = 1.37 \times 10^{-16}$ erg/degree C) and K is an arbitrary additive constant independent of volume but not necessarily independent of temperature. The combination of (12) and (13) gives

$$pV = NkT \tag{14}$$

as the equation of state for an ideal gas.

4. SOME THERMODYNAMIC RELATIONS

Important thermodynamic relations can be deduced from the fact that dE, $d\Psi$, dX and dZ are perfect differentials of the state variables. Thus from (10) it follows that

$$S = -\left(\frac{\partial \Psi}{\partial T}\right)_{\xi_j}; \quad F_j = -\left(\frac{\partial \Psi}{\partial \xi_j}\right)_T. \tag{15}$$

From the first of the expressions in (15), the free energy itself can be written in the form

$$\Psi = E + T\left(\frac{\partial \Psi}{\partial T}\right)_{\xi_j}. \tag{16}$$

This is sometimes called the Gibbs-Helmholtz equation. By differentiating S in (15) partially with respect to ξ_j and F_j with respect to T we obtain

$$\left(\frac{\partial S}{\partial \xi_j}\right)_T = \left(\frac{\partial F_j}{\partial T}\right)_{\xi_j}. \tag{17}$$

When the ξ_j reduce to a single parameter, namely V, and the corresponding F_j becomes p, this is known as one of Maxwell's thermodynamic relations [2] Three other relations can be derived by expressing in similar fashion the fact that dE, dX and dZ are perfect differentials. They are set down here for convenient reference. The first is (written in general form)

$$\left(\frac{\partial T}{\partial \xi_j}\right)_S = -\left(\frac{\partial F_j}{\partial S}\right)_{\xi_j}. \tag{18}$$

[2] Cf. *op. cit.*, p. 296.

The other two are usually written only for the case in which F_j reduces to p and ξ_j becomes V. Then they are

$$\left(\frac{\partial T}{\partial p}\right)_S = \left(\frac{\partial V}{\partial S}\right)_p, \tag{19}$$

$$\left(\frac{\partial S}{\partial p}\right)_T = -\left(\frac{\partial V}{\partial T}\right)_p. \tag{20}$$

The heat capacity is an important concept which we shall meet later. By definition the heat capacity of a substance at constant volume is the heat absorbed per degree change in temperature at constant volume, or

$$C_V = \left(\frac{\Delta Q}{\partial T}\right)_V = T\left(\frac{\partial S}{\partial T}\right)_V = \left(\frac{\partial E}{\partial T}\right)_V. \tag{21}$$

The last step came from the first law (5) with $\Sigma F_j d\xi_j = p\,dV$. We can also define a heat capacity at constant pressure, thus:

$$C_p = \left(\frac{\Delta Q}{\partial T}\right)_p = \left(\frac{\partial E}{\partial T}\right)_p + \left(\Sigma F_j \frac{\partial \xi_j}{\partial T}\right)_p. \tag{22}$$

If the parameters reduce to the volume alone and F_j becomes the pressure p, (22) may be written

$$C_p = \left(\frac{\partial E}{\partial T}\right)_p + p\left(\frac{\partial V}{\partial T}\right)_p \tag{23}$$

The general formula

$$C_p - C_V = \left(\frac{\partial E}{\partial T}\right)_p - \left(\frac{\partial E}{\partial T}\right)_V + p\left(\frac{\partial V}{\partial T}\right)_p \tag{24}$$

becomes the well-known formula

$$C_p - C_V = Nk \tag{25}$$

for the special case of an ideal gas. When applied to one gram of substance, the heat capacity becomes the usual specific heat, denoted by c_V and c_p.

5. RÉSUMÉ

With the basic principles discussed in the preceding sections of this chapter it has proved possible to give a coherent description of a large number of physical and chemical phenomena. This is not a textbook of thermodynamics and hence we shall not pursue the purely thermodynamic method of description in a detailed fashion.[3] Rather we are now interested in seeing how the statistical point of view provides an interpretation of thermodynamics in terms of the atomic constitution of matter. Several different ways of doing this have been devised. Those which we shall consider in this book are: (a) the classical statistics of Maxwell and Boltzmann; (b) the classical kinetic theory; (c) the statistical mechanics of Gibbs; (d) the statistical mechanics of Darwin and Fowler; (e) the quantum statistics. In each case the statistical theory strives to set up a number of statistical quantities analogous to the state variables of thermodynamics and beginning with very general postulates to derive a set of relations among them which can be interpreted as physically equivalent to the thermodynamic relations we have just discussed. The hope exists, furthermore, that the statistical point of view will provide an even deeper understanding of physical phenomena than thermodynamics by suggesting laws which are not susceptible of thermodynamic derivation.

Our method of procedure will be, to a certain extent, an historical one; we shall examine the older physical statistical methods first. This is the natural order, for the more recent quantum statistics employs the same fundamental ideas as the earlier statistics and it will be desirable to have the latter firmly in mind before proceeding to the former. It is hoped that in this way the reader will get a clearer view of the whole subject than if we tried to adopt a unified point of view and abandoned the historical approach entirely. We shall indeed find that the different methods of presenting classical statistics lead essentially to the same result when applied to the same problem. Some may therefore take the stand that a discussion of all methods is superfluous. On the other hand the greater the number of ways in which we can look at a problem the more profound and thorough should be our understanding of it.

PROBLEMS

1. In the schematic diagram A and B represent equal volumes. A is occupied by a mass m of an ideal gas at pressure p and temperature T, while B is a perfect vacuum. Calculate the change in entropy which results when a hole is opened in the partition between A and B, allowing the gas to move freely from A to B.

[3] At this point the reader may wish to consult any one of a number of standard, more or less elaborate, treatments of thermodynamics, e.g., "Textbook of Thermodynamics," by P. Epstein, John Wiley and Sons, New York, 1937; "Thermodynamics," by E. Fermi, Prentice-Hall, New York, 1937; "Heat and Thermodynamics," by M. W. Zemansky, McGraw-Hill, New York, 1937. Of particular interest to physicists in view of the discussion in the later chapters of the present volume is P. W. Bridgman's "Thermodynamics of Electrical Phenomena in Metals," Macmillan, New York, 1935.

2. Compute the change in entropy involved in mixing 1,000 grams of water at 80° C with 500 grams of water at 15° C. Assume that the specific heat of water is constant and equal to 1 cal/gram degree C.

3. Two grams of hydrogen have an initial volume corresponding to a pressure of 76 cm of Hg and temperature 20° C. The volume being kept constant, the gas is heated to temperature 80° C. It is then allowed to expand at constant tempera-ture to double its original volume. How much heat has been absorbed by the gas and how much work has been done on it? Determine the same quantities when the gas is first allowed to expand to double its volume, the temperature being kept con-stant at 20° C, and is then heated at constant volume from 20° to 80° C. In each case also calculate the total change in the internal energy of the gas.

4. From eq. (17) of this chapter derive the Clausius-Clapeyron equation, viz.,

$$L = T\left(\frac{\partial p}{\partial T}\right)_V (\Delta V_s)_T,$$

where L = latent heat of vaporization and $(\Delta V_s)_T$ is the change in specific volume between liquid and vapor phases at constant temperature T.

If the specific volume of water at 100° C is 1 cm³/gram, while that of steam is 1,686 cm³/gram find the change in the boiling point of water produced by lowering the pressure by 10 cm of Hg in the neighborhood of 76 cm of Hg.

If the difference in specific volume between the liquid and solid phases of water at 0° C is 0.1 cm³/gram, find the depression of the freezing point of water associated with an increase in pressure of one atmosphere.

5. It is shown in Chapter IV (eq. 84) that the free energy of an ideal gas with N particles in volume V at temperature T is

$$\Psi = - NkT\left[\log\left(\frac{V}{N} \cdot \frac{(2\pi mkT)^{3/2}}{h^3}\right) + 1\right].$$

Use eq. (16) of this Chapter to find the expression for the total energy of the gas.

Given one mole of an ideal gas under standard conditions of temperature and pressure. Find the change in free energy if the volume is doubled at constant tem-perature. Find the change in free energy if the temperature is raised by 1° C while the volume is kept constant.

6. Derive the expression for the entropy of an ideal gas from the application of Problem 5 to eq. (15) of this chapter.

7. By applying eq. (25) of this chapter to the special case of hydrogen, show how the mechanical equivalent of heat may be calculated.

CHAPTER IV

CLASSICAL MAXWELL-BOLTZMANN STATISTICS

1. STATISTICAL DISTRIBUTION OF N OBJECTS IN μ GROUPS

The fundamental problem of what has come to be called the Maxwell-Boltzmann statistics is the following: Given a large number of objects, N, e.g., molecules of a gas, it is desired to distribute these with respect to some property they all possess, e.g., position in space, velocity or kinetic energy. It will be convenient to think of this property as associated with a set of μ boxes, with a definite value of the property attached to each box. We shall first assume that the objects are indistinguishable, that they move freely and exert no forces on each other, and that it is just as likely that a particular object shall lie in one box as in any other. We can then readily compute the probability of an arrangement in which there are N_1 objects in the first box, N_2 in the second, N_3 in the third, $\cdots$, and N_μ in the μth, by finding the number of independent ways in which this distribution can be achieved. From eq. (2') of Chapter II the number of ways of choosing N_1 of the N objects to place in the first box is simply

$$\binom{N}{N_1} = \frac{N!}{N_1!(N-N_1)!}.$$ (1)

Similarly the number of ways of choosing N_2 objects out of the remaining $(N-N_1)$ to place in the second box is

$$\binom{N-N_1}{N_2} = \frac{(N-N_1)!}{N_2!(N-N_1-N_2)!}.$$ (1')

Clearly then the *total* number of ways required is the product

$$\binom{N}{N_1}\binom{N-N_1}{N_2}\cdots\binom{N-N_1-N_2-\cdots-N_{\mu-1}}{N_\mu},$$ (2)

which can be reduced to the following form

$$\left[\begin{matrix}N\\\mu\end{matrix}\right] = \frac{N!}{N_1!N_2!\cdots N_\mu!}.$$ (3)

For simplicity we shall use the square bracket to denote this expression.

The *probability* associated with the above distribution will be $\begin{bmatrix} N \\ \mu \end{bmatrix}$ divided by the total number of ways of distributing the N objects among the μ boxes without regard for the number of objects in each box. By a simple generalization of the argument in Sec. 1 of Chapter II, the latter number is μ^N. Hence the probability desired is simply

$$P_\mu^N = \frac{\begin{bmatrix} N \\ \mu \end{bmatrix}}{\mu^N}. \tag{4}$$

Boltzmann's Thermodynamic probability W

Equation (4) can be immediately generalized to the case where the *a priori* probabilities of each box are not equal. Suppose that they are actually given by $g_1, g_2, \cdots g_\mu$, respectively, where, since we here assume that these are actual mathematical probabilities, we have

$$\sum_{j=1}^{\mu} g_j = 1. \tag{5}$$

Then the probability that N_1 objects are in the first box, N_2 in the second, etc., if there were only one way in which to realize this distribution, would be

$$g_1^{N_1} g_2^{N_2} \cdots g_\mu^{N_\mu}.$$

Since however the number of ways of making this distribution is $\begin{bmatrix} N \\ \mu \end{bmatrix}$, the total probability becomes

$$P_\mu^N = \begin{bmatrix} N \\ \mu \end{bmatrix} g_1^{N_1} g_2^{N_2} \cdots g_\mu^{N_\mu}. \tag{6}$$

This reduces to (4) when $g_1 = g_2 = \cdots = g_\mu = 1/\mu$.

We now ask the following question: Given an aggregate of N objects whose number remains constant, for what type of distribution among μ boxes will P_μ^N have the maximum value? Intuition answers the question by saying that the required distribution is that for which the number in the jth box is

$$N_j = N g_j. \tag{7}$$

Let us see whether we can confirm this conjecture. The problem is to make P_μ^N a maximum subject to the condition

$$\sum_{j=1}^{\mu} N_j = N = \text{constant}. \tag{8}$$

Choose any set of N_j satisfying the condition (8). If we can find the conditions which $g_1 \cdots g_j \cdots g_\mu$ must satisfy in order to make P_μ^N a maximum subject to (5), we shall have solved the problem. We write (6) in the form

$$\log P_\mu^N = \log \begin{bmatrix} N \\ \mu \end{bmatrix} + \Sigma N_j \log g_j, \qquad (9)$$

and find it simpler to make $\log P_\mu^N$ a maximum subject to the condition (5). But $\log P_\mu^N$ is stationary if any slight but arbitrary variation in the g_j leads to zero variation in $\log P_\mu^N$. The meaning of $\log P_\mu^N$ assures that in the present case the stationary value will be a maximum. Hence the mathematical formulation of the problem is

$$\delta \log P_\mu^N = 0, \qquad (10)$$

subject to

$$\sum_{j=1}^{\mu} \delta g_j = 0, \qquad (11)$$

where we use the symbol δ to denote an arbitrary variation. We then have

$$\sum_{j=1}^{\mu} \frac{N_j \delta g_j}{g_j} = 0 \qquad (12)$$

subject to (11). Let us solve (11) for δg_1 in terms of the rest

$$\delta g_1 = -\sum_{j=2}^{\mu} \delta g_j. \qquad (13)$$

Substitute this into (12) and obtain

$$\delta g_2 \left(\frac{N_2}{g_2} - \frac{N_1}{g_1} \right) + \cdots + \delta g_\mu \left(\frac{N_\mu}{g_\mu} - \frac{N_1}{g_1} \right) = 0. \qquad (14)$$

In this expression $\delta g_2, \cdots \delta g_\mu$ are completely arbitrary, since by giving them any consistent values (proper fractions, of course) we can still choose δg_1 to satisfy the condition (11). Hence the only way to satisfy (14) is to have identically

$$\frac{N_1}{g_1} = \frac{N_2}{g_2} = \cdots = \frac{N_\mu}{g_\mu} = N. \qquad (15)$$

The fact that the constant ratio is N is, of course, a result of (5) and (8). This checks the intuitive deduction.

We have indeed carried out the deduction (15) somewhat indirectly. In actuality the g_j are fixed quantities and the distribution sought is the set of N_j for which P_μ^N is a maximum subject to (8).

Suppose, however, that we have the correct set of N_j. If we substitute them into (9), to secure the required maximum we must still have (15) satisfied. As a matter of fact we could start with (9) and vary the N_j subject to (8) keeping the g_j fixed. This involves using Stirling's formula for the factorials in $\begin{bmatrix} N \\ \mu \end{bmatrix}$. It will yield the result (15), as the reader can show, but the method we have used is simpler.

The reader should see the connection between the distribution given by eq. (15) and the special one treated in Sec. 9 of Chapter II and expressed in eq. (53) of that chapter.

2. THE CANONICAL DISTRIBUTION

We now wish to generalize the distribution problem of Sec. 1 by assigning to each box a certain property which will be possessed by any object in that box. To fix the ideas clearly, let us imagine that the objects are material particles and the property is kinetic energy. We again assume that the particles are free. The energy E_j will be assigned to the jth box: whenever a particle is in that box it possesses precisely this energy value. The total energy of the aggregate of particles is thus $E = \Sigma N_j E_j$. The problem is now to distribute the particles among the boxes in such a way that the distribution probability P_μ^N will be a maximum subject not only to the condition of Sec. 1, viz., that the total number of particles remains constant, but also to the additional condition that the total energy of the aggregate remains unchanged. It will be assumed that the boxes have the *a priori* probabilities $g_1 \cdots g_\mu$ as in Sec. 1.

As before we shall work with $\log P_\mu^N$. From (9) using (3), we have

$$\log P_\mu^N = \log N! - \Sigma \log N_j! + \Sigma N_j \log g_j. \qquad (16)$$

The analytical formulation of the problem is

$$\delta \log P_\mu^N = 0, \qquad (17)$$

subject to

$$\delta \Sigma N_j = 0; \quad \delta \Sigma N_j E_j = 0. \qquad (18)$$

In all sums, unless otherwise specified, it will be assumed that j runs from 1 to μ.

From Stirling's formula (eq. 25 of Chapter II)

$$\log N! = N \log N - N + \tfrac{1}{2} \log 2\pi + \tfrac{1}{2} \log N. \qquad (19)$$

If N is sufficiently large the terms $\frac{1}{2} \log 2\pi$ and $\frac{1}{2} \log N$ are negligible compared with the first two terms on the right. We shall consistently neglect them for the sake of simplicity. This might seem to be an invalid procedure in $\log N_j!$ when N_j is small, as it can quite possibly be. However the error involved will still be small even here, because the terms $\log N_j!$ for small N_j make only a very small contribution to the whole sum. Condition (17) now becomes

$$\Sigma \left(\log \frac{g_j}{N_j} \right) \delta N_j = 0, \tag{20}$$

and conditions (18)

$$\Sigma \delta N_j = 0; \quad \Sigma E_j \delta N_j = 0. \tag{21}$$

Note that the E_j are definitely fixed and the only possible variation in energy comes from the δN_j. The maximization problem is now carried out by the use of Lagrange's undetermined multipliers.[1] We choose the initially arbitrary constant multipliers γ_1 and γ_2 and, remembering (20) and (21), write

$$\Sigma \left(\log \frac{g_j}{N_j} + \gamma_1 + \gamma_2 E_j \right) \delta N_j = 0. \tag{22}$$

We now pick γ_1 and γ_2 to satisfy the equations

$$\log \frac{g_1}{N_1} + \gamma_1 + \gamma_2 E_1 = 0,$$
$$\log \frac{g_2}{N_2} + \gamma_1 + \gamma_2 E_2 = 0. \tag{23}$$

This we have a right to do, since γ_1 and γ_2 are arbitrary. Equation (22) now becomes

$$\sum_{j=3}^{\mu} \left(\log \frac{g_j}{N_j} + \gamma_1 + \gamma_2 E_j \right) \delta N_j = 0, \tag{24}$$

and the variations $\delta N_3, \cdots, \delta N_\mu$ occurring here are now completely arbitrary. For all j, therefore, we have

$$\log \frac{g_j}{N_j} = - \gamma_1 - \gamma_2 E_j,$$

or

$$N_j = g_j e^{\gamma_1 + \gamma_2 E_j}. \tag{25}$$

[1] Cf., Leigh Page, "Introduction to Theoretical Physics," second edition, p. 311. D. Van Nostrand Co., New York, 1935.

It is now convenient to replace γ_1 and γ_2 by two new parameters ψ and Θ defined by the equations

$$\gamma_1 = \frac{\psi}{\Theta} + \log N\mu,$$

$$\gamma_2 = -\frac{1}{\Theta}. \tag{26}$$

The distribution formula (25) then takes the form

$$N_j = \mu g_j N e^{\psi/\Theta} e^{-E_j/\Theta}. \quad = \mu g_j N e^{\frac{\psi - E_j}{\Theta}} \tag{27}$$

The parameters ψ and Θ can at once be determined, at least in principle, as follows. We have from (8)

$$\Sigma N_j = N e^{\psi/\Theta} \cdot \Sigma \mu g_j e^{-E_j/\Theta} = N,$$

whence

$$\psi = -\Theta \log \Sigma \mu g_j e^{-E_j/\Theta}, \tag{28}$$

which gives ψ in terms of Θ. To get the latter consider the total energy

$$E = N e^{\psi/\Theta} \cdot \Sigma \mu g_j E_j e^{-E_j/\Theta}$$

$$= N \cdot \frac{\Sigma \mu g_j E_j e^{-E_j/\Theta}}{\Sigma \mu g_j e^{-E_j/\Theta}}. \tag{29}$$

In this way we see that ψ and Θ are expressible in terms of E, N, g_j and E_j. The actual evaluation of ψ and Θ from these transcendental equations cannot, of course, be carried through in closed form. We shall hope, however, in the subsequent discussion to give them a physical interpretation. Incidentally (29) also provides an expression for the *average* energy per particle in the distribution, viz.,

$$\bar{E} = \frac{E}{N} = \frac{\Sigma g_j E_j e^{-E_j/\Theta}}{\Sigma g_j e^{-E_j/\Theta}}. \tag{30}$$

The distribution defined by (27) is usually termed a *canonical* distribution. Since

$$e^{-\psi/\Theta} = \Sigma \mu g_j e^{-E_j/\Theta}, \tag{31}$$

an alternative way of expressing this type of distribution is clearly

$$N_j = \frac{N g_j e^{-E_j/\Theta}}{\Sigma g_j e^{-E_j/\Theta}}. \tag{27'}$$

This eliminates the parameter ψ from the distribution formula. The parameter Θ is termed the distribution *modulus*. It is clear that it must have the dimensions of energy and so must ψ. We have said nothing so far about the sign of Θ which might be considered arbitrary. However, from (27′) it is clear that negative Θ would lead to indefinitely large values of N_j for increasingly large E_j. As a matter of fact, investigation shows that Θ must be positive if condition (17) is to correspond to a maximum rather than a minimum of $\log P_\mu^N$. By disregarding g_j, positive Θ makes the number of particles in the jth box decrease exponentially with the energy assigned to that box. Of course the distribution is affected by the choice of *a priori* probabilities g_j.

Our understanding of the canonical distribution law (27′) will be enhanced by the consideration of a few special illustrations. First suppose that $g_j = 1/\mu$ for all j and $E_j = E/N$ for all j. Inspection of (27′) for this case shows that for all j

$$N_j = \frac{N}{\mu},$$

corresponding to a uniform distribution. If we forego the restriction on g_j, save for $\Sigma g_j = 1$, the resulting distribution becomes

$$N_j = N g_j,$$

i.e., the same as that already studied in Sec. 1.

For the second illustration imagine that E_j is an integral multiple of a certain fundamental energy unit ε, i.e., $E_j = (j-1)\varepsilon$ where j, as usual, takes the values $1,2,3,\ldots$. Further assume that μ is so large that we can effectively consider the sums over j from 1 to μ as infinite series. For simplicity we shall suppose that the g_j are all equal. Therefore since $e^{-\varepsilon/\Theta} < 1$

$$\Sigma e^{-E_j/\Theta} = \Sigma e^{-(j-1)\varepsilon/\Theta} = \frac{1}{(1 - e^{-\varepsilon/\Theta})}.$$

Moreover by a simple extension of this

$$\Sigma (j-1)\varepsilon \cdot e^{(j-1)\varepsilon/\Theta} = \frac{\varepsilon e^{-\varepsilon/\Theta}}{(1 - e^{-\varepsilon/\Theta})^2}.$$

In the sums j runs from 1 to ∞. Consequently (30) yields for the average energy

$$\bar{E} = \frac{\varepsilon}{e^{\varepsilon/\Theta} - 1}. \tag{32}$$

We shall later have occasion to appreciate the larger significance of (32) (cf. Sec. 10, Chapter VIII), but for the present let us use it as a means of getting a somewhat clearer light on Θ. Solving (32) for Θ yields

$$\Theta = \frac{\varepsilon}{\log\left(1 + \dfrac{\varepsilon}{\bar{E}}\right)}. \tag{33}$$

Suppose that $\varepsilon << \bar{E}$, which is not too far-fetched an assumption. Then we have the interesting approximation

$$\Theta \sim \bar{E}, \tag{33'}$$

or the modulus Θ is approximately equal to the average energy per particle. We shall investigate later a generalization of (33'). From (28) we now have for the parameter ψ

$$\psi = -\frac{\varepsilon}{\log(1 + \varepsilon/\bar{E})} \cdot \log \frac{\mu}{1 - e^{-\log(1+\varepsilon/\bar{E})}},$$

which yields approximately

$$\psi \sim -\bar{E} \log \mu \frac{\bar{E}}{\varepsilon}. \tag{34}$$

If we choose to set $\Psi = N\psi$, we can further write this

$$\Psi \sim -E \log \mu \frac{E}{N\varepsilon}$$

in terms of the total energy. The distribution formula for this special case is

$$N_j = Ne^{-(j-1)\varepsilon/\Theta} \cdot (1 - e^{-\varepsilon/\Theta}), \tag{35}$$

or approximately

$$N_j \sim Ne^{-(j-1)N\varepsilon/E} \cdot (1 - e^{-N\varepsilon/E}). \tag{36}$$

An illustration of more practical importance than the above is provided by a collection of linear simple harmonic oscillators, all with frequency ν. It is shown by quantum mechanical reasoning [2] (also cf. Chapter VIII) that the possible energy values of a linear harmonic oscillator are given by

$$E_j = (j - \tfrac{1}{2})h\nu, \quad j = 1,2,3, \cdots \tag{37}$$

where h is Planck's constant of action (6.55×10^{-27} erg sec). The a priori probabilities are all equal. Assuming again that the number of states is very large, we have

$$\Sigma e^{-E_j/\Theta} = \Sigma e^{-(j-\frac{1}{2})h\nu/\Theta} = \frac{e^{-h\nu/2\Theta}}{1 - e^{-h\nu/\Theta}}. \tag{38}$$

[2] Cf. Lindsay and Margenau, "Foundations of Physics," p. 430.

Consequently the distribution function takes the form

$$N_j = Ne^{-(j-1)h\nu/\Theta} \cdot (1 - e^{-h\nu/\Theta}) \tag{39}$$

which is identical with (35) with $\varepsilon = h\nu$. However, a somewhat different and very interesting situation presents itself with regard to the average energy per oscillator. If we differentiate (38) with respect to Θ the result is

$$\Sigma E_j e^{-E_j/\Theta} = \frac{h\nu}{2} \cdot e^{-h\nu/2\Theta} \cdot \frac{(1 + e^{-h\nu/\Theta})}{(1 - e^{-h\nu/\Theta})^2} \tag{40}$$

and from (30) this gives

$$\bar{E} = \frac{h\nu}{2} \cdot \frac{(1 + e^{-h\nu/\Theta})}{(1 - e^{-h\nu/\Theta})} = \frac{h\nu}{2} + \frac{h\nu}{e^{h\nu/\Theta} - 1}. \tag{41}$$

The significant feature of this result is that, unlike (32), the average energy no longer vanishes when Θ becomes zero. In fact

$$(\bar{E})_{\Theta=0} = \frac{h\nu}{2} = E_1. \tag{42}$$

We shall later learn to call this a " zero-point " energy. It is clear that this situation will always arise when the lowest possible energy value is different from zero as it is in the present case.

In the collection of simple harmonic oscillators considered above the *a priori* probabilities are all equal. It turns out that if the collection contains two dimensional harmonic oscillators, this situation no longer prevails. Rather the g_j increase linearly with j, so that we can write

$$g_j = \frac{j}{C}, \quad (j = 1,2,3,\cdots)$$

where C is a constant depending on the number of energy boxes. Division by this constant is necessary to make g_j a probability in the sense in which we are using the term. Actually this constant plays no role so far as the average energy is concerned. Irrespective of the value of C, eq. (30) gives for the average energy

$$\bar{E} = \frac{\Sigma j E_j e^{-E_j/\Theta}}{\Sigma j e^{-E_j/\Theta}}. \tag{43}$$

Quantum mechanics yields for the two-dimensional oscillator

$$E_j = jh\nu.$$

Consequently

$$\bar{E} = \frac{h\nu \Sigma j^2 e^{-jh\nu/\Theta}}{\Sigma j e^{-jh\nu/\Theta}}. \tag{44}$$

Now by differentiating $\Sigma e^{-jh\nu/\Theta} = 1/(e^{h\nu/\Theta} - 1)$ with respect to Θ, we secure

$$\Sigma j e^{-jh\nu/\Theta} = \frac{e^{h\nu/\Theta}}{(e^{h\nu/\Theta} - 1)^2}. \qquad (45)$$

A second differentiation yields

$$\Sigma j^2 e^{-jh\nu/\Theta} = \frac{e^{h\nu/\Theta}(e^{h\nu/\Theta} + 1)}{(e^{h\nu/\Theta} - 1)^3}. \qquad (46)$$

Consequently

$$\bar{E} = h\nu + \frac{2h\nu}{e^{h\nu/\Theta} - 1}. \qquad (47)$$

This should be compared with (41) and the change in the "zero-point" energy noted.

3. PROPERTIES OF THE CANONICAL DISTRIBUTION. INTERPRETATION OF THERMODYNAMIC RELATIONS

It is now in order to study some properties of the canonical distribution and to indicate analogies with the important thermodynamic relations.

Let us evaluate the expression for $\log P_\mu^N$ (eq. 16) in the case of a canonical distribution. We have

$$\log P_\mu^N = N \log N - N - \Sigma \left(N_j \log \frac{N_j}{g_j} - N_j \right). \qquad (48)$$

Substitution of N_j from (27) yields ultimately on reduction, if we denote the canonical value of P_μ^N by P_c,

$$\log \mu^N P_c = \frac{E - \Psi'}{\Theta} = \log w, \qquad (49)$$

where we have again replaced $N\psi$ by Ψ', and where in what follows we shall always consider $\mu^N P_c$ replaced by w. We shall refer to the latter as the "statistical probability" for a canonical distribution.

We shall now imagine that the system of particles undergoes a change in its total energy, taking place in two ways, viz., (a) by a change dE_j in the amount of energy associated with each box, and (b) by a change in the distribution over the boxes, the change in the number of particles in the jth box being denoted by dN_j. The total change in energy then appears as

$$dE = d\Sigma N_j E_j = \Sigma E_j dN_j + \Sigma N_j dE_j. \qquad (50)$$

There is another way of looking at this which is rather expeditious and moreover will prove very useful when we come to alternative presentations.

Let us introduce the transformation

$$\zeta = e^{-1/\Theta}. \tag{51}$$

We can then write from (29)

$$E = \frac{N\Sigma\mu g_j E_j \zeta^{E_j}}{\Sigma\mu g_j \zeta^{E_j}}. \tag{52}$$

We shall moreover find it convenient to denote $\Sigma\mu g_j \zeta^{E_j}$ by a special symbol and use Z for this purpose. Thus

$$Z = \Sigma\mu g_j \zeta^{E_j}. \tag{53}$$

Now

$$\zeta \frac{\partial Z}{\partial \zeta} = \Sigma\mu g_j E_j \zeta^{E_j}, \tag{54}$$

and therefore

$$E = \frac{N\zeta}{Z} \frac{\partial Z}{\partial \zeta} = N\zeta \frac{\partial \log Z}{\partial \zeta}. \tag{55}$$

This proves to be a very useful mode of expression for the energy of the system. We may call Z the distribution function. Later we shall find something very like this called the *partition function* in the method of Darwin and Fowler (Chapter VII). We shall now consider the total change in E associated with a change in the modulus ζ (or Θ) and the changes in E_j, the latter being lumped in the change in Z. Now we shall assume that the function Z depends on ζ as well as on certain external coordinates, namely the $\xi_1 \cdots \xi_n$ already mentioned in connection with the thermodynamical treatment in Sec. 2, Chapter III. When we carry out the differentiation with this in mind we get for the total change in E

$$dE = \left(N\frac{\partial \log Z}{\partial \zeta} + N\zeta\frac{\partial^2 \log Z}{\partial \zeta^2} \right) d\zeta + N\sum_{\lambda=1}^{n}\zeta\frac{\partial}{\partial \xi_\lambda}\left(\frac{\partial \log Z}{\partial \zeta} \right) d\xi_\lambda. \tag{56}$$

Next we proceed to consider the work done in the change in the external coordinates. For a particle in the jth state in which the energy is E_j our alteration in ξ_λ brings into play a force $-\dfrac{\partial E_j}{\partial \xi_\lambda}$ and the work done by this particle when all the parameters change by $d\xi_1, d\xi_2 \cdots d\xi_n$ is

$$-\sum_{\lambda} \frac{\partial E_j}{\partial \xi_\lambda} d\xi_\lambda. \tag{57}$$

Now the average number of particles in the jth state is N_j, given by (27) or (27'), which by employing (53) can be written in the form

$$N_j = \frac{\mu N g_j \zeta^{E_j}}{Z}. \tag{58}$$

Consequently the contribution to the work by all particles in the jth state is $N_j \sum_\lambda \frac{\partial E_j}{\partial \xi_\lambda} d\xi_\lambda$ and that by all systems in all states is clearly

$$dW = -\frac{N}{Z} \sum_j \sum_\lambda \mu g_j \zeta^{E_j} \frac{\partial E_j}{\partial \xi_\lambda} d\xi_\lambda. \tag{59}$$

From the fact that

$$\sum_\lambda \frac{\partial \log Z}{\partial \xi_\lambda} = \sum_\lambda \frac{\partial}{\partial \xi_\lambda}\left(\log \sum_j \mu g_j \zeta^{E_j}\right) = \frac{1}{Z} \cdot \sum_\lambda \sum_j \mu g_j \zeta^{E_j} \log \zeta \frac{\partial E_j}{\partial \xi_\lambda}, \tag{60}$$

we can write

$$dW = -\frac{N}{\log \zeta} \sum_\lambda \frac{\partial \log Z}{\partial \xi_\lambda} d\xi_\lambda. \tag{61}$$

Therefore the change in the total energy of the system plus the external work done by the system is

$$dE + dW = N\left[\frac{\partial \log Z}{\partial \zeta} + \zeta \frac{\partial^2 \log Z}{\partial \zeta^2}\right] d\zeta$$

$$+ N\left[\sum_\lambda \zeta \frac{\partial}{\partial \xi_\lambda}\left(\frac{\partial \log Z}{\partial \zeta}\right) - \frac{1}{\log \zeta} \sum_\lambda \frac{\partial \log Z}{\partial \xi_\lambda}\right] d\xi_\lambda. \tag{62}$$

Let us now go back to the expression (49) for $\log w$. From (28), (51) and (53) this may be written

$$\log w = -E \log \zeta + N \log Z. \tag{63}$$

The change in $\log w$ when Θ and the ξ_λ alter therefore is

$$d \log w = -dE \log \zeta - \frac{E d\zeta}{\zeta} + N \frac{\partial \log Z}{\partial \zeta} d\zeta + N \sum_\lambda \frac{\partial \log Z}{\partial \xi_\lambda} d\xi_\lambda. \tag{64}$$

From (55) it is clear that the two middle terms in (64) cancel each other, so that finally

$$d \log w = -dE \log \zeta + N \sum_\lambda \frac{\partial \log Z}{\partial \xi_\lambda} d\xi_\lambda.$$

If we divide through by $-\log \zeta$ we get

$$-\frac{d \log w}{\log \zeta} = dE - \frac{N}{\log \zeta} \sum_\lambda \frac{\partial \log Z}{\partial \xi_\lambda} d\xi_\lambda.$$

But from (51) and (61) this at once becomes

$$\Theta \, d \log w = dE + dW. \tag{65}$$

This very interesting relation evidently bears a close analogy to the first law of thermodynamics (eqs. 1 and 4, Chapter III). We can indeed look upon it as the statistical equivalent of the first law if we are willing to identify the increment of quantity of heat transferred to the system of particles as $\Theta d \log w$. Let us then write

$$\frac{\Delta Q}{\Theta} = d \log w. \tag{66}$$

Now the statistical quantity $\log w$ has the property that its value depends solely on the state of the system in its canonical distribution and does not depend on how the system got into that state. It is therefore competent to serve as a statistical analogue of a thermodynamical state variable. In fact we see from (66) that if we interpret the statistical canonical distribution modulus Θ as a universal constant k times the absolute temperature T, we can write [3]

$$d[k \log w] = \frac{\Delta Q}{T}. \tag{67}$$

Comparison with eq. (2) in our discussion of thermodynamics in Chapter II suggests that we interpret the left side of (67) as the change in *entropy* of the system and write

$$d[k \log w] = dS. \tag{68}$$

The integration of (68) then yields for the statistical interpretation of entropy

$$S = k \log w + C, \tag{69}$$

where C is an arbitrary additive constant of integration. We are entitled to choose for C the constant quantity which will make (69) agree best with the known thermodynamical properties of the entropy.

---

[3] k turns out to be the Boltzmann gas constant with the value $1 \cdot 37 \times 10^{-16}$ ergs/°C (Cf. Secs. 1 and 2, Chapter V).

With this in mind we find it advantageous to choose $C = -k \log N!$ and write our statistical definition of entropy in the form

$$S = k \log \left(\frac{w}{N!}\right). \tag{69'}$$

We may indeed proceed to define $w/N!$ as the "effective" statistical probability for the canonical distribution. Examination of the preceding sections of this chapter discloses that if we had used it in place of w no change would have resulted in the canonical distribution. In Chapter VIII we shall see a close connection between the definition (69') in classical statistics and the quantum mechanical definition of entropy. It is well to emphasize that the relations (68) and (69') are dependent on the fact that the system of particles is canonically distributed. Since the equations of thermodynamics refer to systems in equilibrium it is therefore appropriate to assume that the canonical distribution is the statistical analogue of equilibrium. This corresponds well with the fact that $\log P_c$ (and likewise $\log w$) is a maximum for a canonical distribution as compared with any other distribution of the same system of particles with the same energy. The same is of course true for $\log (w/N!)$. If there *were* a configuration of greater probability than the canonical distribution we should expect that the system would not rest in equilibrium until it had attained this more probable state. On this view a system with a fixed number of particles and given energy not in an equilibrium state will correspond to a smaller value of $\log (w/N!)$. But such a system will tend to approach a state of greater probability and this is the statistical interpretation of the irreversible tendency of the entropy of a closed system to increase; the latter has already been emphasized in the thermodynamic definition of entropy in Sec. 2, Chapter III. There is, to be sure, a fundamental difference between the second law of thermodynamics and the law based on the assumption (69) or (69'). According to the second law, the entropy of a closed system *always* increases in a non-cyclic, irreversible process. According to the statistical interpretation it is only *probable* that the entropy will increase. From the very nature of the statistical definition of entropy there is no necessity that the entropy must always increase under the conditions stated. There will always be indeed a finite probability that it will decrease. This may be looked upon as the price we have to pay for the statistical interpretation.

We can illustrate the above situation by attempting to treat the change in entropy during a given process, as statistically defined in

(68), as a measure of the irreversibility of the process. Suppose the system changes from state 1, where the statistical probability is w, to state 2 with probability $w + \Delta w$. It seems appropriate to take the measure of the irreversibility in going from 1 to 2 as the ratio $(w + \Delta w)/w$. We shall call this z. Then

$$\log z = \log \frac{w + \Delta w}{w} = \Delta \log w,$$

whence

$$z = e^{\Delta \log w} = e^{\Delta S/k}.$$

As an example, consider the process involved in the passage of 1 erg of heat energy from a body at 21°C to another body at 20°C brought in contact with the first. If we replace the process by an equivalent *reversible* one, i.e., one carried out ideally with infinite slowness, we can calculate the entropy change ΔS by (67) and get on substitution of the data $\Delta S/k = 8.5 \times 10^{10}$. Hence in this case $z > 10^{10^{10}}$, indicating a high degree of irreversibility. It is rather interesting to consider what happens when the quantity of heat energy transferred is only 10^{-11} erg. Then $z = e^{0.85}$, which is less than 3. Indeed as the amount of energy transferred becomes smaller and smaller, $z \to$ unity and w for the two states approaches the same value. For very small energy transfers the process becomes less and less irreversible from the statistical standpoint. This casts a further interesting light on the significance of the statistical interpretation of entropy.

It is now not a difficult matter to find the statistical analogues of the other important thermodynamic variables. Consider again the Helmholtz free energy (eq. 6 of Chapter III)

$$\Psi = E - TS.$$

With the statistical interpretation of S this becomes

$$\Psi = E - kT \log w + kT \log N!. \tag{70}$$

But now compare this with eq. (49). Let us set as usual

$$\Theta = kT. \tag{71}$$

Then from (28) and (49) and the use of Stirling's formula

$$\Psi = -NkT \left(\log \frac{Z}{N} + 1 \right) \tag{72}$$

is the statistical expression for the free energy in terms of the partition function as we have introduced it in eq. (53). This of course assumes that the constant k, whose value is not specified by the statistical theory, is chosen correctly (cf. Secs. 1 and 2, Chapter V).

We should be able to use the expression (72) to derive the equation of state of the system from eq. (12) of Chapter III. Thus the pressure should be given by the equation

$$p = \frac{\partial}{\partial V}\left[NkT \left(\log \frac{Z}{N} + 1 \right) \right]$$

$$= NkT \frac{\partial \log Z}{\partial V} . \tag{73}$$

If therefore we were to derive the expression for the partition function Z for a system of free particles and in particular its dependence on the physical volume occupied by the system, eq. (73) should reduce to the well-known equation of state of a perfect gas, viz.,

$$pV = RT, \tag{74}$$

where R is the so-called gas constant. Now it is clear from the form of (73) that in order for it to yield (74) it is essential that

$$Z = KV, \tag{75}$$

where K is independent of V, though it may contain the mass of the particles, the parameter Θ, etc., and must have the dimensions of reciprocal volume. In the next section we attempt the calculation of Z.

4. DISTRIBUTION OR PARTITION FUNCTION FOR A SYSTEM OF FREE PARTICLES. FREE ENERGY OF AN IDEAL GAS

The problem is to obtain for an ideal gas the volume dependence of the function

$$Z = \Sigma \mu g_j e^{-E_j/\Theta}, \tag{76}$$

where

$$E_j = \frac{1}{2m} (p_{jx}^2 + p_{jy}^2 + p_{jz}^2) . \tag{77}$$

All particles have the same mass, m, and the p_{jx}, p_{jy} and p_{jz} are the component momenta along the x, y, z axes respectively of a particle in the jth box. Since the gas is assumed to be ideal, the energy is kinetic only. Before we can use (77) to evaluate (76), we must introduce the appropriate *a priori* probabilities g_j. From our previous discussion (cf. Chapter II, Sec. 9) it is reasonable to assume that g_j is proportional to the size of the jth box. Clearly, however, size here does not refer merely to physical volume but also to momentum interval as well. Let us suppose that a particle in the jth box has its configuration coordinates in the volume element $\Delta x_j\,\Delta y_j\,\Delta z_j$ about the rectangular coordinates x_j, y_j, z_j, and its momentum components in the momentum interval $\Delta p_{jx}\Delta p_{jy}\Delta p_{jz}$ in the neighborhood of the momentum components p_{jx}, p_{jy}, p_{jz}. It is then natural to suppose that g_j will be equal to $\Delta x_j\Delta y_j\Delta z_j\Delta p_{jx}\Delta p_{jy}\Delta p_{jz}$ divided by the total " volume " of the six-dimensional space defined by the coordinates $x_j, y_j, z_j, p_{jx}, p_{jy}, p_{jz}$ and whose total extent is given by the range of variation allowed to these coordinates. We have now to decide whether the coordinates shall be allowed to vary continuously or in discrete amounts. We shall make the assumption, which will prove of value in the later discussion of quantum statistics, that the six-dimensional space under consideration has a cellular structure in which the cell has volume h^3, where h is a fundamental constant having the dimensions of momentum times displacement.   This assumption means that no matter how much $x_j, y_j, z_j, p_{jx}, p_{jy}, p_{jz}$ vary among themselves

$$\Delta x_j\Delta y_j\Delta z_j\Delta p_{jx}\Delta p_{jy}\Delta p_{jz} > h^3. \tag{78}$$

We shall now assume further that there are μ cells available. Hence finally

$$g_j = \frac{\Delta x_j\Delta y_j\Delta z_j\Delta p_{jx}\Delta p_{jy}\Delta p_{jz}}{\mu h^3}. \tag{79}$$

Consequently the partition function becomes

$$Z = \frac{1}{h^3}\cdot\sum_j e^{-(p_{jx}^2+p_{jy}^2+p_{jz}^2)/2m\Theta}\Delta x_j\Delta y_j\Delta z_j\Delta p_{jx}\Delta p_{jy}\Delta p_{jz}. \tag{80}$$

Now since the coordinates are all independent of each other and since the exponential term does not involve any configuration coordinates we can carry out the summation over the Δx_j, etc., independently of the momenta and have

$$\sum_j \Delta x_j\Delta y_j\Delta z_j = V, \tag{81}$$

where V is the physical volume occupied by the particles. Since the Δp_{jx}, etc., can be made as small as we please subject only to condition (78), we shall assume that to a very high degree of approximation (h being assumed to be a very small constant) we can replace the summation over the p_{jx}, etc., by a triple integration. It should be emphasized that this replacement of a finite sum by a definite integral is here purely a matter of mathematical convenience and has nothing fundamentally to do with the essential nature of the Maxwell-Boltzmann statistics. In the evaluation of the integral we shall further suppose that the limits for each variable are $-\infty$ and $+\infty$ respectively. Actually there will be finite maximum and minimum values of the momentum components for any actual aggregate of particles. However the exponential integrand renders the choice of infinite limits a very acceptable approximation (cf. the remarks after eq. 30 in Chapter II). Now by a simple transformation and extension of eq. (23) of Chapter II, we have

$$\int_{-\infty}^{+\infty} \int_{-\infty}^{+\infty} \int_{-\infty}^{+\infty} e^{-(p_x^2 + p_y^2 + p_z^2)/2m\Theta} dp_x dp_y dp_z = (2\pi m\Theta)^{3/2}. \qquad (82)$$

Hence

$$Z = \frac{V}{h^3} \cdot (2\pi m\Theta)^{3/2}. \qquad (83)$$

This is indeed of the form of eq. (75) in the last section and thus leads to the correct equation of state for an ideal gas by substitution into eq. (73). From the form of the partition function for an ideal gas as obtained in (83) it results that the free energy (72) is an *extensive* quantity, i.e., at given temperature it is directly proportional to the number of particles and does not depend directly on the volume of the system. In fact if we substitute from (83) into (72), the result for the free energy of an ideal gas is

$$\Psi = -NkT \left[\log \left(\frac{V}{N} \cdot \frac{(2\pi mkT)^{3/2}}{h^3} \right) + 1 \right]. \qquad (84)$$

If two systems are combined so that the density and temperature remain the same the free energy of the combination is the sum of the free energies of the individual systems. It is again assumed that the constant k is chosen correctly.

5. EQUIPARTITION OF ENERGY IN A SYSTEM OF FREE PARTICLES. ENTROPY OF AN IDEAL GAS

We can at once extend the results of the preceding section in an interesting fashion to obtain an expression for the average energy per particle of the system. If we differentiate

$$Z = \Sigma \mu g_j e^{-E_j/\Theta} = \frac{V}{h^3} \cdot (2\pi m\Theta)^{3/2}$$

with respect to Θ we obtain

$$\frac{1}{\Theta^2} \Sigma \mu g_j E_j e^{-E_j/\Theta} = \frac{3V}{2h^3} (2\pi m)^{3/2} \Theta^{1/2}. \qquad (85)$$

Hence (eq. 30)

$$\overline{E} = \frac{\Sigma g_j E_j e^{-E_j/\Theta}}{\Sigma g_j e^{-E_j/\Theta}} = \frac{3}{2}\Theta. \tag{86}$$

This significant result gives the average energy directly in terms of the distribution modulus. It is possible to interpret the equation as expressing the *equipartition* of the kinetic energy among the various degrees of freedom of the individual particles. Each of the latter has three degrees of freedom. If we assign each degree of freedom on the average the amount of energy $\Theta/2$, the total per particle is $3\Theta/2$, which is the equivalent of (86). As a matter of fact this interpretation is confirmed by computing the average energy per particle for the component motion along the x axis only, which at once yields $\Theta/2$. From the symmetry of the integrand in (82) the same result will follow for the y and z degrees of freedom. We reach therefore the general conclusion that on the average the kinetic energy of an aggregate of free particles in a canonical distribution is distributed equally among their degrees of freedom. It is important to emphasize that the result (86) depends for its validity on the approximation of sums by integrals. We shall see that this is true for any statistics in which discrete cells or boxes are employed. The situation is rather different in the method of Gibbs, which will be treated in Chapter VI. We should further emphasize that the system to which the equipartition principle applies is an aggregate of independent particles, possessing kinetic energy only. In any case we shall find the equipartition principle of considerable value in our future discussion of aggregates of particles. In particular we shall use it in connection with the kinetic theory of gases which will be reviewed in the next chapter.

It will be of interest to apply eq. (86) to the derivation of the entropy of an ideal gas. From the definition (69') we have

$$S = k \log w - kN \log N + kN. \tag{87}$$

But

$$k \log w = E/T + Nk \log Z,$$

where E is the total energy of the gas, which from (86) becomes $E = 3NkT/2$ (with Θ replaced by kT, as before). The use of (83) coupled with substitution into (87) yields finally for the entropy of the ideal gas

$$S = \frac{5}{2} kN + kN \log \left[\frac{V}{N} \cdot \frac{(2\pi m k T)^{3/2}}{h^3} \right]. \tag{88}$$

It follows that the entropy is an extensive quantity in the same sense as the free energy, as discussed in Sec. 4.   The reader should note that this result would not have been obtained if we had defined the entropy simply as $S = k \log w$.   It is the choice of the additive constant $-k \log N!$ which assures that S shall have the extensive property.[4]

PROBLEMS

1. Derive the distribution law $N_j = N g_j$ (eq. 7 of this chapter) by varying the N_j subject to $\Sigma N_j = 1$, while keeping the g_j fixed.

2. Find the expression for the free energy of the set of independent linear simple harmonic oscillators whose possible energy values are given by $E_j = (j - \frac{1}{2})h\nu$, $(j = 1,2,3 \cdots)$ (cf. eq. 37).   Do the same for a set of two-dimensional oscillators for which the average energy is given by (47).

3. From the partition function Z for a set of independent linear simple harmonic oscillators derive the expression for the entropy.

4. Show that if the entropy is defined as $S = k \log w$, it is not an extensive quantity for any ideal gas and that the same is true of the corresponding free energy.

5. Derive the expression for the *Gibbs* free energy, $\Psi + pV$, for an ideal gas. Do the same for the enthalpy (cf. Sec. 3, Chapter III).

6. In a canonical distribution of N free particles find the expression for the number of particles having kinetic energy included between E and $E + dE$.   Find the ratio between the number of particles with energy in the range dE about the average energy $\bar{E} = 3\Theta/2$ and the number of particles with energy in the same range dE about an energy differing by 1 per cent from $\bar{E}$.

7. Compute the " effective statistical probability " for the canonical distribution of one mole of an ideal gas under standard conditions.

8. The methods of this chapter may be applied to an aggregate of independent particles which move in an external conservative force field characterized by the potential function $\phi(x, y, z)$.   Find the general form of the partition function of such an aggregate.   Specialize to the case in which the force field is the constant gravitational field near the surface of the earth.

---

[4] This point is well brought out in Mayer and Mayer, "Statistical Mechanics," pp. 114 ff.   John Wiley & Sons, 1940.

CHAPTER V

THE KINETIC THEORY OF GASES

1. THE VIRIAL AND THE EQUATION OF STATE OF AN IDEAL GAS

It is assumed that the reader is acquainted with the fundamental assumptions of the kinetic theory of gases from at least an elementary point of view. It is the intention of this chapter to review briefly its chief results, emphasizing in particular the points of contact with the statistical theory of the preceding chapter.

The kinetic theory envisages a gas as composed of a very large number of material particles called molecules moving with widely varying velocities in all directions and colliding with each other and with the walls of the confining vessel. The collisions with the walls are assumed to be responsible for the pressure of the gas while the average kinetic energy of the molecules is connected with the observed temperature of the gas. The first fundamental task of the kinetic theory is to provide a theoretical deduction of the equation of state of the gas, i.e., the relation connecting pressure, volume and temperature (cf. Sec. 3, Chapter 3). There are several ways of attacking this problem.[1] The one presented here is somewhat different from that used in elementary books, being based on the so-called *virial* of Clausius.

We shall confine our attention first to an ideal gas, in which the molecules are mass particles in the form of elastic spheres with radii very small compared with their average distance apart, so that indeed their dimensions can be neglected. They are assumed to be free particles exerting no mutual forces and all having the same mass m. We shall suppose their number is N and number their coordinates x_i, y_i, z_i in some inertial system with the subscript i which runs from 1 to N. Consider the following function of the coordinates

$$M = \tfrac{1}{2} \sum_{i=1}^{N} m(x_i^2 + y_i^2 + z_i^2). \tag{1}$$

[1] Cf. Sir James Jeans, "Dynamical Theory of Gases," Chapter VI. Cambridge, 1930. The reader may also consult with profit other recent books on kinetic theory, e.g., L. B. Loeb, "Kinetic Theory of Gases," Chapters II and V, McGraw-Hill, New York, 1927; and E. H. Kennard, "Kinetic Theory of Gases," Chapters I and V, McGraw-Hill, New York, 1938.

This does not appear to have immediate physical significance. But let us differentiate with respect to the time. Using the dot notation for time differentiation, we obtain

$$\dot{M} = \sum_{i=1}^{N} m(x_i \dot{x}_i + y_i \dot{y}_i + z_i \dot{z}_i). \tag{2}$$

A second time differentiation gives

$$\ddot{M} = \sum_{i=1}^{N} m(\dot{x}_i^2 + \dot{y}_i^2 + \dot{z}_i^2) + \sum_{i=1}^{N} m(x_i \ddot{x}_i + y_i \ddot{y}_i + z_i \ddot{z}_i). \tag{3}$$

We shall now proceed to form an average of a somewhat different nature from any hitherto considered in this book, namely an average over the *time*. The coordinates, component velocities and component accelerations of the particles are of course functions of the time. Hence the quantity $\ddot{M}$ will depend on the time. Its time average is

$$\overline{\overset{t}{\ddot{M}}} = \frac{1}{\tau} \int_0^\tau \ddot{M} dt = \frac{1}{\tau} (\dot{M}_\tau - \dot{M}_0), \tag{4}$$

where $\dot{M}_0$ is the value of $\dot{M}$ at the initial time $t = 0$ and $\dot{M}_\tau$ its value at time τ. Since the system of particles is confined to a finite space, the x_i, y_i, z_i coordinates are bounded at all times. The component velocities $\dot{x}_i, \dot{y}_i, \dot{z}_i$ will also be bounded. Consequently the difference $\dot{M}_\tau - \dot{M}_0$ in (4) is bounded and therefore as τ increases $\overline{\ddot{M}_\tau} \rightarrow 0$. From this we conclude that

$$\overline{\sum_{i=1}^{N} \frac{m}{2} (\dot{x}_i^2 + \dot{y}_i^2 + \dot{z}_i^2)} = -\tfrac{1}{2} \overline{\sum_{i=1}^{N} m(x_i \ddot{x}_i + y_i \ddot{y}_i + z_i \ddot{z}_i)}, \tag{5}$$

where the averages are taken over a sufficiently long time. The quantity on the left-hand side is the time average of the total kinetic energy of the system. The quantity on the right-hand side may be written in slightly different form if we replace $m\ddot{x}_i$ by F_{x_i}, the x component of the resultant force acting on the ith particle. Similar replacement of the y and z component accelerations yields for the right-hand side

$$\Omega = -\tfrac{1}{2} \overline{\sum_{i=1}^{N} (x_i F_{x_i} + y_i F_{y_i} + z_i F_{z_i})}. \tag{6}$$

The quantity Ω was called by Clausius the *virial* of the system. The relation (5) then states that for a system in canonical distribution *the total average kinetic energy is equal to its virial.* This is the virial theorem.

Let us now calculate the virial for an ideal gas by considering that the force components which enter eq. (6) are merely those involved in the collisions between the molecules and the walls. This means that F_{x_i}, etc., have non-vanishing values only for the values of x_i, y_i, z_i at the walls. These forces arise because of the change in momentum experienced by the molecules in their reflection from the walls. It

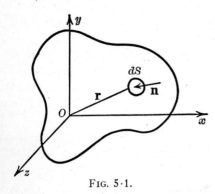

FIG. 5·1.

might seem difficult to compute them; but we must recall that it is the time average which is involved in eq. (6). The average wall forces can be effectively replaced by the integrated *pressure* which according to the postulates of the kinetic theory is indeed the average effect of the continual bombardment of the walls by the molecules. Figure 5·1 represents a portion of the surface of the containing vessel. Let us consider the area element $\mathbf{n}dS$ in this surface, where $\mathbf{n}$ is the unit vector normal to the surface at dS. This element has the position vector

$$\mathbf{r} = \mathbf{i}x + \mathbf{j}y + \mathbf{k}z \qquad (7)$$

in the chosen system of rectangular coordinates. The average force exerted on the system by the element of area is a vector directed oppositely to $\mathbf{n}$ and of magnitude pdS, if we denote the pressure of the gas by p. The components of this force along the axes are then

$$- pdS \cos \alpha, \quad - pdS \cos \beta, \quad - pdS \cos \gamma,$$

where $\cos \alpha$, $\cos \beta$, $\cos \gamma$ are the direction cosines of $\mathbf{n}$. The summation in (6) over all the molecules is now conveniently replaced by an integral over the whole surface of the containing vessel. Consequently we have for the virial

$$\Omega = \frac{p}{2} \int (x \cos \alpha + y \cos \beta + z \cos \gamma)dS. \qquad (8)$$

Since by definition

$$\mathbf{n} = \mathbf{i} \cos \alpha + \mathbf{j} \cos \beta + \mathbf{k} \cos \gamma,$$

we can transform (8) to

$$\Omega = \frac{p}{2} \int \mathbf{r} \cdot \mathbf{n} \, dS. \tag{9}$$

We can now employ the divergence theorem (often called Gauss' theorem) in vector analysis [2] to write

$$\Omega = \frac{p}{2} \int \nabla \cdot \mathbf{r} \, dV, \tag{10}$$

where the integral is now the volume integral of the divergence of $\mathbf{r}$ over the whole volume of the containing vessel. But

$$\nabla \cdot \mathbf{r} = \frac{\partial x}{\partial x} + \frac{\partial y}{\partial y} + \frac{\partial z}{\partial z} = 3.$$

Hence finally

$$\Omega = \tfrac{3}{2}pV. \tag{11}$$

From the virial theorem we therefore draw the conclusion that the total average kinetic energy of the molecules of the ideal gas is equal to $3pV/2$, or

$$\overset{t}{\bar{E}} = \tfrac{3}{2}pV. \tag{12}$$

Having reached this point we cannot go further toward the actual equation of state without introducing a macroscopic interpretation of $\overset{t}{\bar{E}}$. There are two possibilities. In the first place, we may arbitrarily but plausibly assume that the total average energy characterizes the temperature of the gas, so that constant temperature implies constant $\overset{t}{\bar{E}}$. With this association (12) becomes at once Boyle's law for an ideal gas. If we wish to be more specific we can introduce the statistical considerations of the preceding chapter and assume that the molecules are canonically distributed with respect to their kinetic energy. To be sure this is passing beyond the methods of kinetic theory as commonly understood, but it forms a useful bridge between the kinetic and statistical points of view. We shall then suppose that the total average kinetic energy $\overset{t}{\bar{E}}$ is the same as $N\bar{E}$, where N is the number of molecules and $\bar{E}$ the average energy per molecule in a canonical distribution. But in Sec. 5 of Chapter IV we have shown that

$$N\bar{E} = \tfrac{3}{2}N\Theta.$$

[2] See Leigh Page, "Introduction to Theoretical Physics," second edition, p. 32. D. Van Nostrand Co., New York, 1935.

Hence (12) becomes

$$pV = N\Theta. \tag{13}$$

But the equation of state of an ideal gas is known to be

$$pV = RT, \tag{14}$$

where T is the temperature on the Kelvin scale and R is the gas constant appropriate to the gas in question and its mass. If (13) is to be the kinetic-statistical analogue of (14) it is clear that we must have

$$\Theta = \frac{R}{N} T. \tag{15}$$

In words, the modulus of the canonical distribution is directly proportional to the Kelvin temperature of the gas and the coefficient of proportionality is the gas constant per molecule. This is the quantity which has received the name of Boltzmann's gas constant k, i.e.,

$$k = \frac{R}{N}, \tag{16}$$

and

$$\Theta = kT. \tag{17}$$

With this assignment the kinetic statistical derivation of the equation of state of an ideal gas may be considered complete.

2. SOME SIMPLE KINETIC THEORY PROPERTIES OF AN IDEAL GAS

The simple kinetic theory described in the preceding section leads to some interesting properties of an ideal gas. We shall review these briefly here.

If we write the kinetic energy in the form

$$\sum_{i=1}^{N} \frac{m}{2} (\dot{x}_i^2 + \dot{y}_i^2 + \dot{z}_i^2) = \sum_{i=1}^{N} \frac{m}{2} v_i^2$$

it follows that we can express the average in terms of a *root-mean-square velocity*

$$v_m = \sqrt{\overline{v^2}} \tag{18}$$

as follows

$$\sum \frac{m}{2} v_i^2 = \overline{E}^t = \frac{Nm}{2} v_m^2. \tag{19}$$

Equation (12) then becomes

$$pV = \tfrac{1}{3} Nm v_m^2. \tag{20}$$

The value of v_m can be estimated very easily from the fact that the density of the gas is given by

$$\rho = \frac{Nm}{V},$$ (21)

whence

$$v_m = \sqrt{\frac{3p}{\rho}}.$$ (22)

The substitution of the atmospheric pressure in dynes/square centimeter and the density of hydrogen under standard conditions ($T = 273°$ K, pressure 76 cm of Hg) yields $v_m = 1,900$ meters/sec approximately for hydrogen, in so far as hydrogen can be considered an ideal gas.   Actually v_m for an ideal gas does not depend on the pressure. From (14) we readily write

$$v_m = \sqrt{\frac{3kT}{m}},$$ (23)

indicating that for a given gas v_m depends solely on the absolute temperature.   Precise knowledge of the mass of a single molecule, e.g., that of hydrogen, then suffices for the determination of k.   Using the value $m_{H_2} = 3.32 \times 10^{-24}$ gram leads to

$$k = 1.37 \times 10^{-16} \text{ ergs/degree C.}$$ (24)

Coming back to the ideal gas law in the form

$$pV = NkT,$$ (25)

we observe that since k is a universal constant, N is the same for equal volumes of all ideal gases at the same temperature and pressure. This is the law of Avogadro.   In particular since the chemical molecular weights are proportional to the actual molecular masses, it follows that the number of molecules in a gram molecule or mole of any ideal gas is a universal constant.   This is the Avogadro number, now generally given as

$$N_A = 6.03 \times 10^{23},$$ (26)

whose best evaluation is from electrochemical data, namely the value of the Faraday Q or charge necessary to evolve one chemical equivalent of any element in an electrolytic process coupled with the fundamental electric charge e.   We have indeed

$$Q = N_A e,$$

and with $Q = 9,650$ emu and $e = 1.6 \times 10^{-20}$ emu, N_A is found to be 6.03×10^{23}. The Avogadro number is not, of course, confined to an ideal gas. According to atomic theory it is a genuine universal constant giving the number of molecules in a mole of any element or compound.

No difficulty should be experienced in deducing from the above simple considerations other important results of elementary kinetic theory, including Graham's effusion law, according to which the effusion velocity through small orifices of a gas at constant temperature and pressure varies inversely as the square root of the density, and Dalton's law of partial pressures that the pressure of a mixture of two gases is equal to the sum of the pressures which each would exert individually if alone in the same volume.

The kinetic theory also has something of interest to say about the specific heats of a gas (Sec. 4, Chapter III). The total average energy per gram of an ideal gas whose molecules are single mass particles is from (19)

$$E_m = \frac{v_m^2}{2} = \frac{3}{2}\frac{kT}{m}. \tag{27}$$

Consequently the specific heat at constant volume is

$$c_V = \left(\frac{\partial E_m}{\partial T}\right)_V = \frac{3}{2}\frac{k}{m}. \tag{28}$$

Multiplying both numerator and denominator of (28) by N_A gives

$$c_V = \frac{3}{2}\frac{kN_A}{M} = \frac{3}{2}R_m, \tag{29}$$

where M is the molecular weight and R_m the gas constant per gram of gas. For the rare gas argon, for example, $R_m = 2.1 \times 10^6$ ergs/gram degree and hence (29) yields (in terms of the more familiar calories/gram degree C)

$$c_V = 0.075 \text{ cal/gram degree C.}$$

This agrees very closely with the experimentally observed value at room temperature.

For a gas whose molecules consist of more than one mass particle, we can no longer assume that the average energy per gram is given by (27), since the internal kinetic energy of the constituent parts of the molecule relative to its center of mass must be considered. We may account for this by writing in place of (27)

$$E_m = (1 + \beta)\frac{v_m^2}{2}, \tag{30}$$

where β represents the ratio of the average internal kinetic energy to the average kinetic energy of translation of the center of mass of the molecule. It will have the same value for all gases whose molecules have the same constitution. We then get

$$c_V = \frac{3}{2}(1 + \beta)\frac{k}{m}. \tag{31}$$

For example, if a molecule consists of two particles of equal mass rotating about some axis perpendicular to the line joining them, it develops that $\beta = \frac{2}{3}$ so that

$$c_V = \frac{5}{2}\frac{k}{m}. \tag{32}$$

This choice of β is dictated by the equipartition principle. There are three degrees of freedom of translation of the center of mass of the system of two particles whereas there are two degrees of freedom of rotation, namely about two mutually perpendicular independent axes also perpendicular to the line joining the two particles. Now if the equipartition principle applies also to rotational energy we should expect that at given temperature the ratio of the average kinetic energy of rotation to that of translation would be precisely $\frac{2}{3}$. This is the basis of the choice in (32).[3] This formula holds well for hydrogen. The substitution of m_{H_2} and k into (32) gives indeed

$$c_V = 2.46 \text{ cal/gram degree C}$$

in fairly close agreement with the measured value for hydrogen at room temperature.

The ratio of the specific heat at constant pressure to that at constant volume, $\gamma = c_p/c_V$ can also be handled by the application of the preceding considerations to eq. (25) of Chapter III. The latter can be rewritten in terms of the actual specific heats (instead of the heat capacities) as follows

$$c_p - c_V = R_m, \tag{33}$$

it being understood that comparable units are employed on both sides. For monatomic gases we therefore have from eq. (29)

$$\frac{c_p}{c_V} = \gamma = \frac{5}{3}. \tag{34}$$

This ratio is found to hold pretty exactly for the rare gases of the

[3] See, for example, Kennard, *op. cit.*, p. 365, for a proof that the equipartition principle holds equally well for rotational as for translational energy.

atmosphere. For diatomic gases like hydrogen and oxygen, on the other hand, we have from (32)

$$\gamma = \tfrac{7}{5} \tag{35}$$

in rather good agreement with experimental results for the quasi-ideal diatomic gases. As the complexity of constitution of the molecule increases, c_V increases and we expect γ to approach unity. This again is experimentally confirmed to a considerable extent. For the statistical theory of specific heats, cf. Chapter IX.

3. COLLISIONS AND MEAN FREE PATH OF A GAS

In our discussion so far we have entirely neglected the possibility that the molecules of a gas may collide with each other. We have indeed assumed effectively that the molecules are geometrical points. If they are actually possessed of finite extension, however, they will be bound to hit each other in their flight and such collisions conceivably should have an important bearing on the properties of a gas.

For the elementary considerations of the present section we shall assume that the molecules are perfectly elastic spheres of diameter D. Suppose that all the molecules save one are instantaneously at rest, whereas that one moves with respect to the others with average relative velocity $\bar{v}_r$. Denote the average number of collisions per second experienced by any molecule by Z_c. The distance between successive collisions is called the *free path* of the molecule and the average value of a large number of free paths is termed the *mean free path*. We shall denote it by λ. Clearly, if the average velocity of the molecules is given by v_m, we have the fundamental relation

$$\lambda = \frac{v_m}{Z_c}. \tag{36}$$

Naturally the precise value of λ for given Z_c depends on the value chosen for the average velocity. The root-mean-square velocity is the one usually adopted.

The average number of collisions per second for any spherical molecule of diameter D is the same as the average number of collisions per second for a single spherical molecule of *radius* D moving through a field of *point* molecules. Consequently we can get an approximate value for Z_c by multiplying the average number of molecules per unit volume by the volume of the right circular cylinder traced out by a circle of radius D moving with the average relative velocity $\bar{v}_r$. Thus

$$Z_c = \pi D^2 \bar{v}_r n, \tag{37}$$

where n is here the number of molecules per unit volume. In order to utilize (37) it is necessary to evaluate $\bar{v}_r$ in terms of v_m. This can be readily done in the simple special case for which all the molecules have the same velocity magnitude, viz., v_m. Consider the two molecules

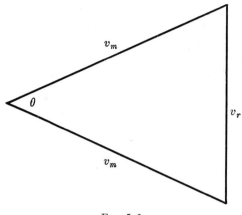

FIG. 5·2.

whose paths make the angle θ with each other (cf. Fig. 5·2). The relative velocity is clearly

$$v_r = 2v_m \sin \frac{\theta}{2}. \tag{38}$$

Hence

$$\overline{v}_r = 2v_m \overline{\sin \frac{\theta}{2}}, \tag{39}$$

and we must calculate the average of $\sin (\theta/2)$ over the whole collection of molecules. Now if we fix our attention on a single molecule the probability of finding another molecule with its velocity included in the angular region $d\theta$ between θ and $\theta + d\theta$ from the direction of the first molecule is simply

$$\tfrac{1}{2} \sin \theta \, d\theta. \tag{40}$$

This may be seen from the fact that we are assuming the velocity directions of the molecules to be symmetrically distributed so that no particular direction has greater *a priori* probability than any other. Hence the fractional number of molecules having their velocity directions at any instant included within the range θ and $\theta + d\theta$ with any arbitrary direction is the ratio of the solid angle included between

θ and $\theta + d\theta$ to the whole solid angle about a point, viz., 4π. This ratio is readily seen, however, to be

$$2\pi \sin \theta \, \frac{d\theta}{4\pi},$$

or the value given in (40). Hence, from the general definition of an average quantity

$$\overline{\sin \frac{\theta}{2}} = \frac{1}{2} \int_0^\pi \sin \frac{\theta}{2} \cdot \sin \theta \, d\theta. \tag{41}$$

Note that the integration over θ is taken between the limits 0 and π. We see indeed that

$$\frac{1}{2} \int_0^\pi \sin \theta \, d\theta = 1. \tag{42}$$

The evaluation of the integral in (41) leads at once to

$$\overline{\sin \frac{\theta}{2}} = \frac{2}{3},$$

and hence from (39)

$$\bar{v}_r = \tfrac{4}{3} v_m. \tag{43}$$

Consequently (37) becomes

$$Z_c = \tfrac{4}{3}\pi D^2 n v_m, \tag{44}$$

and the mean free path is

$$\lambda = \frac{3}{4\pi D^2 n}. \tag{45}$$

This result was first obtained by Clausius.[4] The mean free path is thus seen to depend on the number of molecules per unit volume and the diameter of each. The former quantity n can readily be obtained from the Avogadro number and the fact that the volume of a mole of any ideal gas is equal to 22.41×10^3 cm^3 under standard conditions of temperature and pressure. Hence approximately at $0°$ C and 76 cm of Hg

$$n = 2.70 \times 10^{19}. \tag{46}$$

How shall we get a measure of D? Many methods are available,[5] but we shall consider only one. This has to do with the *viscosity* of a gas, in itself an interesting topic.

[4] Cf. Kennard, *op. cit.*, p. 105.
[5] Cf. Loeb, *op. cit.* Appendix I, pp. 523 ff.

4. ELEMENTARY KINETIC THEORY OF VISCOSITY

The viscosity of a gas is one of the most significant effects of the molecular motion within the gas on the large scale motion of the gas as a whole. It will be recalled that in all actual fluids the motion of any part of the fluid is to a certain extent resisted by the rest. This effect is attributed to a so-called viscous force which each layer of fluid exerts on the immediately adjacent layer. Newton made the assumption that the viscous force is directly proportional to the flow velocity gradient or rate of change of velocity with distance normal to the direction of flow. Moreover, it is also assumed that the viscous force is proportional to the area of the contiguous layers. The constant of proportionality is called the coefficient of viscosity, or more briefly, the viscosity of the fluid. If we denote the area in question by A, the flow velocity gradient by dV/ds, and the viscosity by η, the viscous force then may be written

$$F = \eta A \frac{dV}{ds}. \tag{47}$$

The viscosity is thus the viscous force per unit area per unit velocity gradient. In absolute units its dimensions are dyne second/square centimeter. In these units the value for water at 20° C is 0.01. As might be expected, the viscosity values for gases are very much smaller. That for hydrogen at 0° C is 8.4×10^{-5} in absolute units. The viscosity of liquids decreases as the temperature increases, but that of gases increases with the temperature.

The explanation of the viscosity of a liquid is probably to be found in considerable measure in the cohesive forces between the constituent parts. This explanation is not available for ideal gases in which such forces are ignored. Yet even a gas like hydrogen, which at ordinary temperatures approaches close to the ideal variety in its other properties, possesses definitely measurable viscosity. Maxwell was the first to give a kinetic theory description of the viscosity of a gas in terms of the motion of the molecules and in particular the transfer of momentum by the random motion of the molecules from one moving layer of gas to another. An elementary discussion based on this idea follows.

Consider a gas which is flowing as a whole from left to right. Draw the parallel horizontal planes A, P, and B (Fig. 5·3) which contain the direction of flow, and suppose the flow velocity of the gas in plane A is V_1, while that in plane B is V_2, where A and B are chosen a distance apart equal to 2λ. The plane P is equidistant from

A and B. If we make the assumption that all the molecules have the velocity v_m, the average number of molecules traveling *downward* across unit area of P per second is $nv_m/6$ while on the average the same number of molecules travel *upward* across unit area of P per second. Because of the way the planes have been drawn, the molecules mentioned have suffered their last collisions (before striking P) in the planes A or B. If we assume that in passing through A or B each one instantaneously acquires the appropriate flow velocity V_1 or V_2, it follows that the $nv_m/6$ downward-moving molecules convey from A to the gas below P the flow momentum $nv_m/6 \cdot m V_1$ per second

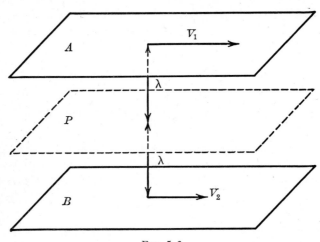

FIG. 5·3.

per unit area while the $nv_m/6$ upward-moving molecules convey from B to the gas above P the flow momentum $nv_m/6 \cdot m V_2$ per second per unit area. Now from Newton's second law the downward transfer of momentum per second per unit area, viz., $nv_m/6 \cdot m V_1$ represents the tangential stress exerted by the gas *above* the plane P on the gas below, while the upward transfer of momentum per second per unit area, viz., $nv_m/6 \cdot m V_2$ represents the tangential stress exerted by the gas below the plane P on the gas above. The equal and opposite reaction (Newton's third law) on the gas below is therefore $-nv_m/6 \cdot m V_2$. Hence the *resultant* tangential drag on unit area of the gas immediately below P is given by

$$nv_m/6 \cdot m(V_1 - V_2).$$

By definition this corresponds to F/A in eq. (47). Moreover the velocity gradient in the neighborhood of P is clearly to a good approximation

$$\frac{dV}{ds} = \frac{(V_1 - V_2)}{2\lambda}.$$

Hence the viscosity η becomes at once

$$\eta = \frac{nmv_m\lambda}{3} = \frac{\rho v_m\lambda}{3}, \tag{48}$$

where ρ is the density of the gas. This fundamental relation has been derived here by a rather crude method making use of somewhat questionable assumptions. More careful and elaborate deductions are to be found in the standard kinetic theory textbooks.[6] By substituting for v_m from (23) and λ from (45), the expression for η becomes

$$\eta = \frac{\sqrt{3kmT}}{4\pi D^2}. \tag{49}$$

This brings out the interesting fact that the viscosity of a gas should be independent of the pressure and therefore of the density. This prediction was first made by Maxwell who also verified it experimentally over a wide range of values. The variation with the square root of the absolute temperature has also received ample experimental verification. For a description of experimental methods of measuring η, Loeb's book may be consulted. Equations (48–49) may now be used to obtain numerical estimates of λ, D, and Z_c. Thus for hydrogen under standard conditions we obtain

$$\lambda = 1.7 \times 10^{-5} \text{ cm.}$$

$$D \sim 10^{-8} \text{ cm.}$$

$$Z_c \sim 10^{10} \text{ sec}^{-1}.$$

5. THE MAXWELLIAN DISTRIBUTION OF VELOCITIES

Although at the very beginning of this review of kinetic theory we included among the fundamental ideas the assumption that the molecules may differ in velocity, in the applications so far considered, particularly those in Sec. 3, we have actually assumed that effectively all the molecules move with the root-mean-square velocity v_m. It now remains to be seen how the variation in velocity may be taken

---

[6] Cf. Kennard, *op. cit.*, pp. 138 ff.; Loeb, *op. cit.*, pp. 180 ff. Also cf. Page, *op. cit.*, p. 343.

into account. We must first consider how the molecules are distributed on the average with respect to their velocities. This is the main problem of kinetic theory and many deductions have been given, the most famous being those of Maxwell and Boltzmann. From the purely dynamical point of view the problem is to consider an aggregate of confined elastic spheres which are continually colliding with each other, with the velocity of each sphere usually changing at each collision. However at any given instant there will be a certain number of spheres having velocities lying within any initially prescribed velocity interval. It is a fundamental assumption of kinetic theory that this number ultimately reaches a value which does not vary with the time as long as the gas represented by the aggregate remains in a state of equilibrium. The problem is to find this number. Boltzmann attacked it from the standpoint of the average effect of the elastic impacts on the velocities of the individual particles. Maxwell disregarded impacts altogether and considered the distribution of velocities from the standpoint of pure probabilities. There has been much argument about these deductions. We shall not go into either but merely show how the distribution they arrived at more or less immediately emerges from the application of the classical statistics of Chapter IV to an aggregate of particles, with the assumption that the state of equilibrium is represented completely by a canonical distribution with respect to the energy of the particles. The distribution of velocities is then obtained at once from the canonical distribution, eq. (27) or eq. (27') of Chapter IV with E_j as the kinetic energy of a particle of mass m and velocity components v_{x_j}, v_{y_j}, v_{z_j}. In accordance with eq. (17) of this chapter we set $\Theta = kT$. For the partition function $\Sigma \mu g_j e^{-E_j/\Theta}$ we use the expression for Z given in eq. (83) of Chapter IV. The *a priori* probability g_j is that given in (79) of Chapter IV. With these substitutions, the number of molecules having their velocity components in the interval $v_x, v_x + \Delta v_x$; $v_y, v_y + \Delta v_y$; $v_z, v_z + \Delta v_z$ may be written

$$\Delta N = N \left(\frac{m}{2\pi kT}\right)^{3/2} e^{-m/2kT \cdot (v_x^2 + v_y^2 + v_z^2)} \Delta v_x \Delta v_y \Delta v_z. \tag{50}$$

This is the Maxwellian velocity distribution formula. If we denote $(m/2\pi kT)^{3/2} e^{-mv^2/2kT}$ (with $v^2 = v_x^2 + v_y^2 + v_z^2$) by $f(v)$, we have

$$\frac{\Delta N}{N} = f(v) \Delta v_x \Delta v_y \Delta v_z. \tag{51}$$

The function $f(v)$ is the well-known probability or Gauss error function already introduced in Chapter II (cf. Fig. 2·1). The fractional number of molecules per unit velocity interval in the neighborhood of v is a symmetrical function of the resultant velocity, with the result that the average velocity is zero.

Often a more useful type of distribution law than (51) is that for the fractional number of molecules having resultant velocity magnitude in the interval from v to $v + \Delta v$. This distribution thus disregards the direction of the velocity. If we imagine a momentum space in which each point represents a possible resultant momentum value for a molecule, the points corresponding to molecules with resultant momentum magnitudes between mv and $mv + m\Delta v$ will lie in a spherical shell of radius mv

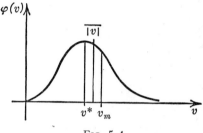

Fig. 5·4.

and thickness $m\Delta v$, with volume $4\pi m^3 v^2 \Delta v$. Denoting by $(\Delta N)'$ the number of molecules corresponding to this volume gives

$$\frac{(\Delta N)'}{\Delta N} = \frac{4\pi m^3 v^2 \Delta v}{m^3 \Delta v_x \Delta v_y \Delta v_z}. \tag{52}$$

By substitution for ΔN from (50) the desired distribution formula then proves to be

$$\frac{(\Delta N)'}{N} = 4\pi v^2 \left(\frac{m}{2\pi kT}\right)^{3/2} e^{-mv^2/2kT} \Delta v = \phi(v)\,\Delta v. \tag{53}$$

The plot of $\phi(v)$ yields the non-symmetrical curve shown in Fig. 5·4.

We can use the non-symmetrical Maxwell distribution to calculate some average values of the velocity. First we shall compute the velocity corresponding to ϕ_{max}. This will be denoted by v^* and is obtained by solving $\dfrac{d\phi(v)}{dv} = 0$. We get

$$v^* = \sqrt{\frac{2kT}{m}}. \tag{54}$$

Next, the average of the absolute value of v is given by

$$\overline{|v|} = \int_0^\infty v\phi(v)\,dv.$$

On employing partial integration there results

$$\overline{|v|} = \frac{2}{\sqrt{\pi}} v^* \sim 1.13\, v^*. \tag{55}$$

We have already introduced the root-mean-square velocity as the most important average velocity in kinetic theory. The evaluation of v^2 from (53) yields

$$\overline{v^2} = \int_0^\infty v^2 \phi(v)dv = \frac{3kT}{m}, \tag{56}$$

with

$$v_m = \sqrt{\frac{3kT}{m}}, \tag{57}$$

in agreement with the result of the simple theory at the beginning of this chapter. We have indicated in Fig. 5·4 the fact that

$$v_m > \overline{|v|} > v^*.$$

In practically all subsequent applications we shall employ v_m.

The average kinetic energy can also be found from (56) with the usual result, i.e.,

$$\overline{E_{\text{kin}}} = \tfrac{3}{2}kT. \tag{58}$$

Many attempts have been made to verify the formula (53) experimentally. One of the more recent ones is that of Zartman,[7] who studied the deposition of evaporated bismuth atoms on the inside of a revolving cylinder and obtained a "velocity spectrum" in good agreement with the Maxwell law.[8]

6. APPLICATION OF THE MAXWELL DISTRIBUTION TO COLLISIONS

The discussion of collisions and mean free path given in Sec. 3 can now be generalized to include the assumption of the Maxwell distribution. Let us consider the collisions between the set of molecules having velocity components in the interval v_x, $v_x + dv_x$, etc., to be denoted as set 1 for convenience and the set having velocity components in the interval V_x, $V_x + dV_x$, etc., to be denoted as set 2. The relative velocity of a molecule in set 1 with respect to a molecule in set 2 has the magnitude

$$v_r = \sqrt{(V_x - v_x)^2 + (V_y - v_y)^2 + (V_z - v_z)^2}. \tag{59}$$

---

[7] *Phys. Rev.* **37**, 383 (1931).

[8] For a discussion of these and other similar experiments, the reader is referred to Kennard, *loc. cit.*, pp. 71 f. See also "Atomic Physics," Univ. of Pittsburgh Staff, second edition, p. 11, 1937.

The average number of collisions per second which any single molecule of set 2 makes is (from Eq. 37)

$$Z'_c = \pi D^2 n \bar{v}_r = \pi D^2 n \left(\frac{m}{2\pi kT}\right)^{3/2} \int\int\int_{-\infty}^{+\infty} v_r e^{-mv^2/2kT} dv_x dv_y dv_z, \quad (60)$$

where the average is taken over *all* the molecules in unit volume by allowing v_x, v_y, v_z to take on all possible values. Evidently Z'_c is a function of V_x, V_y, V_z. What we wish is the average number of collisions suffered by a molecule of *any* velocity. To get this from (60) we must multiply by the probability of finding a molecule of set 2 and then integrate once more over the velocities. Thus the desired collision rate is finally

$$Z_c = \pi D^2 n \left(\frac{m}{2\pi kT}\right)^3 \int\int\int\int\int_{-\infty}^{+\infty} v_r e^{-m(v^2+V^2)/2kT} .$$

$$dv_x dv_y dv_z d V_x d V_y d V_z. \quad (61)$$

To evaluate the integral (61) we introduce the following transformation

$$V_x = \alpha - \frac{a}{2} ; \qquad v_x = \alpha + \frac{a}{2}$$

$$V_y = \beta - \frac{b}{2} ; \qquad v_y = \beta + \frac{b}{2} \qquad (62)$$

$$V_z = \gamma - \frac{c}{2} ; \qquad v_z = \gamma + \frac{c}{2} .$$

Then

$$v_r = \sqrt{a^2 + b^2 + c^2}.$$

and substitution into (61) yields

$$Z = \pi D^2 n \left(\frac{m}{2\pi kT}\right)^3 \int\int\int\int\int_{-\infty}^{+\infty} \sqrt{a^2 + b^2 + c^2}.$$

$$e^{-(m/kT)\cdot(\alpha^2+\beta^2+\gamma^2)} e^{-(m/4kT)\cdot(a^2+b^2+c^2)} \cdot d\alpha d\beta d\gamma \, dadbdc, \quad (63)$$

where we have used the fact that

$$d V_x d V_y d V_z dv_x dv_y dv_z = \frac{\partial(V_x, V_y, V_z, v_x, v_y, v_z)}{\partial(\alpha, \beta, \gamma, a, b, c)} d\alpha d\beta d\gamma dadbdc. \quad (64)$$

$\dfrac{\partial(V_x, \cdots)}{\partial(\alpha, \cdots)}$ is the Jacobian of the transformation, i.e.,

$$\frac{\partial(V_x, \cdots)}{\partial(\alpha, \cdots)} = \begin{vmatrix} \dfrac{\partial V_x}{\partial \alpha} & \dfrac{\partial V_y}{\partial \alpha} & \dfrac{\partial V_z}{\partial \alpha} & \dfrac{\partial v_x}{\partial \alpha} & \dfrac{\partial v_y}{\partial \alpha} & \dfrac{\partial v_z}{\partial \alpha} \\ \cdot & \cdot & \cdot & \cdot & \cdot & \cdot \\ \cdot & \cdot & \cdot & \cdot & \cdot & \cdot \\ \dfrac{\partial V_x}{\partial c} & \dfrac{\partial V_y}{\partial c} & \dfrac{\partial V_z}{\partial c} & \dfrac{\partial v_x}{\partial c} & \dfrac{\partial v_y}{\partial c} & \dfrac{\partial v_z}{\partial c} \end{vmatrix}. \tag{65}$$

In the present case this reduces to *unity*, leading to (63). To evaluate (63) we note first that

$$\int\!\!\!\int\!\!\!\int_{-\infty}^{+\infty} e^{-(m/kT)\cdot(\alpha^2+\beta^2+\gamma^2)} d\alpha\, d\beta\, d\gamma = \left(\frac{\pi kT}{m}\right)^{3/2}.$$

There remains the triple integration over a, b, c. We transform to spherical coordinates, i.e.,

$$a = w \sin\theta \cos\phi, \quad b = w \sin\theta \sin\phi, \quad c = w \cos\theta,$$

whence

$$a^2 + b^2 + c^2 = w^2,$$

and

$$da\,db\,dc = w^2 \sin\theta\, d\theta\, d\phi\, dw.$$

This yields

$$\int\!\!\!\int\!\!\!\int_{-\infty}^{+\infty} (\ ) da\,db\,dc = \int_0^{2\pi} \int_0^{\pi} \int_0^{+\infty} w^3 e^{-(mw^2/4kT)} \sin\theta\, d\theta\, d\phi\, dw$$

$$= 2\pi \left(\frac{4kT}{m}\right)^2,$$

and therefore the final result is

$$Z_c = 2\sqrt{2\pi}\, D^2 n \sqrt{\frac{2kT}{m}} = 4\sqrt{\frac{\pi}{3}}\, D^2 n v_m. \tag{66}$$

This value of Z_c should be compared with that in eq. (44) which we obtained on the assumption that all the molecules move with the velocity v_m. Since $\pi/3$ is very close to unity, the difference between the two formulas is slight, amounting in fact to only a little over 2 per cent. While it is decidedly unsafe to generalize on the basis of a single illustration, this result does suggest that the invocation of the Maxwell distribution does not alter the general functional form of simple kinetic theory formulas but may be expected merely to introduce a slightly altered numerical multiplying factor. This presumption is realized to some extent by more extensive study, though the change in the factor may indeed be larger than in the case just discussed.

The value of the mean free path obtained from (66) turns out to be

$$\lambda = \frac{\sqrt{3/\pi}}{4D^2 n}, \tag{67}$$

differing very slightly from our more simple version in eq. (45).

7. TRANSPORT PHENOMENA

The phenomenon of viscosity as described by the kinetic theory of gases is an illustration of a group of effects known under the heading of *transport* phenomena. Other well-known illustrations are heat conduction and diffusion. It is not our intention to give a detailed discussion of these effects which are usually extensively treated in the standard kinetic theory texts.[9] However, it will be worth while to discuss them qualitatively and give for reference some of the fundamental formulas, particularly with a view to the influence of the Maxwell distribution on the results.

We have already mentioned viscosity in Sec. 4 and have given a "derivation" of a sort for the coefficient of viscosity of a gas. The application of the Maxwell law to the problem is a rather involved matter but finally leads to the result

$$\eta = 0.310 \rho v_m \lambda, \tag{68}$$

differing from the value in eq. (48) by the difference between $\frac{1}{3}$ and 0.310. Actually the problem proves to be more complicated than even the Maxwell distribution would make it; in fact account must be taken of the fluctuations which occur from the precise Maxwell distribution and which exert a considerable influence on the viscosity which tends to increase the numerical factor [10] in (68) to nearly 0.5.

The conduction of heat through a gas, like that through a solid, takes place whenever a temperature gradient exists. The thermal conductivity κ is defined by the fundamental equation

$$\frac{dQ}{dt} = -\kappa \frac{dT}{dx}, \tag{69}$$

[9] Cf., for example, Kennard, *op. cit.*, pp. 135 ff.

[10] This will be true only for an infinitely rare gas. This result is due to Chapman. For the reference, consult Kennard, *op. cit.*, p. 147.

where dQ/dt is the rate of flow of heat per unit area per second in the x direction and dT/dx is the temperature gradient in this direction. From the standpoint of kinetic theory thermal conduction is due to the transfer of the energy of the on-the-average faster moving molecules from the high temperature region to the lower temperature region. Of course molecules from the low temperature region also move to the higher temperature region but they carry less energy and hence there is a *net* transfer of energy in the direction of decreasing temperature. We can even give a simple theory of thermal conduction by considering the transfer of energy from one layer of a gas to another just as we treated the transfer of momentum in the simplified discussion of viscosity in Sec. 4.

Let us refer once more to Fig. 5·3 and assume that the average kinetic energy per molecule in plane A is E_1 while that in plane B is E_2. By utilizing assumptions similar to those employed in Sec. 4, we arrive at the conclusion that the $nv_m/6$ molecules which cross unit area per second moving downward from A, transfer the kinetic energy $nv_m/6 \cdot E_1$, while those moving upward from B, transfer the amount $nv_m/6 \cdot E_2$. There is thus a net transfer of kinetic energy of

$$\frac{nv_m}{6} (E_1 - E_2)$$

over a distance of 2λ. But we can write

$$\frac{E_1 - E_2}{2\lambda} = \frac{dE}{ds},$$

where dE/ds is the gradient of kinetic energy in the direction of temperature change. The rate of flow of heat energy per unit area per second then becomes

$$\frac{dQ}{dt} = -\frac{nv_m\lambda}{3}\frac{dE}{ds}, \tag{70}$$

where the negative sign emphasizes that the flow takes place along the negative gradient. Now we can get a connection with (69) by observing that

$$\frac{dE}{ds} = \frac{dE}{dT}\frac{dT}{ds}, \tag{71}$$

whence

$$\kappa = \frac{1}{3} nv_m\lambda \frac{dE}{dT}. \tag{72}$$

But $n \dfrac{dE}{dT}$ is the specific heat of the gas at constant volume per unit volume and divided by the density is the ordinary specific heat c_V (eq. 28). Hence for an ideal homogeneous gas this simplified theory yields

$$\kappa = \tfrac{1}{3}\rho v_m \lambda c_V = \eta c_V. \qquad (73)$$

This is an extremely interesting result, connecting as it does the thermal conductivity with the viscosity and specific heat at constant volume. All these are independently measurable quantities so that the relation provides a good test of the success of kinetic theory. Since the derivation is idealized and all intermolecular action is ignored, we cannot expect indeed that (73) will be satisfied exactly for any gas though there should be agreement in order of magnitude. A table of experimental values quoted by Kennard [11] indicates that the ratio $\kappa/\eta c_V$ for the rare gases helium, neon, and argon averages about 2.45. For hydrogen, nitrogen, and oxygen the ratio is around 2. It is interesting to note that for the gases with more complicated molecules like NH_3, the ratio drops to approximately 1.5. It is clear that the relation (73) has only order of magnitude validity and further study is necessary to establish an accurate relation. This has been done by Chapman (cf. Kennard, as before, for references) who found that for monatomic gases (73) should be replaced by $\kappa = 5/2 \cdot \eta c_V$. This is in good agreement with experiment. On the other hand for polyatomic gases Eucken has derived the formula $\kappa = 1/4 \cdot (9\gamma - 5)\eta c_V$ (with $\gamma = c_p/c_V$) which is also in excellent agreement with experiment.

Diffusion takes place in a gas composed of two or more different kinds of molecules where the concentrations vary from point to point. The result is an eventual evening out of differences of composition with the ultimate attainment of uniform concentration throughout the gas. Kinetic theory describes this process in terms of the greater probability of molecules of a given kind to move from a region of high concentration to one of low concentration than in the reverse direction. This, of course, tends to wipe out differences in concentration. Diffusion may be described quantitatively in terms of the diffusion coefficient. Suppose the gas contains two different kinds of molecules with concentration n_1 and n_2 (number of molecules per unit volume). These are functions of both space and time. An analysis of the problem, into which we shall not go, shows that for

----

[11] *Op. cit.*, p. 180.

an ideal gas the variation of n_1 and n_2 with t and x,y,z is expressible by the fundamental differential equations

$$\frac{\partial n_1}{\partial t} = D\nabla^2 n_1,$$

$$\frac{\partial n_2}{\partial t} = D\nabla^2 n_2. \tag{74}$$

In these equations D is called the *diffusion coefficient* for the mixture of the two gases. It has the dimensions of square centimeters/second. The reader will note the interesting resemblance between eqs. (74) and the ordinary differential equation for heat conduction, obtained from the definition eq. (69). Thus if T is the absolute temperature

$$\frac{\partial T}{\partial t} = \frac{\kappa}{\rho c_V} \cdot \nabla^2 T. \tag{75}$$

A simplified theory of diffusion due to Meyer leads to the following equation connecting D with the mean free path

$$D = \frac{1}{3}\left(\frac{n_2 v_{m1}\lambda_1 + n_1 v_{m2}\lambda_2}{n_1 + n_2}\right), \tag{76}$$

where the subscript 1 refers to the molecules of the first kind and 2 to those of the second kind. It must be noted that the mean free paths in this formula are those given in terms of the root-mean-square velocity. The formula (76) takes no account of the Maxwell distribution nor of the more recent Chapman theoretical considerations. Kennard's book should be consulted for their effect.

8. THE BOLTZMANN *H*-THEOREM

In Sec. 5 we introduced the Maxwell distribution of velocities of the molecules of a gas as a kinetic representation of the canonical distribution of particles in an aggregate with respect to their kinetic energy. This was based on purely statistical considerations in accordance with which the canonical distribution and hence the Maxwell distribution is the most likely one because there are more ways in which it can be realized than any other. As such we took it to correspond to the state of equilibrium of the aggregate. From the standpoint of pure kinetic theory this might appear to be a somewhat gratuitous assumption. When we realize that the molecules are in the continual process of changing their velocities by collision, how can we be sure that *any* steady distribution of velocities will ever be obtained, or that if such does occur the distribution may not actually be different from the Maxwellian? It is worth pointing out that these questions do not arise in a strictly statistical theory. Nevertheless they are fundamental in kinetic theory. They were answered by Boltzmann,[12] and the answer is included in his celebrated H-theorem. Boltzmann investigated the quantity

$$H = \int f \log f \, dk, \qquad (77)$$

where

$$f = f(v_x, v_y, v_z, t) \qquad (78)$$

is the velocity distribution function, e.g., the Maxwell $f(v)$ in our eq. (51) (divided by the constant $(m/2\pi kT)^{3/2}$ to make it non-dimensional) and $dk = dv_x \, dv_y \, dv_z$. The integral in (77) is a triple one with the limits from $- \infty$ to $+ \infty$. We have indicated in (78) that f may be a function of the time; it is not, of course, in the Maxwellian case.

Boltzmann proceeded to form dH/dt from (77) in terms of $\partial f/\partial t$. The latter quantity can be expressed in terms of f itself by means of a rather general and somewhat elaborate study of the effect of collisions on the distribution function. We shall not go into this, but merely state that without specification of the precise form of f, it develops that

$$\frac{dH}{dt} \leq 0. \qquad (79)$$

In words, the function H cannot increase with the time. In particular for a *steady* distribution dH/dt must vanish. But from the form of dH/dt, its vanishing implies necessarily that f have the Maxwellian form. The Maxwellian distribution then is the only steady one, i.e., the only one which does not change with the time. This is the essential content of the H-theorem. However, one can go on to show that H has a minimum value for the Maxwell distribution as compared with all others having the same v_m, i.e., the same average energy. Hence we see that the effect of the collisions is to make f ultimately assume the Maxwellian form if at any initial instant it does not possess it. One could even get an idea of the rapidity with which the Maxwell distribution is approached by computing dH/dt. For ideal gases under ordinary conditions of temperature and pressure this rate is very rapid indeed. It can be shown [13] that if the initial distribution is non-Maxwellian and the mean square velocity com-

---

[12] K. Akad. Wiss. (Wien) Sitzungsberichte **66**, 275 (1872).
[13] Cf. Jeans, op. cit., p. 243.

ponents in the three coordinate directions differ, the time in which
the difference between any two such components becomes $1/e$ of its
initial difference is of the order of

$$\tau = \frac{\eta}{p}, \tag{80}$$

where η is as usual the viscosity and p the pressure. This time was
called by Maxwell the " relaxation time." Thus for hydrogen at $0°$ C
and standard conditions

$$\tau \sim 8.4 \times 10^{-11} \text{ sec.}$$

It will be noticed that this is comparable with the time taken by a
hydrogen molecule under these conditions to traverse a free path
equal to the mean free path. It gives a good idea of how quickly
any deviations from the Maxwell distribution may be expected to
disappear.

In our later study of statistical mechanics we shall find an interesting connection between the H function of Boltzmann and the
entropy. The theorem (79) will be found indeed to have a close relation with the law of increasing entropy of an isolated system.

9. EQUATION OF STATE OF A REAL GAS. VIRIAL FOR INTERACTION FORCES

The treatment of kinetic theory in this chapter has been limited
to the ideal gas in which forces between the individual molecules,
aside from those arising from collisions, are entirely neglected. Much
of the lack of precise agreement between the results of kinetic theory
and the behavior of actual gases has been traced to this neglect. For
example, the equation of state

$$pV = NkT,$$

derived from the simple kinetic theory in Sec. 1, describes a real gas
accurately only when it is well above its critical temperature. Efforts
have naturally been made to obtain a more satisfactory equation of
state by taking into account molecular interaction. In spite of the
years of investigation from Maxwell's time to the present, this subject
can hardly be considered to be in satisfactory condition from a
theoretical point of view. However, in this section we present an
introduction to the subject, adopting the method of the virial already
used for the ideal gas in Sec. 1.

We shall suppose that the interaction forces in question are *central*,
i.e., depend only on the distance r_{ij} from the ith to the jth particle

If m_i is the mass of the ith particle and m_j that of the jth, it will be assumed that the force between the two may be expressed as $m_i m_j f(r_{ij})$. Hence the x component of the force may be written as

$$F_{ij}^x = m_i m_j f(r_{ij})(x_i - x_j)/r_{ij}, \qquad (81)$$

where x_i and x_j are the x coordinates of the two particles respectively. We must now apply this to the computation of Ω in eq. (6). Consider first simply the two particles i and j. The contribution to the virial arising from their mutual interaction is then

$$-\frac{1}{2} m_i m_j \frac{f(r_{ij})}{r_{ij}} \overline{[x_i(x_i - x_j) + x_j(x_j - x_i) + \text{similar terms in } y \text{ and } z]},$$

which becomes on reduction and combination of terms

$$-\tfrac{1}{2} m_i m_j \overline{f(r_{ij})r_{ij}}. \qquad (82)$$

There is an important point about (82) which deserves attention. Due to the symmetrical average distribution of the particles the average force on each is zero (save close to the walls of the container). We must be careful not to conclude, however, that therefore $\overline{f(r_{ij})r_{ij}} = 0$.

Summing over the whole aggregate of particles we have

$$-\tfrac{1}{2} \sum_{i, j} m_i m_j \cdot \overline{f(r_{ij})r_{ij}},$$

where the summation is extended over all pairs of particles. If now we combine this with the contribution to the virial due to the surface forces (eq. 11), the virial theorem yields

$$\tfrac{3}{2} NkT = \tfrac{3}{2} pV - \tfrac{1}{2} \sum_{i, j} m_i m_j \overline{f(r_{ij})r_{ij}}. \qquad (83)$$

The equation of state then takes the general form

$$pV = NkT + \tfrac{1}{3} \sum_{i, j} m_i m_j \overline{f(r_{ij})r_{ij}}. \qquad (84)$$

If we were acquainted with the precise nature of the intermolecular forces, i.e., the $f(r_{ij})$, and could evaluate the sum involved in the second term on the right-hand side of (84) we should have a theoretical deduction of the exact equation of state of any real gas. However, we do not know the intermolecular forces, except in so far as better information about them is being obtained by quantum mechanical studies which are not considered in the present purely classical treatment. Of course one might try various force laws and see how the resulting equations compare with the empirically known equations of state. The difficulty comes, however, in carrying out the evaluation of the summation for any force law. We can at any rate draw certain semi-quantitative conclusions from the general expression (84). In the first place we can recall the bearing of an important observation of Maxwell on the equation. From a certain point of view the equation says that the pressure of a gas may be thought of as arising from two sources, i.e., (a) the motion of the molecules symbolized by the term NkT in (84) and, (b) the intermolecular forces symbolized by the summation term in (84). One finds it interesting to ask what would be the result of assuming that the pressure arises primarily from the forces rather than from the motions. This of course would imply *repulsive* forces between the molecules. But Maxwell observed that in this case Boyle's law pV = constant at constant temperature would demand that $f(r_{ij})$ should vary as $1/r_{ij}$, for only in this way could $\Sigma f(r_{ij})r_{ij}$ be made constant. But this inverse distance force law would lead to the result that the force action of the portion of the gas far away from a particular molecule would be greater than that near at hand. (Recall that the number of molecules in the neighborhood of a particular molecule goes up roughly as the square of the distance from the molecule.) This would produce differences of pressure in vessels of the same volume but different shape, even at the same temperature—an anomaly not observed. Maxwell therefore concluded that most of the reason for the pressure of a gas on the molecular theory must be sought in the kinetic energy term and the summation term must be considered a correction only.

If we consider the intermolecular forces as cohesive in nature, i.e., as attractive but falling off in intensity very sharply with the distance, we can estimate the summation $\Sigma m_i m_j r_{ij} f(r_{ij})$ rather readily as follows. Let us first replace $m_i m_j f(r_{ij})$ by $\phi(r_{ij})$. Consider the interaction between the group of molecules in volume dV placed for convenience at the origin of a system of spherical coordinates and the group in volume dV' all at distance r from the first group. Let n as usual denote the number of molecules per unit volume and neglect to a first approximation the effect of the cohesive forces on the uniformity of spatial distribution. Then the contribution of the forces between the two groups to the sum in question becomes

$$n^2 dV dV' r\phi(r)dr.$$

The total contribution for the whole gas will be obtained by integrating the above over dV and dV' and dividing by 2 to avoid counting the volume twice. Let $dV' = 4\pi r^2 dr$. We need not worry over the precise upper limit of the integration since $\phi(r)$ is assumed to fall off very rapidly with r. Hence

$$\overline{\Sigma r\phi(r)} = \frac{4\pi n^2}{2} \int dV \int_0^\infty r^3\phi(r)dr. \qquad (85)$$

The average required by the definition of the virial is here effectively implied in the procedure of taking the *average* number of particles per unit volume. The $\int_0^\infty r^3\phi(r)dr$ is a negative constant which we may call $-a'$, while $\int dV = V$, the total volume of the gas. Hence

$$\overline{\Sigma r\phi(r)} = -\frac{2\pi N^2 a'}{V}. \qquad (86)$$

Equation (84) then becomes

$$p = \frac{NkT}{V} - \frac{2}{3}\frac{\pi N^2 a'}{V^2}.$$

If further we let $2/3 \cdot \pi N^2 a' = a$, a constant which does depend, of course, on the total amount of gas, the equation of state becomes

$$\left(p + \frac{a}{V^2}\right) V = NkT. \qquad (87)$$

When the molecules get very close together it is necessary to assume that the attractive forces become repulsive. The calculation of the contribution of these repulsive forces to the virial is a more complicated matter. It is carried out by Jeans [14] and leads to the result that we must *add* to the virial the term

$$\frac{3bNkT}{V}, \qquad (88)$$

where b has the value

$$b = \tfrac{2}{3}N\pi D^3, \qquad (89)$$

the molecules still being supposed to be elastic spheres with diameter D. The result of (88) is to modify eq. (84) still further. If b/V is small the resulting equation may be written

$$\left(p + \frac{a}{V^2}\right)(V - b) = NkT. \qquad (90)$$

[14] *Op. cit.*, p. 131.   Cf. also Loeb, *op. cit.*, p. 138.

This is the familiar van der Waals' equation, which is fairly successful in describing the behavior of many real gases. It is interesting to note that b appears as equal to four times the total volume of all the molecules in the gas. In many discussions of van der Waals' equation it is introduced as a correction to the volume of the gas to allow for the volume actually occupied by the molecules. In the present discussion it arises more properly as a contribution from the very short range repulsive forces which must exist between the molecules.

10. THE BROWNIAN MOTION AND MOLECULAR REALITY

In concluding this brief survey of kinetic theory we encounter a question which must often have been seriously asked in the early days of the theory: Are molecules real? Do they actually exist and can we know about their existence more directly than by the success of the theory as a description of thermodynamical phenomena? From the standpoint of modern physical methodology these questions have little or no meaning. Nevertheless the attempt to answer them led to an exhaustive study of an interesting phenomenon and shed much light on other kinetic properties. The phenomenon takes its name from the English botanist Robert Brown, who in 1827, noticed the irregular but ceaseless motion of small particles, e.g., gamboge, suspended in a liquid. The same phenomenon is also exhibited in striking fashion by smoke particles suspended in air. At first the motion was thought to be of organic origin but after the rise of the kinetic theory it became clear that the only reasonable explanation for it lies in the assumption that the particles are subject to the continual bombardment of the molecules of the surrounding medium. The most complete experimental study of the phenomenon is that of Perrin.[15] The theory has been developed by a number of investigators, including Einstein, Smoluchowski and Langevin. We shall present here the method due to Langevin.[16]

Consider the motion along the x axis of a single particle in a viscous medium. The equation of motion is, by an extension of Stokes' law for the fall of a sphere through a viscous fluid,[17]

$$m\ddot{x} + 6\pi\eta a\dot{x} = X. \qquad (91)$$

Here m is the mass of the particle, supposed to be a sphere of radius a, and the viscosity of the medium is η. The X on the right represents

---

[15] Cf. "Brownian Movement and Molecular Reality," trans. by F. Soddy, Taylor and Francis, London, 1910.

[16] P. Langevin, *Comptes rendus*, **146**, 530 (1908).

[17] See, for example, Page, *op. cit.*, p. 273.

the unknown force due to the molecular impacts. All we know about it is that it is positive as often as it is negative and sufficiently large to maintain motion.

It will be convenient to rewrite eq (91) in terms of $\xi = x - x_0$, which is the actual displacement of the particle in time t if x_0 is the initial distance from the origin. Then multiplying through by ξ, we obtain

$$m\ddot{\xi}\xi + 6\pi\eta a\dot{\xi}\xi = X\xi. \tag{92}$$

We can write at once

$$\frac{d^2\xi^2}{dt^2} = 2\dot{\xi}^2 + 2\ddot{\xi}\xi.$$

Therefore

$$\frac{m}{2}\frac{d^2\xi^2}{dt^2} - m\dot{\xi}^2 + 3\pi\eta a\frac{d}{dt}(\xi^2) = X\xi. \tag{93}$$

If next we average over a large number of identical particles, $\overline{X\xi}$ becomes vanishingly small. We set $z = \overline{\xi^2}$ and get

$$\frac{m}{2}\dot{z} + 3\pi\eta az = m\overline{\dot{\xi}^2}. \tag{94}$$

Now if the particles can be thought of as forming an ideal gas the principle of equipartition of kinetic energy should apply and we can set $m\overline{\dot{\xi}^2} = kT$. Hence eq. (94) becomes

$$\dot{z} = \frac{2kT}{m} - \frac{6\pi\eta az}{m}, \tag{95}$$

which on integration yields

$$z = kT/3\pi\eta a + Ce^{-6\pi\eta at/m}. \tag{96}$$

Here C is a constant of integration. If the density of the material composing the particles is, let us say, about 1.2 grams/cm³; and if the viscosity is that of water, i.e., approximately 0.012 gram/cm sec; and if $a = 0.2 \times 10^{-4}$ cm, we have

$$6\pi\eta a/m \sim 10^8 \text{ sec}^{-1}.$$

Hence as far as any steady state is concerned we may safely neglect the last term in (96). That equation then becomes

$$\frac{d}{dt}\overline{\xi^2} = \frac{kT}{3\pi\eta a},$$

yielding on integration

$$\overline{\xi^2} = kT/3\pi\eta a \cdot \tau + \overline{\xi_0^2} \tag{97}$$

for the mean square displacement along the x axis at time τ, if $\overline{\xi_0^2}$ is the initial mean square displacement. But we can always choose $\overline{\xi_0^2} = 0$ and have finally

$$\overline{\xi^2} = kT/3\pi\eta a \cdot \tau, \tag{98}$$

which is the equation for the Brownian motion first deduced by Einstein, giving the mean square displacement as a linear function of the time. As an illustration consider a typical experiment of Perrin in which 50 gamboge particles all with radii very close to $a = 0.212 \times 10^{-4}$ cm were suspended in water at 20° C. The mean-square displacement component along one direction, which we may take to be the x axis,[18] was measured for the value $\tau = 30$ sec. The result was $\overline{\xi^2} = 4.5 \times 10^{-7}$ cm². Substitution into (98) yields a value for the Boltzmann constant

$$k = 1.23 \times 10^{-16} \text{ ergs/degree C.}$$

This is of the correct order of magnitude and the result may be taken as a confirmation of the essential success of the theory and the value of the Brownian motion for the study of molecular phenomena.

PROBLEMS

1. Use the virial theorem to prove that in an aggregate of particles which are not confined in a box but which nevertheless have their motions bounded and attract each other with a force varying inversely as the square of the distance of separation the time average of the total kinetic energy is equal to minus one-half the time average of the total potential energy.

2. One thousand molecules of hydrogen are in thermal equilibrium at 0° C. Find the number with speeds between 0 and 100 meters/sec; 100 and 200 meters/sec and so on up to 3,000 meters/sec. Plot the results in the form of a curve and indicate on it the positions of v^*, $\overline{|v|}$ and v_m.

3. In Problem 2, find the total number of molecules whose speeds are less than v_m. What is the probability that a molecule shall have its speed lying between v^* and v_m?

4. In Problem 2, find the total number of molecules whose component velocity along the x axis lies between 500 meters/sec and 550 meters/sec, whose component velocity along the y axis lies between -500 meters/sec and -450 meters/sec and whose component velocity along the z axis lies between 600 meters/sec and 650 meters/sec. To what range of directions and resultant speed does this correspond?

5. The mass of an electron is 9×10^{-28} gram. In an ideal gas composed of free electrons, i.e., mutual interaction neglected, calculate the root-mean-square velocity at 0° C. Compare the pressure exerted by the ideal electron gas on the walls of the

---

[18] Strictly speaking one ought to consider the component displacements along the y and z axes also. The analytical treatment is the same as above. Perrin should be consulted for details on this and other experimental points.

confining vessel at $0°$ C with that exerted by helium gas at the same temperature, the number of particles per unit volume being assumed to be the same in each case.

6. Fifty cubic centimeters of a certain mixture of oxygen and nitrogen at $0°$ C contain 2×10^{20} molecules of nitrogen and 5×10^{18} molecules of oxygen. Calculate the partial pressure due to each gas as well as the pressure exerted by the mixture.

7. Generalize the Maxwell distribution (50) to the case of an aggregate of independent particles in the constant gravitational field at the surface of the earth. Relate the result to the well known variation of density with height in the atmosphere.

8. Carry out the evaluation of the Jacobian of the transformation (62) and prove that it is equal to unity. Find the Jacobian of the transformation from rectangular to spherical coordinates.

9. Evaluate the mean free path for hydrogen, helium, and nitrogen molecules under standard conditions. Plot the mean free path of hydrogen molecules as a function of the temperature from $0°$ C to $300°$ C.

10. In van der Waal's equation of state (eq. 90) show that if the critical specific volume, critical pressure and critical temperature are employed as *units* of specific volume, pressure and temperature, respectively, the equation takes the form

$$\left(p' + \frac{3}{v'^2} \right)\left(v' - \frac{1}{3} \right) = \frac{8}{3} T',$$

it being understood that one gram of gas is in question and that $p' = p/p_c$, $v' = v/v_c$, and $T' = T/T_c$. For chlorine at 10 atmospheres and $T = 293°$ K, find the values of v. Which value corresponds to the purely gaseous state?

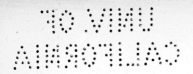
CHAPTER VI

CLASSICAL STATISTICAL MECHANICS

1. THE CHARACTERISTICS OF STATISTICAL MECHANICS

The discussion of the preceding chapters on the application of the statistical method to physics may arouse wonder regarding the next step in this study. Conceivably we might develop the kinetic theory further. This, however, would necessarily involve the detailed study of forces between molecules, lying outside the purely statistical ideas. These matters are sufficiently discussed in professional treatises on kinetic theory. We have seen that a rational foundation for thermodynamics is provided by the Maxwell-Boltzmann statistics as treated in Chapter IV. This might appear to satisfy all our needs and render further investigation unnecessary save for the mere enumeration and solution of specific applications which after all are a part of thermodynamics anyway.

The reader will certainly have noted, however, as a somewhat queer circumstance that whereas the kinetic theory employs mechanical ideas in its set-up, the Maxwell-Boltzmann statistics is essentially non-mechanical. Fundamentally all its results are based on the distribution of objects or entities of any sort in groups with respect to some property or properties. Moreover the entities in question are assumed to be independent and without mutual influence. It is true we have introduced a few special applications of the Maxwell-Boltzmann point of view to mechanical systems consisting of free particles.[1] Further progress would now appear to be possible in the construction of a new point of view in which mechanical and statistical concepts are welded together from the beginning in a single unified theory. The postulates of such a theory, with which we shall associate the name statistical mechanics, will necessarily appear general and abstract. Nevertheless we can hope that they will serve as a rational basis for thermodynamics in the sense that the theorems deduced from them will form the laws of thermodynamics and that from the results of the

---

[1] Moreover in Sec. 9, Chapter V, we discussed the kinetic theory for a gas with interacting particles, but this transcends the strictly logical application of the Maxwell-Boltzmann statistics.

102

theory we can calculate (as averages, of course) the significant functions in the thermodynamical equations. If such a theory turns out to be successful, its very generality should guarantee its universal applicability.

The first to found statistical mechanics in the formal sense just explained was J. Willard Gibbs.[2] We shall refer to the method of Gibbs as classical statistical mechanics and it will form the subject matter of the present chapter. With the advent of quantum theory, statistical mechanics has turned in a new direction which will be considered in detail in the latter part of this book. The fundamental ideas of Gibbs, however, are as important today as they were in his own time and no serious student of statistical mechanics can afford to neglect them.

Since statistical mechanics employs in its formulation the concepts of advanced mechanics and in particular the canonical equations of Hamilton, it will be desirable to review these briefly.

2. REVIEW OF ADVANCED MECHANICS

Consider an aggregate of n particles with masses m_1, $m_2 \cdots m_n$ and position vectors $\mathbf{r}_1$, $\mathbf{r}_2 \cdots \mathbf{r}_n$ in some rectangular coordinate system. Thus, if x_j, y_j, z_j are the rectangular coordinates of the jth particle

$$\mathbf{r}_j = \mathbf{i}x_j + \mathbf{j}y_j + \mathbf{k}z_j.$$

It will be supposed that there are external forces acting on the particles; these are denoted by $\mathbf{F}_1$, $\mathbf{F}_2 \cdots \mathbf{F}_n$. According to D'Alembert's principle and the principle of virtual displacements[3] the motion of the aggregate is given by the fundamental equation

$$\sum_{j=1}^{n} (m_j \ddot{\mathbf{r}}_j - \mathbf{F}_j) \cdot \delta\mathbf{r}_j = 0. \tag{1}$$

Here $\delta\mathbf{r}_j$ represents a possible, i.e., virtual, displacement of the jth particle subject to the constraints acting on the system. In general we distinguish between an *actual* displacement which a particle undergoes in time and a possible displacement which it might but does not

[2] "Elementary Principles in Statistical Mechanics," Yale University Press, 1903. See also his Collected Works, Vol. II, Part 1, 1930. This famous volume was once characterized by Henri Poincaré as a "little book, little read because it is a little hard." It is indeed a model of conciseness. There has recently appeared a useful commentary on it by Arthur Haas in "Commentary on the Scientific Writings of J. Willard Gibbs," Vol. II, Yale University Press, 1936.

[3] Cf. Lindsay and Margenau, "Foundations of Physics," p. 102.

necessarily have, by denoting the former as usual by $d\mathbf{r}_j$ and the latter by $\delta\mathbf{r}_j$. A brief examination discloses that δ has the same *formal* properties as a mathematical operator that d possesses. Thus we can write at once

$$\ddot{\mathbf{r}}_j \cdot \delta\mathbf{r}_j = \frac{d}{dt}(\dot{\mathbf{r}}_j \cdot \delta\mathbf{r}_j) - \tfrac{1}{2}\delta(v_j^2), \tag{2}$$

where $v_j^2 = \dot{\mathbf{r}}_j \cdot \dot{\mathbf{r}}_j$, and is the square of the resultant velocity magnitude for the jth particle. Therefore from (1)

$$\sum_{j=1}^{n} \mathbf{F}_j \cdot \delta\mathbf{r}_j = \sum_{j=1}^{n} m_j \ddot{\mathbf{r}}_j \cdot \delta\mathbf{r}_j = \frac{d}{dt}\sum_{j=1}^{n} m_j \dot{\mathbf{r}}_j \cdot \delta\mathbf{r}_j - \delta T, \tag{3}$$

where we have introduced T for the kinetic energy $\sum \dfrac{m_j}{2} v_j^2$. If we integrate both sides of this equation with respect to the time from t_0 to t_1, we get

$$\sum_{j=1}^{n} m_j \dot{\mathbf{r}}_j \cdot \delta\mathbf{r}_j \bigg]_{t_0}^{t_1} = \int_{t_0}^{t_1} \delta T\, dt + \int_{t_0}^{t_1} \sum_{j=1}^{n} \mathbf{F}_j \cdot \delta\mathbf{r}_j\, dt. \tag{4}$$

Let us limit our attention to possible motions all of which have the same initial and final positions respectively; then $\delta\mathbf{r}_j$ will vanish for all j at both t_0 and t_1 and (4) will become

$$\int_{t_0}^{t_1} (\delta T + \Sigma \mathbf{F}_j \cdot \delta\mathbf{r}_j)\, dt = 0. \tag{5}$$

Finally, let us assume that the forces are conservative. This means that a potential energy function $V(x_j, y_j, z_j)$ exists such that

$$-\mathbf{F}_j = \mathbf{i}\frac{\partial V}{\partial x_j} + \mathbf{j}\frac{\partial V}{\partial y_j} + \mathbf{k}\frac{\partial V}{\partial z_j}. \tag{6}$$

Then since

$$\delta V = \sum_{j=1}^{n} \left(\frac{\partial V}{\partial x_j}\delta x_j + \frac{\partial V}{\partial y_j}\delta y_j + \frac{\partial V}{\partial z_j}\delta z_j \right) \tag{7}$$

we can write (5) in the more convenient form [4]

$$\int_{t_0}^{t_1} \delta(T - V)\, dt = 0. \tag{8}$$

---

[4] The mature reader will see at once the connection between (8) and Hamilton's principle. No discussion is needed here, however. Cf. the discussion in Lindsay and Margenau, *op. cit.*, pp. 128 f.

The quantity $T - V$ is usually referred to as the Lagrangian function of the system and denoted by L. It is here a function of the coordinates and their velocities.

We now find it convenient to abandon the rectangular coordinates in favor of generalized coordinates $q_1 \cdots q_f$, which may have any character as long as a knowledge of them as functions of the time is sufficient to fix the position of every particle of the system at any instant. Their number f is called the number of degrees of freedom of the system. In the case of the aggregate of n particles, free to move in three-dimensional space, we clearly have $f = 3n$. Any constraints on the freedom of motion of the system will, of course, decrease f. Now the q's will necessarily be related to the rectangular coordinates, and we shall express the relation in the following way

$$x_j = x_j(q_1 \cdots q_f); \quad y_j = y_j(q_1 \cdots q_f)$$

$$z_j = z_j(q_1 \cdots q_f). \tag{9}$$

The rectangular velocity components become

$$\dot{x}_j = \sum_{k=1}^{f} \frac{\partial x_j}{\partial q_k} \dot{q}_k, \quad \dot{y}_j = \sum_{k=1}^{f} \frac{\partial y_j}{\partial q_k} \dot{q}_k, \quad \dot{z}_j = \sum_{k=1}^{f} \frac{\partial z_j}{\partial q_k} \dot{q}_k. \tag{10}$$

From (10) the kinetic energy T can also be expressed in terms of the generalized coordinates and generalized velocities $\dot{q}_1 \cdots \dot{q}_f$. It can be shown that T has the form of a homogeneous quadratic function of the $\dot{q}_j$. Thus

$$T = \sum_{i,\,k=1}^{f} a_{ik}\dot{q}_i\dot{q}_k, \tag{11}$$

where the a_{ik} are functions of the q_j. Clearly, since the potential energy V for a conservative system is a function of the x_j, y_j, z_j only, it will also depend solely on the q_j. The problem is to examine eq. (8), keeping in mind that $L = T - V$ is a function of the q_j and $\dot{q}_j$. We could then obtain the Lagrangian equations of motion in the fashion followed in many books. Since these are not the ones useful for statistical mechanics, however, we proceed otherwise.

Let us introduce the quantity p_j defined by

$$p_j = \frac{\partial L}{\partial \dot{q}_j}. \tag{12}$$

This will be called the *momentum conjugate* to q_j. It is, of course, a generalized momentum component and only reduces to the ordinary momentum of Newtonian mechanics when $\dot{q}_j$ is an actual velocity. It will turn out to be a more important quantity for our further considerations than $\dot{q}_j$. Next we bring in the function H defined in the following way

$$H = \sum_{j=1}^{f} p_j \dot{q}_j - L. \tag{13}$$

The function H is known as the Hamiltonian function of the system. From its construction it might appear to be a function of the q_j, $\dot{q}_j$ and p_j. Actually it reduces explicitly to a function of the q_j and p_j. For let us find how H changes when the q_j, $\dot{q}_j$ and p_j change by dq_j, $d\dot{q}_j$ and dp_j respectively. We have

$$dH = \sum_{j=1}^{f} \left(p_j d\dot{q}_j + \dot{q}_j dp_j - \frac{\partial L}{\partial q_j} dq_j - \frac{\partial L}{\partial \dot{q}_j} d\dot{q}_j \right). \tag{14}$$

From the definition of p_j in (12), the first and last terms in the parenthesis cancel and we are left with

$$dH = \sum_{j=1}^{f} \left(\dot{q}_j dp_j - \frac{\partial L}{\partial q_j} dq_j \right), \tag{15}$$

substantiating our statement that H is an explicit function of the q_j and p_j only. We shall denote this by writing H in the form $H(q_j, p_j)$ which is an abbreviation of the longer form $H(q_1 \cdots q_f, p_1 \cdots p_f)$. This notation will be used extensively in what follows.

Equation (8) now takes the form

$$\int^{t_1} \delta \left[\sum_{j=1}^{f} p_j \dot{q}_j - H(p_j, q_j) \right] dt = 0, \tag{16}$$

which immediately becomes

$$\int_{t_0}^{t_1} \left[\sum_{j=1}^{f} \dot{q}_j \delta p_j + \sum_{j=1}^{f} p_j \delta \dot{q}_j - \sum_{j=1}^{f} \frac{\partial H}{\partial q_j} \delta q_j - \sum_{j=1}^{f} \frac{\partial H}{\partial p_j} \delta p_j \right] dt = 0. \tag{17}$$

Partial integration yields

$$\int_{t_0}^{t_1} \sum_{j=1}^{f} p_j \delta \dot{q}_j dt = - \int_{t_0}^{t_1} \sum_{j=1}^{f} \dot{p}_j \delta q_j dt,$$

since all the δq_j and δp_j vanish at t_0 and t_1. Therefore (17) becomes

$$\int_{t_0}^{t_1} \left[\sum_{j=1}^{f} \dot{q}_j \delta p_j - \sum_{j=1}^{f} \frac{\partial H}{\partial p_j} \delta p_j - \sum_{j=1}^{f} \dot{p}_j \delta q_j - \sum_{j=1}^{f} \frac{\partial H}{\partial q_j} \delta q_j \right] dt = 0. \tag{18}$$

Now except for the restriction on the δq_j and δp_j at t_0 and t_1, they are otherwise completely and independently arbitrary. The only way in which (18) can be satisfied under these conditions is to have the integrand vanish identically for all δq_j and δp_j. The independence of the q_j and p_j then implies that we must have

$$\frac{\partial H}{\partial p_j} = \dot{q}_j,$$

$$\frac{\partial H}{\partial q_j} = - \dot{p}_j.$$

(19)

These $2f$ equations of the first order are known as the canonical equations of motion, or alternatively as the Hamiltonian equations of motion.

The connection between the Hamiltonian $H(p_j, q_j)$ and the better known functions T and V becomes clear from its definition (13). Since V is independent of the $\dot{q}_j$, we have

$$p_j = \frac{\partial T}{\partial \dot{q}_j},$$

(20)

and (13) becomes

$$H = \sum_{j=1}^{f} \frac{\partial T}{\partial \dot{q}_j} \dot{q}_j - T + V.$$

(21)

If we differentiate T in (11) with respect to $\dot{q}_j$, then multiply by $\dot{q}_j$ and sum, the result is [5]

$$\sum_{j=1}^{f} \frac{\partial T}{\partial \dot{q}_j} \dot{q}_j = 2T.$$

(22)

Hence

$$H = T + V.$$

(23)

In other words, for a conservative system the Hamiltonian function is simply the total energy expressed as a function of the generalized coordinates and conjugate momenta. For example, for a simple harmonic oscillator with one degree of freedom

$$H = \frac{p^2}{2m} + \frac{kq^2}{2},$$

(24)

[5] This follows at once, of course, from Euler's theorem on homogeneous functions.

the mass of the system being m and the stiffness k. The Hamiltonian equations (19) reduce to two, viz.,

$$\frac{\partial H}{\partial q} = kq = -\dot{p} \tag{25}$$

$$\frac{\partial H}{\partial p} = \frac{p}{m} = \dot{q}. \tag{26}$$

The second equation is identical with the definition $p = \partial L/\partial \dot{q}$, while the first equation is the ordinary Newtonian equation of simple harmonic motion.

An important property of the canonical equations (19) is their invariance of form with respect to an arbitrary transformation of generalized coordinates of the form

$$Q_j = Q_j(q_1 \cdots q_f), \qquad j = 1, 2 \cdots, f. \tag{27}$$

If we denote by T' the kinetic energy in terms of Q_j and $\dot{Q}_j$ and define the new conjugate momentum P_j by

$$P_j = \frac{\partial T'}{\partial \dot{Q}_j}, \tag{28}$$

it develops that we still have

$$\frac{\partial H'}{\partial P_j} = \dot{Q}_j$$

$$\frac{\partial H'}{\partial Q_j} = -\dot{P}_j, \tag{29}$$

where H' is the function of P_j and Q_j obtained by substituting from (27) and (28) into the original Hamiltonian $H(p_j, q_j)$. The fact that the Hamiltonian equations are written in terms of generalized coordinates, of course suggests this invariance property. We shall find it useful in the development of statistical mechanics.

3. PHASE SPACE

The task of statistical mechanics is the description of the behavior of large scale bodies in the form of solids and fluids by assuming them to be dynamical systems with f degrees of freedom, where in general $f \gg 1$. The complete specification of the state of the system is given by the $2f$ coordinates and conjugate momenta $q_1 \cdots q_f, p_1 \cdots p_f$. From this point of view the state is termed the *phase* of the system. It is customary to think of the $2f$ quantities constituting the phase as

being represented geometrically by a point in a $2f$ dimensional orthog-
onal space called the *phase space* of the system. Each system has its
own phase space. As the p's and q's vary with the time the phase
point moves and traces out a path in phase space. This path is not
entirely arbitrary since the p's and q's satisfy the Hamiltonian equations of motion (19).

It will be worthwhile to illustrate by a special case which lends
itself to easy visualization even though it does not satisfy the condition $f \gg 1$ and hence is not of much importance in practical applications: the simple harmonic oscillator for which $f = 1$. Here $H = p^2/2m$
$+kq^2/2$, where m and k are the mass and stiffness of the oscillator
respectively, and the Hamiltonian equations become

$$\dot{p} = -kq, \quad \dot{q} = \frac{p}{m}. \tag{30}$$

The phase space is two-dimensional, viz., the pq plane.
Every point of this plane
represents a possible phase
of a dynamical system of one
degree of freedom. If the
total energy of the oscillator
is constant and equal to E its
corresponding phase points
are those lying on the elliptical path (cf. Fig. 6·1)

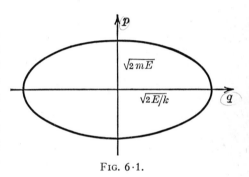

FIG. 6·1.

$$\frac{p^2}{2m} + \frac{kq^2}{2} = E. \tag{31}$$

This ellipse has the semi-major axis $\sqrt{2E/k}$ and the semi-minor axis
$\sqrt{2Em}$. At any particular instant the phase of the oscillator is represented by some point on the ellipse. As time passes and the actual
oscillator goes through its various phases in physical space we can
think of the corresponding phase point as moving about the ellipse
and repeating this motion periodically with the period equal to
$2\pi\sqrt{m/k}$, the actual period of the oscillator; incidentally this is equal
to the *area* of the phase ellipse divided by the energy. The rate at
which the phase point traverses the ellipse is given by eqs. (30). If the
energy does not remain constant, the phase path will be more complicated, but if E is restricted to lie between two values E_1 and E_2, the
path will certainly lie in the phase space between the two ellipses

corresponding to E_1 and E_2 respectively. We shall have occasion to utilize this situation later. However, for the moment it will be simpler to confine our attention to a conservative system. It will be noticed that the phase curve in Fig. 6·1 nowhere crosses itself. No phase path representing a dynamical system can ever cross itself; such a situation would violate the fundamental characteristic of a dynamical system that the precise knowledge of the q's and p's at one instant suffices to specify the phase for all past or future time. However, it is of interest to observe that since according to quantum mechanics this precise knowledge is never available (cf. the indeterminacy principle), infinitely sharp phase paths have no meaning in quantum theory and must be replaced by paths of *finite* width, or phase ribbons, as they may be called. In the present chapter we shall ignore this and restrict ourselves to the classical point of view.

4. THE GIBBSIAN ENSEMBLE

We are now prepared to introduce the concept of an *ensemble*. Let us imagine a collection of a great many dynamical systems all having the same Hamiltonian function. They might, for example, be a collection of simple harmonic oscillators, all with the same mass and stiffness. We shall suppose that their phases are not the same but are in fact distributed over a wide variety of possible phase values. If they are oscillators, their phases at any instant might correspond to points selected at random on the phase ellipse in Fig. 6·1. The collection in question is termed an *ensemble*. It must be emphasized that such an ensemble is a purely mental construction and has no concrete existence. This introduces at once an element of abstractness into statistical mechanics not shared by classical particle dynamics. We are asked to *contemplate* at once a very large number of copies of a dynamical system distributed somehow over all the phases possible for such a system. The copies of the system composing the ensemble will be termed the *elements* of the ensemble.

Each element in the ensemble is represented by a point in phase space. For the oscillator ensemble, these points form the loci of the ellipse in Fig. 6·1 if the energy of the system is fixed or, if it is not fixed, occupy the whole family of ellipses corresponding to the allowed range of E. Consider the latter case. In any given area of the phase space there will be at a given instant a certain number of phase points corresponding to elements of the ensemble. This enables us to introduce the concept of *phase density*. About any point in phase space we construct a small region and take the limit of the number of phase points divided by the size of the region as the latter grows smaller. Clearly to give meaning to this quantity the number of elements must be very large and distributed more or less continuously. We shall refer to the phase density as D.

Consider again our illustration of the oscillator and suppose the ensemble consists of N elements with energies included between E_1 and E_2. The *average* density of the corresponding points in phase space will then be

$$\bar{D} = \frac{1}{2\pi} \sqrt{\frac{k}{m}} \frac{N}{(E_2 - E_1)}$$

in the phase region between the two ellipses characterized by E_2 and E_1 respectively and zero everywhere else. The actual density may be constant throughout the region and equal to the average, or it may vary and be a function of p and q. For example, the density may vary directly with the energy, i.e., $D = KE$. Let us investigate this for a moment. The total number of elements of the ensemble is given in perfectly general fashion by

$$N = \int D d\phi, \tag{32}$$

where $d\phi$ is the element of volume of the phase space, and is given in general by

$$d\phi = dq_1 \cdots dq_f \cdot dp_1 \cdots dp_f. \tag{33}$$

The integration is carried out over the whole portion of phase space occupied by the ensemble. In the present illustration $d\phi = dp\,dq$ and (32) becomes

$$N = K \iint E \, dp \, dq,$$

the integration being taken over the whole of the appropriate phase space, i.e., the area contained between the two ellipses for E_1 and E_2. We can write simply

$$dp \, dq = 2\pi \sqrt{\frac{m}{k}} \, dE,$$

and obtain

$$N = 2\pi K \sqrt{\frac{m}{k}} \int_{E_1}^{E_2} E dE = \pi K \sqrt{\frac{m}{k}} (E_2^2 - E_1^2).$$

If we speak generally instead of a specific illustration, we may say that D will be a function of the $p_1 \cdots p_f, q_1 \cdots q_f$ as well as the time, and the number of elements of the ensemble in $d\phi$ will be [6]

$$dN = D(p_j, q_j, t)d\phi. \tag{34}$$

If D does not depend on the time explicitly the ensemble is termed *stationary*. In general, however, we expect D to change with the time so that the phase points occupying at a given instant a certain portion of the phase space may be thought of as moving out of that region into another one with the passage of time.

Since the element of volume $d\phi$ is to play such an important role in statistical mechanics, it is of importance to see how it behaves with respect to an arbitrary transformation of coordinates in configuration space. Suppose we transform the phase variables $q_1 \cdots q_f, p_1 \cdots p_f$ to the system $Q_1 \cdots Q_f, P_1 \cdots P_f$, where

$$\begin{aligned}
Q_j &= Q_j(q_1 \cdots q_f) \\
P_j &= P_j(q_1 \cdots q_f, p_1 \cdots p_f).
\end{aligned} \tag{35}$$

From the property of the functional determinant already alluded to in eq. (64) of Chapter V, we have

$$dQ_1 \cdots dQ_f \cdot dP_1 \cdots dP_f$$

$$= \frac{\partial(P_1 \cdots P_f, Q_1 \cdots Q_f)}{\partial(p_1 \cdots p_f, q_1 \cdots q_f)} dq_1 \cdots dq_f \cdot dp_1 \cdots dp_f. \tag{36}$$

The effect of the transformation will be clear from an evaluation of the Jacobian, which is of the form

$$\frac{\partial(P_1 \cdots Q_f)}{\partial(p_1 \cdots q_f)} = \begin{vmatrix}
\dfrac{\partial P_1}{\partial p_1} & \cdots & \dfrac{\partial P_f}{\partial p_1} & \dfrac{\partial Q_1}{\partial p_1} & \cdots & \dfrac{\partial Q_f}{\partial p_1} \\
\cdots & \cdots & \cdots & \cdots & \cdots & \cdots \\
\dfrac{\partial P_1}{\partial p_f} & \cdots & \dfrac{\partial P_f}{\partial p_f} & \dfrac{\partial Q_1}{\partial p_f} & \cdots & \dfrac{\partial Q_f}{\partial p_f} \\
\dfrac{\partial P_1}{\partial q_1} & \cdots & \dfrac{\partial P_f}{\partial q_1} & \dfrac{\partial Q_1}{\partial q_1} & \cdots & \dfrac{\partial Q_f}{\partial q_1} \\
\cdots & \cdots & \cdots & \cdots & \cdots & \cdots \\
\dfrac{\partial P_1}{\partial q_f} & \cdots & \dfrac{\partial P_f}{\partial q_f} & \dfrac{\partial Q_1}{\partial q_f} & \cdots & \dfrac{\partial Q_f}{\partial q_f}
\end{vmatrix}. \tag{37}$$

But since $\dfrac{\partial Q_j}{\partial p_k} = 0$ for all j and k from 1 to f the determinant at once

---

[6] Note that $D(p_j, q_j, t)$ is an abbreviation for $D(p_1 \cdots p_f, q_1 \cdots q_f, t)$ as usual.

breaks down into the product of two determinants, i.e.,

$$\frac{\partial(P_1 \cdots Q_f)}{\partial(p_1 \cdots q_f)} = \begin{vmatrix} \dfrac{\partial P_1}{\partial p_1} & \cdots & \dfrac{\partial P_f}{\partial p_1} \\ \cdots\cdots\cdots \\ \dfrac{\partial P_1}{\partial p_f} & \cdots & \dfrac{\partial P_f}{\partial p_f} \end{vmatrix} \cdot \begin{vmatrix} \dfrac{\partial Q_1}{\partial q_1} & \cdots & \dfrac{\partial Q_f}{\partial q_1} \\ \cdots\cdots\cdots \\ \dfrac{\partial Q_1}{\partial q_f} & \cdots & \dfrac{\partial Q_f}{\partial q_f} \end{vmatrix} \cdot \tag{38}$$

Let us denote the transformed Hamiltonian by $K(P_1 \cdots P_f, Q_1 \cdots Q_f)$. Then from eqs. (12) and (20), since the system is assumed to be conservative,

$$P_j = \frac{\partial K}{\partial \dot{Q}_j}.$$

Consequently we have

$$\frac{\partial P_j}{\partial p_k} = \frac{\partial}{\partial p_k}\frac{\partial K}{\partial \dot{Q}_j} = \sum_{l=1}^{f}\frac{\partial^2 K}{\partial \dot{Q}_l \partial \dot{Q}_j}\frac{\partial \dot{Q}_l}{\partial p_k}, \tag{39}$$

which makes it possible to write

$$\frac{\partial P_j}{\partial p_k} = \frac{\partial}{\partial \dot{Q}_j}\sum_{l=1}^{f}\frac{\partial K}{\partial \dot{Q}_l}\frac{\partial \dot{Q}_l}{\partial p_k} = \frac{\partial}{\partial \dot{Q}_j}\frac{\partial K}{\partial p_k}, \tag{40}$$

since the $\dot{Q}_l$ are linear functions of the p's with coefficients involving the q's and therefore $\dfrac{\partial \dot{Q}_l}{\partial p_k}$ is a function of the q's alone. But $\dfrac{\partial K}{\partial p_k} = \dfrac{\partial H}{\partial p_k} = \dot{q}_k$ and hence (40) yields

$$\frac{\partial P_j}{\partial p_k} = \frac{\partial \dot{q}_k}{\partial \dot{Q}_j}. \tag{41}$$

But

$$\dot{q}_k = \sum_{l=1}^{f}\frac{\partial q_k}{\partial Q_l}\dot{Q}_l,$$

whence

$$\frac{\partial \dot{q}_k}{\partial \dot{Q}_j} = \frac{\partial q_k}{\partial Q_j} = \frac{\partial P_j}{\partial p_k} \tag{42}$$

The expression on the right of (38) then becomes

$$\begin{vmatrix} \dfrac{\partial q_1}{\partial Q_1} & \cdots & \dfrac{\partial q_f}{\partial Q_1} \\ \cdots\cdots\cdots \\ \dfrac{\partial q_1}{\partial Q_f} & \cdots & \dfrac{\partial q_f}{\partial Q_f} \end{vmatrix} \cdot \begin{vmatrix} \dfrac{\partial Q_1}{\partial q_1} & \cdots & \dfrac{\partial Q_f}{\partial q_1} \\ \cdots\cdots\cdots \\ \dfrac{\partial Q_1}{\partial q_f} & \cdots & \dfrac{\partial Q_f}{\partial q_f} \end{vmatrix}$$

Now, from the general rule for multiplying determinants, if we denote by C_{ij} the ij term in the product determinant, we have

$$C_{ij} = \sum_{k=1}^{f} \frac{\partial q_k}{\partial Q_i} \frac{\partial Q_j}{\partial q_k} = \frac{\partial Q_j}{\partial Q_i} = \delta_{ji}, \qquad (43)$$

where δ_{ji} is the Kronecker symbol which equals unity for $i = j$ and is zero otherwise. Hence the product determinant is just the diagonal determinant

$$\begin{vmatrix} 1 & 0 & 0 & 0 & \cdots & 0 \\ 0 & 1 & 0 & 0 & \cdots & 0 \\ \cdot & \cdot & \cdot & \cdot & \cdot & \cdot \\ 0 & 0 & 0 & 0 & \cdots & 1 \end{vmatrix}$$

whose value is unity. Since the functional determinant is unity we have demonstrated the invariance of the volume element $d\phi$ in phase space with respect to an arbitrary point transformation.

5. LIOUVILLE'S THEOREM. THE EQUATION OF CONTINUITY IN STATISTICAL MECHANICS

Let us now consider a region of phase space and the "flow" of phase points through it. We can think of this region as enclosed by a hyper-surface whose "area" element will be denoted by $d\sigma$. We then generalize the divergence theorem of ordinary three-vectors to the $2f$ dimensional phase space. Thus for a generalized vector function of the phase space, $\mathbf{V}$, with components $V_{q_1}, V_{q_2} \cdots V_{q_f}, V_{p_1} \cdots V_{p_f}$ we *define* the divergence of $\mathbf{V}$ as

$$\nabla \cdot \mathbf{V} = \sum_{j=1}^{f} \left(\frac{\partial V_{q_j}}{\partial q_j} + \frac{\partial V_{p_j}}{\partial p_j} \right). \qquad (44)$$

If we denote by V_n the component of $\mathbf{V}$ normal to $d\sigma$ the divergence theorem becomes

$$\int V_n d\sigma = \int \sum \left(\frac{\partial V_{q_j}}{\partial q_j} + \frac{\partial V_{p_j}}{\partial p_j} \right) d\phi, \qquad (45)$$

where the "volume" integral on the right is taken over the whole phase region under consideration and the "surface" integral on the left is taken over the hyper-surface enclosing this region. Now apply this to the case where $\mathbf{V}$ is the vector with components $D\dot{q}_1, \cdots D\dot{q}_n$, $D\dot{p}_1 \cdots D\dot{p}_n$. Thus $D\dot{q}_1$ is the rate of flow of phase points per unit area in the q_1 "direction." The vector $\mathbf{V}$ may then be said to represent "phase flow," and $\int V_n d\sigma$ represents the net phase outflow from the phase region bounded by the hyper-surface over which the integration is taken. But this phase efflux must be compensated by a change in phase density inside the volume. In symbols

$$\int V_n d\sigma = -\int \frac{\partial D}{\partial t}\, d\phi, \tag{46}$$

whence from (45)

$$\int \left(\frac{\partial D}{\partial t} + \sum_{j=1}^{f} \frac{\partial(D\dot{q}_j)}{\partial q_j} + \sum_{j=1}^{f} \frac{\partial(D\dot{p}_j)}{\partial p_j} \right) d\phi = 0. \tag{47}$$

Since the phase region over which the integration is extended is arbitrary, the result in (47) may be written in general

$$\frac{\partial D}{\partial t} + \sum_{j=1}^{f} \left(\frac{\partial(D\dot{q}_j)}{\partial q_j} + \frac{\partial(D\dot{p}_j)}{\partial p_j} \right) \cdot 0. \tag{48}$$

It will be noted at once that this is analogous to the equation of continuity in hydrodynamics. It can be written in physically more significant form by carrying out the indicated differentiations. Then

$$\frac{\partial D}{\partial t} + D \sum_{j=1}^{f} \left(\frac{\partial \dot{q}_j}{\partial q_j} + \frac{\partial \dot{p}_j}{\partial p_j} \right) + \sum_{j=1}^{f} \left(\dot{q}_j \frac{\partial D}{\partial q_j} + \dot{p}_j \frac{\partial D}{\partial p_j} \right) = 0.$$

But from the canonical equations (19) it follows that for any j

$$\frac{\partial \dot{q}_j}{\partial q_j} + \frac{\partial \dot{p}_j}{\partial p_j} = 0.$$

Moreover

$$\sum \left(\frac{\partial D}{\partial q_j} \dot{q}_j + \frac{\partial D}{\partial p_j} \dot{p}_j \right)$$

is the time rate of change of D due to the changes in the p's and q's. Consequently (48) becomes

$$\frac{dD}{dt} = 0, \tag{49}$$

which says that the *total* time rate of change of D, the phase density, vanishes. This theorem, known as Liouville's theorem, means that to one following the motion of the phase points in an ensemble the density does not change with the time. At any given place in phase space, the density may change, to be sure, but what may be called the *motional* change vanishes. Thus if we consider a certain region of phase space containing at a given instant a certain number of phase points, during the passage of time these points move in such a way as to occupy an equal phase volume at every instant, even though the "shape" of the volume may alter. This result is referred to by Gibbs as the *principle of conservation of density-in-phase*.[7]

The importance of this theorem for statistical mechanics can scarcely be over-emphasized. Not only is it basic for the further theoretical development but it has also been used directly to simplify physical problems. One of these is the study of the motion of electrons in the earth's magnetic field which is of great significance for the investigation of cosmic rays.[8]

Gibbs also has shown how Liouville's theorem may be used with little or no further mathematical manipulation to prove the invariance of the element of phase volume.[9]

In the special case of a *stationary* ensemble $\dfrac{\partial D}{\partial t} = 0$, and the theorem becomes

$$\sum_{j=1}^{f} \left(\frac{\partial D}{\partial q_j} \dot{q}_j + \frac{\partial D}{\partial p_j} \dot{p}_j \right) = 0. \tag{50}$$

It can be shown that if D is a function of the energy E alone (50) follows directly. Hence Liouville's theorem will lead to $\dfrac{\partial D}{\partial t} = 0$, i.e. the ensemble is stationary. The proof follows. Here

$$\frac{\partial D}{\partial q_j} = \frac{\partial D}{\partial E} \frac{\partial E}{\partial q_j}, \quad \frac{\partial D}{\partial p_j} = \frac{\partial D}{\partial E} \frac{\partial E}{\partial p_j}.$$

But from the canonical equations

$$\frac{\partial E}{\partial q_j} = \frac{\partial H}{\partial q_j} = -\dot{p}_j \quad \text{and} \quad \frac{\partial E}{\partial p_j} = \frac{\partial H}{\partial p_j} = \dot{q}_j,$$

Hence

$$\dot{q}_j \frac{\partial D}{\partial q_j} + \dot{p}_j \frac{\partial D}{\partial p_j} = \frac{\partial D}{\partial E} (-\dot{q}_j \dot{p}_j + \dot{p}_j \dot{q}_j) = 0,$$

and therefore (50) follows. Therefore an ensemble for which the phase density is a function of the energy alone must be stationary.

[7] For an alternative derivation which is purely analytical in character, cf. Lindsay and Margenau, *op. cit.*, pp. 221 ff.

[8] Cf. G. Lemaitre and M. S. Vallarta, *Phys. Rev.*, **43**, 87 (1933).

[9] Gibbs, *op. cit.*, p. 11.

A simple illustration of Liouville's theorem is provided by a system consisting of a single charged particle with charge e moving in a uniform electric field of intensity F. The Hamiltonian function for such a particle is

$$H = \frac{p^2}{2m} - eFq,$$

where it is assumed that the field is directed along the positive q axis. An ensemble representing such a system with constant energy E_1 would have elements corresponding to the phase points located on the parabola E_1 in the pq plane (cf. Fig. 6·2). Let us, however, imagine an ensemble with phase points located in the phase region ϕ, between the two parabolas corresponding to total energies E_1 and E_2 respectively and between the parallels to the q axis defined by the values p_1 and p_2 respectively. If the phase values of the elements of this ensemble correspond to $t = 0$, at the expiration of time t the phase points of the ensemble for the system will no longer lie in ϕ_1. Rather they will

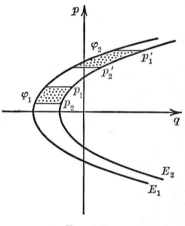

FIG. 6·2.

have moved into the new phase region ϕ_2 bounded by the momentum values p_1' and p_2', where

$$p_1' = p_1 + \dot{p}t, \quad p_2' = p_2 + \dot{p}t.$$

From the canonical equations, $\dot{p} = eF$. Now the phase "volume" occupied by the ensemble at $t = 0$ is the area

$$\phi_1 = \frac{(E_2 - E_1)}{eF} (p_2 - p_1),$$

while the phase "volume" occupied by the ensemble at time t is

$$\phi_2 = \frac{(E_2 - E_1)}{eF} (p_2' - p_1').$$

But from the expressions for p_1' and p_2' it follows that $p_2' - p_1' = p_2 - p_1$ and hence $\phi_2 = \phi_1$. As time passes the same set of phase points occupy equal "volumes" of phase space. Therefore the density-in-phase must remain the same, as Liouville's theorem requires. The reader will note that the shape of the successive phase regions occupied by the ensemble changes though the "volume" is invariant.

6. THE FUNDAMENTAL POSTULATE OF STATISTICAL MECHANICS

It is now necessary to provide some connection between the ensemble, which is a purely abstract mental construct, and the dynamical system whose behavior the ensemble has been created to describe. We do this by means of a fundamental postulate, the statement of which, however, demands the introduction of an additional concept. This is the *phase probability*. If we have N elements in the ensemble and the phase density is D, the probability of choosing at random an element whose phase is included in the region $d\phi$ about the phase point $q_1 \cdots q_f, p_1 \cdots p_f$, is defined to be

$$P d\phi = (D/N) d\phi, \tag{51}$$

where $P(q_j, p_j, t)$ is called the probability coefficient, and we obviously have

$$P(p_j, q_j, t) = \frac{D(p_j, q_j, t)}{N}. \tag{52}$$

Evidently from (32)

$$\int P d\phi = \frac{1}{N} \int D d\phi = 1. \tag{53}$$

That is, the probability of choosing an element at random from the whole phase space of the ensemble is unity.

The basic postulate now runs as follows: The probability that at a given instant, t, the physical system being described shall have its phase included in the region $d\phi$ about the value $q_1 \cdots q_f, p_1 \cdots p_f$ is the same as the probability $P d\phi$ of choosing at random from the ensemble corresponding to the physical system an element included in the phase region $d\phi$. It is essential here once again to distinguish between the actual physical system which assumes its possible phase values one after another as time passes and the imaginary copies which compose the ensemble, whose elements correspond to all possible phase values of the system visualized simultaneously.

The practical value of the basic postulate is that it provides a definite physical meaning for the *average* over the ensemble of any physical quantity characteristic of the system being described. Thus if $\chi(q_1 \cdots q_f, p_1 \cdots p_f)$ is a physical quantity which is a function of the q's and p's of the physical system, we shall define the average of χ over the ensemble as

$$\bar{\chi} = \int \chi P d\phi, \tag{54}$$

the integration being taken as usual over the whole phase space occupied by the ensemble. From the fundamental postulate it now follows that $\bar{\chi}$ is the value of the quantity χ which we should expect on the *average* to measure for the system when it is in a state of equilibrium, viz., the only state in which we can contemplate the act of measurement. The calculation of average values over the ensemble will then be the principal task of statistical mechanics, for these averages are taken as the actual physical values encountered in measurement and entering into the laws characterizing the experimentally observed behavior of the system. The essential difference between the average over an ensemble and the kind of average considered in the statistical distributions of Chapter IV should be carefully noted. Thus, for example, the average energy $\bar{E}$ in eq. (30) of Chapter IV refers to the average energy *per particle* in an actual physical aggregate of particles canonically distributed. The average defined by (54) is on the contrary an average of the quantity in question for the whole physical system described by the ensemble. This point will be illustrated and emphasized again in the study of special types of ensembles (cf. the end of Sec. 9 of this chapter).

7. THE MICROCANONICAL OR ENERGY-SHELL ENSEMBLE

It is now necessary to consider some special types of ensembles, for clearly the fundamental postulate of the previous section can not be applied unless we have a definite distribution of elements to which to apply it. Let us consider the ensemble whose elements have energies lying in the interval from E_0 to $E_0 + \Delta E$, for which in other words

$$E_0 \leq H(q_1 \cdots q_f, p_1 \cdots p_f) \leq E_0 + \Delta E. \qquad (55)$$

This interval constitutes in phase space what may be called an *energy shell*. We shall assume that the phase points of the ensemble fill this shell everywhere densely. The ensemble itself is usually called a *microcanonical* ensemble, a name whose significance will be understood better later. As a matter of fact it might more appropriately be termed an *energy-shell* ensemble.

Now from Liouville's theorem $dD/dt = 0$; if further we suppose that the ensemble is stationary, i.e., $\partial D/\partial t = 0$, it follows from (50) that there is no change in phase density along any phase curve. Hence along every phase curve the density remains constant both in space and time. From this we infer that D has the same value throughout the energy shell. To be sure, in order to reach this conclusion, we have made a tacit hypothesis, namely that every possible phase curve of the system fills the shell densely or at any rate that each such phase curve passes infinitely close to every point of the shell. This is the celebrated ergodic or quasi-ergodic hypothesis. It has received much attention in discussions of statistical mechanics. It is not difficult to show that the strict assumption that the phase curve passes through every point in the energy shell or on the energy surface leads to logical contradiction. The strict ergodic hypothesis is therefore usually replaced by the less stringent quasi-ergodic hypothesis that ultimately the phase curve passes as close as one requires to every point in the shell. Applied to the actual physical system the hypothesis effectively means that the system will ultimately get infinitely close to every possible phase value consistent with the restriction to constant energy or limited energy variation. So stated, the assumption has a plausible ring. The purely mathematical problems which it poses, however, are

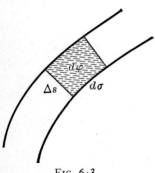

FIG. 6·3.

considerable. For a consideration of these the reader is referred to P. S. Epstein.[10] Let $\Delta\phi$ be the phase volume of the energy shell. What we wish to do is to specialize eq. (54) so as to obtain a convenient expression for the *average* of any function of the phase over the microcanonical ensemble. We construct the diagram shown in Fig. 6·3 where a portion of the energy shell is shown schematically. Here $d\sigma$ represents a portion of the energy "surface" defined by $H(p_1 \cdots p_f,\ q_1 \cdots q_f) = E_0$ and Δs is the "normal" to this surface which extends to the other bounding surface of the phase volume occupied by the ensemble, viz., $H = E_0 + \Delta E$. Then for the element of phase volume of the ensemble we may write

$$d\phi = \Delta s \cdot d\sigma, \tag{56}$$

where further $\Delta\phi = \displaystyle\int d\phi$ over the space between the energy surfaces. We now get

$$Pd\phi = \frac{D}{N} \cdot d\phi = \frac{d\phi}{\Delta\phi}, \tag{57}$$

since $\displaystyle\int Dd\phi = N$, where N is the total number of elements in the ensemble, and we can take D outside of the integral sign because of

[10] "Commentary on the Scientific Writings of J. Willard Gibbs," pp. 465 ff. Yale University Press, 1936.

its constancy. But now we can write to an approximation which improves as ΔE grows smaller

$$\frac{\Delta E}{\Delta s} = |\nabla H|, \tag{58}$$

where $|\nabla H|$ is the absolute value of the generalized gradient of the Hamiltonian, viz.,

$$|\nabla H| = \sqrt{\sum_{k=1}^{f}\left(\frac{\partial H}{\partial q_k}\right)^2 + \sum_{k=1}^{f}\left(\frac{\partial H}{\partial p_k}\right)^2}. \tag{59}$$

Its value is of course taken at the energy surface. The volume $\Delta\phi$ of the energy shell depends on E and ΔE. In fact we can write

$$\Delta\phi = \omega(E)\Delta E. \tag{60}$$

As a result of Eqs. (56–60)

$$Pd\phi = \frac{d\sigma}{\omega(E)|\nabla H|}. \tag{61}$$

This enables us to express the average value of any phase function $\chi(q_1 \cdots q_f, p_1 \cdots p_f)$ over the microcanonical ensemble in terms of an integral taken over the inner surface of the energy shell. Thus from (54)

$$\overline{(\chi)}_{mc} = \int \frac{\chi d\sigma}{\omega(E)|\nabla H|}. \tag{62}$$

Before going further with the general treatment, let us specialize the above to the case where the dynamical system is a simple harmonic oscillator. This enables us to visualize a little better what we are doing. In Fig. 6·4 we represent the energy shell for the ensemble as the plane area between the two ellipses whose equations are $H = p^2/2m + kq^2/2 = E_0$ and $p^2/2m + kq^2/2 = E_0 + \Delta E$. The element of "surface" $d\sigma$ of the shell now becomes the element of arc of the ellipse, viz.,

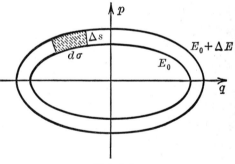

FIG. 6·4.

$$d\sigma = \sqrt{1 + \left(\frac{dp}{dq}\right)^2}\,dq. \tag{63}$$

Moreover

$$|\nabla H| = \sqrt{\left(\frac{\partial H}{\partial p}\right)^2 + \left(\frac{\partial H}{\partial q}\right)^2} = \sqrt{\frac{p^2}{m^2} + k^2 q^2}. \tag{64}$$

$\omega(E)$ is obtained from the dependence of ϕ (here *area*) on the energy. Thus since the area of the ellipse for E_0 is $2\pi \sqrt{\frac{m}{k}} E_0$, the size of the shell is given by

$$\Delta\phi = 2\pi \sqrt{\frac{m}{k}} \Delta E, \tag{65}$$

whence $\omega(E) = 2\pi \sqrt{m/k} = $ constant. We are now prepared to write $Pd\phi$. Thus

$$d\sigma = \sqrt{1 + \frac{m^2 k^2 q^2}{p^2}} \cdot dq$$

and

$$\frac{d\sigma}{|\nabla H|} = \frac{m\, dq}{\sqrt{2mE_0 - mkq^2}}.$$

Hence

$$Pd\phi = \frac{1}{2\pi} \sqrt{mk} \cdot \frac{dq}{\sqrt{2mE_0 - mkq^2}}. \tag{66}$$

It is interesting to observe that $Pd\phi$ reduces precisely to dt/t_0, where t_0 is the period of the oscillator and dt is the time spent in the interval dq. As a check on (66) we can show by direct integration that $\int Pd\phi$ equals unity when the integration is extended over the whole shell. The evaluation of the microcanonical average kinetic and potential energies is of interest. Thus

$$\left(\overline{\frac{p^2}{2m}}\right)_{\text{mc}} = \frac{1}{2\pi} \sqrt{\frac{k}{m}} \int_{-\sqrt{2E_0/k}}^{+\sqrt{2E_0/k}} \frac{p^2 dq}{\sqrt{2mE_0 - mkq^2}} = \frac{E_0}{2}. \tag{67}$$

In similar fashion

$$\left(\overline{\frac{kq^2}{2}}\right)_{\text{mc}} = \frac{E_0}{2}. \tag{68}$$

Thus for the simple harmonic oscillator the averages of the kinetic and potential energies over a microcanonical ensemble are each equal to one-half the characteristic energy of the ensemble. This reminds us of the ordinary mechanical theorem that the *time* average of the kinetic energy of a simple harmonic oscillator is equal to the time average of the potential energy. The connection here is indeed an illustration of the basic postulate discussed in Sec. 6.

It will be observed that in the above example we can write $p^2/2m$ as $\dfrac{p}{2}\dfrac{\partial H}{\partial p}$ and $kq^2/2$ as $\dfrac{q}{2}\dfrac{\partial H}{\partial q}$. This suggests a possible generalization as follows: Let us form the average of the quantity

$$\chi = q_k \frac{\partial H}{\partial q_k}.$$

Then

$$\overline{(\chi)}_{\mathrm{mc}} = \frac{1}{\omega(E_0)} \int q_k \frac{\partial H}{\partial q_k} \cdot \frac{d\sigma}{|\nabla H|}, \tag{69}$$

where $\omega(E_0)$ has been removed from under the integral sign since it has the same value at all points of the energy surface.

Now

$$\frac{\partial H}{\partial q_k} \bigg/ \sqrt{\sum_{j=1}^{f}\left(\frac{\partial H}{\partial q_j}\right)^2 + \sum_{j=1}^{f}\left(\frac{\partial H}{\partial p_j}\right)^2}$$

may be interpreted as the cosine of the "angle" between the normal to the energy surface and the q_k "direction." This follows from the fact that in analogy to the ordinary theory of surfaces $\dfrac{\partial H}{\partial q_1} \cdots \dfrac{\partial H}{\partial q_f}$, $\dfrac{\partial H}{\partial p_1} \cdots \dfrac{\partial H}{\partial p_f}$ are proportional to the "direction cosines" of the normal to the surface

$$H(p_1 \cdots p_f, q_1 \cdots q_f) = E_0.$$

Consequently we may look upon $\dfrac{\partial H}{\partial q_k} \cdot \dfrac{d\sigma}{|\nabla H|}$ as the projection of $d\sigma$ on the $2n$-1 dimensional "plane" normal to the q_k direction. Therefore

$$q_k \frac{\partial H}{\partial q_k} \frac{d\sigma}{|\nabla H|}$$

may be interpreted as the "volume element" $d\phi^*$ of the $2n$ dimensional phase volume enclosed by the energy surface. The same will hold true of

$$p_k \frac{\partial H}{\partial p_k} \frac{d\sigma}{|\nabla H|}.$$

Hence for both we shall have

$$\overline{(\chi)}_{\mathrm{mc}} = \frac{1}{\omega(E_0)} \int d\phi^* = \frac{\phi^*}{\omega(E_0)}. \tag{70}$$

Here ϕ^* is the total phase volume enclosed by the energy surface. We can make an immediate interesting application. For $p_k \dfrac{\partial H}{\partial p_k} = p_k \dot{q}_k$, from the canonical equations (19), and $\Sigma p_k \dot{q}_k = H + L = 2T$, where T is the total kinetic energy. Hence we may refer to $p_k \dot{q}_k$ as $2T_k$, or twice the kinetic energy associated with the kth degree of freedom. From (70) we therefore have

$$(\overline{T}_k)_{mc} = \frac{\phi^*}{2\omega(E_0)}. \tag{71}$$

But since the right-hand side is constant, this implies the equipartition of kinetic energy among the degrees of freedom of the system.

Consider further $q_k \dfrac{\partial H}{\partial q_k} = - q_k \dot{p}_k$ (from 19). If we treat $\dot{p}_k$ as the generalized force associated with the kth degree of freedom, eq. (6) of Chapter V suggests that we may define

$$\Omega = - \tfrac{1}{2}\overline{(\Sigma q_k \dot{p}_k)}_{mc} \tag{72}$$

as the generalized *virial* of the dynamical system under consideration, since it is formed in precisely the same way as the virial of Clausius for an actual physical system of particles. But from the theorem (70), it follows that

$$\Omega = \overline{(\Sigma T_k)}_{mc} \tag{73}$$

or the generalized virial is equal to the microcanonical average of the kinetic energy of the system. This is the statistical mechanical version of the virial theorem.

The reader will find it instructive to verify this result for the simple harmonic oscillator.

8.   COMPONENT SYSTEMS

The physical system represented by the ensemble has so far been thought of as a unitary whole. We now wish to resolve it into a number of component systems assumed to be independent of each other, save for the possibility of energy exchange. Thus if the original system is the aggregate of all the molecules composing a given mass of an ideal gas, a component system might be an individual molecule. Denote the resultant system by S and its k components by $S_1, S_2, \cdots S_k$. If S_j has f_j degrees of freedom and f is the total number of degrees of freedom of S

$$\sum_{j=1}^{k} f_j = f. \tag{74}$$

It should be clear that the same phase space cannot serve for the component and resultant systems. For the resultant system we shall employ what is called a γ space, for the component systems the spaces will be denoted by $\mu_1, \mu_2 \cdots \mu_k$. The phase space μ_j has $2f_j$ dimensions. If we are dealing with molecules in the form of particles with three degrees of freedom, each μ space has six dimensions, and if there are N molecules in the resultant system, the γ space has $6N$ dimensions.

Though we shall conceive the system S to be closed and hence representable by a microcanonical ensemble, it would restrict matters too much to assume the same for the components, since we should like to think of the components as having the possibility of changing their energy by transfer from one to another without altering the energy of the whole. For this reason we shall not be able to construct microcanonical ensembles for the component systems, and the phase points for S_k may occupy *any* part of μ_k. But the phase probability P for the resultant system will presumably somehow depend on the instantaneous energy of the system and we shall in fact assume that P is a function of E alone. For each component system there will also be a phase probability $P_j = P_j(E_j)$ where E_j is the (variable) energy of the jth system and $\Sigma E_j = E_0$. If the ensembles representing S and S_j are stationary, P and P_j will be independent of the time. The problem now is to find the functions $P_j(E_j)$. The probability that the phase points for system S_1 lie in $d\phi_1$ of space μ_1, $\cdots$ those for S_j in $d\phi_j$ of space μ_j, etc. will be by definition

$$P_1 d\phi_1 \cdot P_2 d\phi_2 \cdots P_k d\phi_k.$$

But this must equal the probability that the ensemble for S shall lie in $d\phi$, since the systems have been assumed to be independent. Hence

$$P_1 P_2 \cdots P_k d\phi_1 \cdots d\phi_k = P d\phi. \tag{75}$$

Since $d\phi = d\phi_1 \cdot d\phi_2 \cdots d\phi_k$, we get the functional equation

$$P_1(E_1) \cdot \cdots \cdot P_k(E_k) = P(E_1 + E_2 + \cdots + E_k). \tag{76}$$

We can write (76) in the form

$$\sum_{i=1}^{k} \log P_i(E_i) = \log P, \tag{77}$$

and if we alter E_i by dE_i subject to the condition that $d\Sigma E_i = dE_0 = 0$, the result is

$$d\sum_{i=1}^{k} \log P_i = d \log P,$$

or

$$\sum_{i=1}^{k} \frac{1}{P_i}\frac{dP_i}{dE_i} dE_i = \frac{1}{P}\sum_{i=1}^{k} \frac{\partial P}{\partial E_i} dE_i. \qquad (78)$$

By equating corresponding terms and recalling that $\dfrac{\partial P}{\partial E_i}$ is the same for all i since P is a function of the total energy only, we arrive at

$$\frac{1}{P_1}\cdot\frac{dP_1}{dE_1} = \frac{1}{P_2}\cdot\frac{dP_2}{dE_2} = \cdots = \frac{1}{P_k}\frac{dP_k}{dE_k} = \text{constant} = C, \qquad (79)$$

where C is a negative constant and will be written in the form $-1/\Theta$. Therefore for any j from 1 to k the dependence of P_j on E_j takes the form

$$P_j = C_j e^{-E_j/\Theta}. \qquad (80)$$

The C_j are multiplicative parameters to be evaluated by further conditions placed on the P_j.

9. THE CANONICAL ENSEMBLE

The immediately preceding considerations at once suggest a new type of ensemble in which the energy is not restricted to lie in a shell but is allowed to vary continuously, and in which the fractional number of elements of the ensemble per unit volume of phase space is not constant but varies with the energy. Thus following Gibbs we shall introduce an ensemble such that

$$P d\phi = C e^{-H(q_1 \cdots q_f,\, p_1 \cdots p) /\Theta} d\phi, \qquad (81)$$

with the probability coefficient

$$P = e^{(\psi - H)/\Theta}. \qquad (82)$$

We have here placed $C = e^{\psi/\Theta}$ by the introduction of the new parameter ψ. The meaning of (81) and (82) is this: For a given system the Hamiltonian function is a certain function of the q's and p's. The probability of picking at random an element of the ensemble lying in the phase element $d\phi$ about the point $(q_1 \cdots q_f, p_1 \cdots p_f)$ depends on the position of this point through the Hamiltonian. Consider as an example the simple harmonic oscillator. Here

$$P dp dq = e^{\psi/\Theta} e^{-(p^2/2m + kq^2/2)/\Theta} \cdot dp dq.$$

For small absolute values of p and q, i.e., small total energy of the oscillator, P will be larger than for large values of p and q, which correspond to larger total energy.

In following Gibbs we shall call an ensemble for which the probability coefficient has the form (82) a *canonical ensemble*. Its relation to the canonical distribution discussed in Chapter IV will be discussed in the sequel. Θ is defined as the *modulus* of the ensemble. The second parameter ψ can be expressed in terms of Θ by the relation (from 53)

$$e^{-\psi/\Theta} = \int e^{-H/\Theta} d\phi, \qquad (83)$$

the integral being taken over all the portion of phase space occupied by the ensemble. There would appear to be a certain difficulty about this equation. Inspection shows that it is not dimensionally correct, since on the left we have $e^{-\psi/\Theta}$, a pure number, while $d\phi$ on the right has the dimensions of phase space. We can correct this situation merely by thinking of $d\phi$ as a pure number giving the ratio of the genuine volume element in phase space to an arbitrarily chosen unit volume. This will still enable us to compute ensemble-averages by means of eq. (54).

In the canonical ensemble we have a means of representing statistically a physical system of variable energy, i.e., an *unclosed* system like the component systems S_j mentioned in Sec. 8. We can then look upon the aggregate of such systems S_j, each represented by a canonical ensemble, as a system of constant energy E_0 represented by a microcanonical ensemble. From this point of view a canonical ensemble may be interpreted as a component part of a microcanonical ensemble. There is, however, another possible point of view which considers a microcanonical ensemble as a part of a canonical ensemble. Suppose all the component systems S_j are dynamically similar with the same number of degrees of freedom, etc., e.g., similar molecules. Then they may all be represented in a single phase space which we may call the μ space. We may now divide the μ space into a set of energy shells within each of which the phase density is constant but with P varying from shell to shell according to (82). Here the microcanonical ensemble for each system S_j appears naturally as a component part of a canonical ensemble for the *same* system. To a certain extent this justifies the name associated with it.

Let us now find the probability that the element of a canonical ensemble shall correspond to energy lying in the interval from E_0 to $E_0 + \Delta E$. By the fundamental postulate of Sec. 6, this is equal to the probability that the dynamical system represented by the canonical ensemble shall be found in such a phase interval that its energy lies between E_0 and $E_0 + \Delta E$. But this probability is simply

$$e^{(\psi - E_0)/\Theta} \Delta \phi, \tag{84}$$

where $\Delta \phi$ is the elementary volume in phase space corresponding to the energy shell in question.

Rather more important is the calculation of the average value of any dynamical quantity over a canonical ensemble. Thus if $\chi(q_1 \cdots q_f, p_1 \cdots p_f)$ is such a quantity, we have from (53), (54), and (82)

$$\overline{(\chi)}_c = \int \chi e^{(\psi - H)/\Theta} d\phi = \int \chi e^{-H/\Theta} d\phi \bigg/ \int e^{-H/\Theta} d\phi. \tag{85}$$

Since (85) eliminates the parameter ψ it is often the more convenient form. The integrations in both numerator and denominator are taken over the whole of the phase space occupied by the ensemble.

As an illustration consider the average energy of an oscillator. It will be simplest to express the integrations in terms of the energy itself by using the energy shell as the elementary phase volume and writing $d\phi = 2\pi\sqrt{m/k}\, dE$. Then

$$(\overline{E})_c = \frac{\displaystyle\int_0^\infty E e^{-E/\Theta} dE}{\displaystyle\int_0^\infty e^{-E/\Theta} dE}. \tag{86}$$

For the sake of simplicity we use the limits 0 and ∞, though strictly speaking the upper limit should be finite. Because of the exponential, however, the error due to this change will be slight. The result of the integration turns out to be

$$(\overline{E})_c = \Theta. \tag{87}$$

Incidentally the reader may show that the same result is obtained from the direct expression, using the Hamiltonian of the oscillator,

$$(\overline{E})_c = \frac{\displaystyle\iint_{-\infty}^{+\infty} (p^2/2m + kq^2/2) e^{-(p^2/2m + kq^2/2)/\Theta} dp\, dq}{\displaystyle\iint_{-\infty}^{+\infty} e^{-(p^2/2m + kq^2/2)/\Theta} dp\, dq}.$$

In attempting to generalize the preceding results we proceed to find the canonical average of ϕ^*/ω, where ϕ^* is the total phase volume enclosed by the energy surface $H = E_0$ and $\omega(E) = d\phi^*/dE$ (cf. eq. 60). Thus

$$\overline{(\phi^*/\omega)_c} = \frac{\int_\Phi (\phi^*/\omega)e^{-H/\Theta}d\phi}{\int_\Phi e^{-H/\Theta}d\phi}, \qquad (88)$$

where Φ is the total phase volume over which we are taking the average. If we now replace $d\phi$ by $\omega(E_0)dE$ in the numerator, the expression (88) becomes

$$\overline{(\phi^*/\omega)_c} = \frac{\int_0^{E_{max}} \phi^* e^{-E/\Theta}dE}{\int_\Phi e^{-E/\Theta}d\phi}. \qquad (89)$$

A partial integration of the integral in the numerator yields

$$\overline{(\phi^*/\omega)_c} = \frac{-\phi^*\Theta e^{-E/\Theta}\Big]_0^{E_{max}} + \Theta \int_\Phi e^{-E/\Theta}d\phi^*}{\int_\Phi e^{-E/\Theta}d\phi}. \qquad (90)$$

If now we take E_{max} large enough the integrated part will vanish since the term $e^{-E/\Theta}$ will wipe out $\phi^*\Theta$, as long as ϕ^* depends algebraically on E, which will be true in practice. Moreover in the integral in the denominator we may replace $d\phi$ by $d\phi^*$ merely by a transformation of coordinates, which results, for integration over a sufficiently large volume of phase space, in

$$\overline{(\phi^*/\omega)_c} = \Theta. \qquad (91)$$

This provides an interpretation of the modulus of the canonical ensemble. Now in eq. (71) we have already shown that ϕ^*/ω is itself the average of $2T_j$ (or twice the kinetic energy associated with the jth degree of freedom of the system) taken over a microcanonical ensemble with elements filling the energy shell E_0, $E_0 + \Delta E$ enclosing the phase volume ϕ^*. What we have shown in (91) then reduces to this: the *canonical* average of the microcanonical average kinetic energy corresponding to each degree of freedom of the system is equal to $\Theta/2$, i.e.,

$$\overline{((\overline{T_j})_{mc})_c} = \frac{\Theta}{2} = \overline{T_j}. \qquad (92)$$

We use the single bar to denote the *generalized* average of T_j. Equation (92) signifies equipartition of kinetic energy among the degrees of freedom of the dynamical system.   The generalized average of the total kinetic energy becomes $f \, \Theta/2$, if there are f degrees of freedom. Our present procedure amounts to thinking of the canonical ensemble as consisting of a set of microcanonical ensembles.   The generalized average then naturally is the canonical average of the microcanonical average.

   It is important at this state to compare the meaning of the canonical average of a physical quantity, like the energy, over the ensemble representing the system, with the averages encountered in the simple statistical considerations of Chapters II and IV.   In the so-called canonical distribution of Chapter IV, we found expressions for the average energy, e.g., eq. (30) of that chapter.   This represents the average energy *per particle* of a dynamical system of particles when canonically distributed.   For example, in a system of free particles, as in Sec. 5 of Chapter IV we found the average energy to be $\bar{E} = 3\Theta/2$ (eq. 86 of Chapter IV), where Θ is the modulus of the canonical distribution.   Now it must be emphasized that the average energy over a canonical ensemble means something quite different from this.   The average of a quantity over an ensemble refers, as has already been stated in Sec. 6 of this chapter, to the *expected measured value* of the quantity for the entire dynamical system in a state of equilibrium. Thus, in so far as a canonical ensemble is a suitable statistical representation of a system in equilibrium, the canonical average of the energy is the expected value of the energy of the system when we measure it in a state of equilibrium; it is not the average energy per component particle of the system.   It is essential that this be realized in order that a correct understanding be had of the relation between the Gibbs ensemble method and the Maxwell-Boltzmann method of statistical distribution.   In the latter method we deal with systems in which the total energy is constant and given and we are interested in finding out how the particles of the system are distributed with respect to their energy.   The canonical distribution is that corresponding to maximum probability of realization subject to the constancy of the total number of particles and the total energy.   We hoped to find and did indeed find relations among the various quantities defining the canonical distribution which correspond to known thermodynamical laws.   In the Gibbs statistical mechanical method the energy of the system is no longer looked upon as an absolutely constant quantity. It may indeed fluctuate, but only about an average which it is the task of the theory to calculate.   This average should be the experimentally measured value.   It is also the further task of the theory to develop relations among quantities defined by the ensemble which will correspond to the laws of thermodynamics. The virial theorem and the equipartition of energy are cases in point. Further illustrations will be developed in what follows.

In his development of statistical mechanics Gibbs confined himself largely to the use of the canonical ensemble, and we shall follow this practice in the remainder of this chapter. As the reader has already observed from Sec. 8 the canonical ensemble arises naturally as a suitable representation of a component system whose energy may change by exchange with another component of the same macroscopic system, it being understood that the energy of the latter remains constant. The canonical ensemble is therefore well fitted to represent a system whose energy varies. However, it will later become clear (cf. Sec. 11) that it is also able to provide a very satisfactory statistical representation of a system whose energy is constant. The canonical ensemble is subject to easier analytical manipulation than the micro-canonical ensemble. If it can accomplish the same descriptive ends as the microcanonical ensemble its use will lead to considerable economy of thought. We may make one further remark at this point. We shall later associate the physical concept of temperature with the modulus Θ of the canonical ensemble. This type of ensemble therefore represents a system at constant temperature.

10. THE MAXWELL-BOLTZMANN DISTRIBUTION LAW

One of the searching tests of any statistical theory of dynamical systems is its ability to lead to the proper law for the distribution of velocities. We have now to examine this problem from the standpoint of Gibbs' statistical mechanics. We must first construct a canonical ensemble for a system of n free particles all of mass m having $f(=3n)$ degrees of freedom. The Hamiltonian for such a system is

$$H = \sum_{j=1}^{n} (p_{xj}^2 + p_{yj}^2 + p_{zj}^2)/2m. \tag{93}$$

The phase probability in the corresponding canonical ensemble is now (writing $p_j^2 = p_{xj}^2 + p_{yj}^2 + p_{zj}^2$, for short)

$$P d\phi = \frac{e^{-\Sigma p_j^2/2m\Theta} \prod_{j=1}^{n} dx_j\, dy_j\, dz_j \prod_{j=1}^{n} dp_{xj}\, dp_{yj}\, dp_{zj}}{\int (2f) \int e^{-\Sigma p_j^2/2m\Theta} \prod_{j=1}^{n} dx_j\, dy_j\, dz_j \prod_{j=1}^{n} dp_{xj}\, dp_{yj}\, dp_{zj}}, \tag{94}$$

where the integral in the denominator is $2f$ fold. This, of course, gives the probability associated with an ensemble element of volume $d\phi$ in the neighborhood of the phase $x_1, y_1, z_1, p_{x1}, p_{y1}, p_{z1}, \cdots$ $x_n, y_n, z_n, p_{xn}, p_{yn}, p_{zn}$. From the fundamental postulate of Sec. 6, this is the probability of finding the actual system of f degrees of freedom in the state for which the first particle has coordinates in the neighborhood of x_1, y_1, z_1 and momentum components in the neighborhood of p_{x1}, p_{y1}, p_{z1}, and correspondingly for the other particles.

Now we actually wish the expression for the probability that any one particle (for simplicity we shall take the one denoted by subscript 1) shall have its phase as indicated while the other particles are distributed in *any fashion whatever* consistent with the given total energy and finite volume. From the fundamental postulate and eq. (94) this will be

$$P_1 d\phi_1 =$$

$$\frac{e^{-p_1^2/2m\Theta} d\phi_1 \int (2f-6) \int e^{-\sum\limits_{j=2}^{n} p_j^2/2m\Theta} \prod\limits_{j=2}^{n} dx_j\, dy_j\, dz_j \cdot \prod\limits_{j=2}^{n} dp_{xj}\, dp_{yj}\, dp_{zj}}{\Delta}$$

$$(95)$$

where Δ is the same denominator as in (94) and $d\phi_1 = dx_1 dy_1 dz_1 \cdot dp_{x1} dp_{y1} dp_{z1}$. Note that the integral in the numerator is now $(2f - 6)$ fold. If further we wish the probability that the first particle shall have its momentum components in the neighborhood of p_{x1}, p_{y1}, p_{z1} while its coordinates are unrestricted we have further

$$P_1' d\phi_1' =$$

$$\frac{e^{-p_1^2/2m\Theta} dp_{x1}\, dp_{y1}\, dp_{z1} \int (f-3) \int e^{-\sum\limits_{j=2}^{n} p_j^2/2m\Theta} \prod\limits_{j=2}^{n} dp_{xj}\, dp_{yj}\, dp_{zj}}{\int (f) \int e^{-\sum\limits_{j=1}^{n} p_j^2/2m\Theta} \prod\limits_{j=1}^{n} dp_{xj}\, dp_{yj}\, dp_{zj}} \cdot \quad (96)$$

The integrals in (96) are easy to carry out by iteration of the well-known integral $\iiint e^{-(p_x^2+p_y^2+p_z^2)/2m\Theta}\, dp_x\, dp_y\, dp_z = (2\pi m\Theta)^{3/2}$. The result is that

$$P_1' d\phi_1' = (2\pi m\Theta)^{-3/2} e^{-(p_{x1}^2+p_{y1}^2+p_{z1}^2)/2m\Theta}\, dp_{x1}\, dp_{y1}\, dp_{z1}. \quad (97)$$

In place of the first particle we might have taken *any* particle. We therefore reach the conclusion that the average fractional number of particles having their momentum components in the interval $p_x, p_x + dp_x, \cdots$ becomes

$$\frac{dn}{n} = (2\pi m\Theta)^{-3/2} e^{-(p_x^2 + p_y^2 + p_z^2)/2m\Theta}\, dp_x\, dp_y\, dp_z. \qquad (98)$$

If further we replace p_x by mv_x, etc., this would take the precise form of the Maxwellian velocity distribution (50) in Chapter V, provided indeed we are entitled to replace the characteristic parameter Θ of the ensemble by kT. The temptation is therefore strong to look upon (97) and its equivalent (98) as the statistical mechanical version of the Maxwell-Boltzmann distribution law and to consider the parameter Θ as the statistical mechanical analogue of something proportional to the thermodynamic temperature.

It is worth while pointing out that the restriction to absolutely free particles is not necessary. We can introduce a potential energy function $V(x_j, y_j, z_j)$ into the Hamiltonian. As long as it is a function of the coordinates only, its influence will cancel out in the integration over the coordinates and the final result will still be (97). Of course we can then no longer maintain that *any* position coordinates for the system are as likely as any other: as a result of the forces on the system certain parts of configuration space will in general be preferred by the system, depending on the nature of $V(x_j, y_j, z_j)$.

A further observation is in order on the statistical mechanical interpretation of the Maxwell-Boltzmann distribution law. In the immediately preceding discussion we have tried to develop the analogy with kinetic theory by constructing a Gibbs ensemble for a whole system of free particles. This seems to be the natural course to pursue, but it is interesting to observe that we can achieve the same result by forming the ensemble for a *single* particle. Let us see how this comes about. The Hamiltonian for a system consisting of such a particle of mass m, having kinetic energy only, is

$$H = (p_x^2 + p_y^2 + p_z^2)/2m. \qquad (99)$$

The phase probability for the corresponding canonical ensemble is

$$Pd\phi = \frac{e^{-(p_x^2 + p_y^2 + p_z^2)/2m\Theta}\, dx\, dy\, dz\, dp_x\, dp_y\, dp_z}{\displaystyle\int\!\!\int\!\!\int\!\!\int\!\!\int\!\!\int e^{-(p_x^2 + p_y^2 + p_z^2)/2m\Theta}\, dx\, dy\, dz\, dp_x\, dp_y\, dp_z}. \qquad (100)$$

It must be emphasized that in constructing the canonical ensemble for a single particle we cannot assume that the energy of the particle is fixed. By the very nature of the canonical ensemble we must assume the possibility that the energy of the system being described shall be able to fluctuate. The particle we are here talking about is one whose energy can then have *any* value. It cannot therefore be considered free in the usual dynamical sense, even though we are treating its energy as wholly kinetic.

If we carry out the integration in the denominator of (100), we can write

$$Pd\phi = \frac{e^{-(p_x^2+p_y^2+p_z^2)/2m\Theta} \; dx \; dy \; dz \; dp_x \; dp_y \; dp_z}{\tau(2\pi m\Theta)^{3/2}}, \qquad (101)$$

where τ is the physical volume in which the particle is confined. If further we require the probability that the phase point have momentum values p_x, p_y, p_z in the indicated interval with no restriction on the coordinates x, y, z, we obtain

$$P'd\phi' = (2\pi m\Theta)^{-3/2} e^{-(p_x^2+p_y^2+p_z^2)/2m\Theta} \; dp_x \; dp_y \; dp_z. \qquad (102)$$

This is identical with eq. (98) which gives the average fractional number of particles in a whole aggregate of free particles having their momentum components in the indicated interval. It therefore appears that we need not have considered the whole aggregate in forming the canonical ensemble. A single member suffices. Closer inspection of the situation indicates that the reason for this is that the particles in the aggregate are free and do not affect each other. If the particles were to act on each other with forces, the Hamiltonian would no longer be of the simple form (93) and the possibility of replacing the whole Hamiltonian by that for a single particle in forming the ensemble would no longer exist.

11. DEVIATIONS OF QUANTITIES FROM THEIR AVERAGE VALUES

The utility of statistical mechanics for thermodynamics resides in the *average* quantities computed over an ensemble; these are to be identified with the physically measured values of these quantities. For example, the actually measured energy of a physical system is taken to be the canonical average of the energy over the canonical ensemble representing the system. On the other hand in the ensemble the various elements correspond to different energies and there are then actually wide deviations from the average. This situation appears rather disconcerting when we are trying to represent a system with constant energy by a canonical ensemble. Offhand we should be inclined to say that it could not be done and that we *must* represent such a system by a microcanonical ensemble. That this is not really *always* the case, however, is seen from an examination of the magnitude of the deviations from the average energy in a canonical ensemble.

We need not confine our investigation to the energy. Let χ be *any* function of the coordinates and momenta of the system. The fluctuation or deviation of χ from its canonical average is represented by

$$\xi = \chi - \bar{\chi}. \tag{103}$$

(The bar here indicates *canonical* average without further specification.)   The average deviation is then at once

$$\bar{\xi} = \overline{(\chi - \bar{\chi})} = 0. \tag{104}$$

To get something more significant we introduce the fractional root-mean-square deviation or

$$\alpha = \sqrt{\frac{\overline{\xi^2}}{\bar{\chi}^2}} = \sqrt{\frac{\overline{\chi^2} - \bar{\chi}^2}{\bar{\chi}^2}}. \tag{105}$$

We shall take α as a measure of the average deviation of χ from its average value.   For the sake of being specific let $\chi = H$ and let us confine our comments to an ensemble representing an aggregate of free particles, i.e., an ideal gas, where

$$\bar{H} = \bar{E} = \frac{f\Theta}{2}. \tag{106}$$

As usual f is the number of degrees of freedom of the system.   We replace $1/\Theta$ by z and let $\int e^{-Hz} d\phi = Q$.   Then

$$\frac{dQ}{dz} = -\int He^{-Hz} d\phi = -\bar{E} \cdot Q$$

from the definition of canonical average.   Moreover

$$\frac{d^2Q}{dz^2} = \int H^2 e^{-Hz} d\phi = \overline{E^2} \cdot Q.$$

We therefore have

$$\overline{E^2} - \bar{E}^2 = \frac{d^2Q/dz^2}{Q} - \frac{(dQ/dz)^2}{Q^2} = \Theta^2 \frac{d\bar{E}}{d\Theta}. \tag{107}$$

Hence

$$\alpha = \sqrt{\frac{\overline{E^2} - \bar{E}^2}{\bar{E}^2}} = \frac{\Theta}{\bar{E}} \sqrt{\frac{d\bar{E}}{d\Theta}} = \sqrt{\frac{2}{f}}. \tag{108}$$

Consequently if the number of degrees of freedom of the system is very large, as it will be in the case of a gas, α becomes negligibly small and we are after all justified in using a canonical ensemble to represent the system.

There is another way of looking at the matter which brings out the same point. We may compute the fractional number of elements in a canonical ensemble having energies lying in the range from E to $E + \Delta E$, where E is any energy value. This fractional number will clearly be

$$\frac{\Delta N}{N} = \int_{E}^{E+\Delta E} e^{(\psi - H)/\Theta} d\phi. \tag{109}$$

In this expression $e^{(\psi - H)/\Theta}$ is to be integrated over that portion of phase space for which the Hamiltonian H lies between E and $E + \Delta E$. Now if we restrict the discussion to an ideal gas of n particles of mass m, H has the form (f = number of degrees of freedom = $3n$)

$$H = \frac{1}{2m} \cdot \sum_{j=1}^{f} p_j^2. \tag{110}$$

In evaluating (109) it will be convenient to write $d\phi = d\phi_q d\phi_p$ where $d\phi_q$ is the configuration coordinate part of the phase space volume element and $d\phi_p$ is the momentum part. Then

$$\frac{\Delta N}{N} = \tau^{f/3} \int_{E}^{E+\Delta E} e^{(\psi - H)/\Theta} d\phi_p, \tag{111}$$

where τ = the physical volume occupied by the gas and $\int d\phi_q = \tau^{f/3}$.

Now we shall let the volume in *momentum* space occupied by the points representing systems whose energies lie between 0 and E be Φ_p, where then

$$\Phi_p = \int_{0}^{E} d\phi_p. \tag{112}$$

It is clear that Φ_p is some function of E, and we must now find out what this function is. Let us imagine first that $E = 1$ (unit of energy). The upper limit in (112) is then really equivalent to the relation

$$\frac{1}{2m} \sum_{j=1}^{f} p_j^2 = 1. \tag{113}$$

On the other hand if $E = a^2$, the upper limit in (112) is equivalent to

$$\frac{1}{2m} \sum_{j=1}^{f} p_j^2 = a^2. \tag{114}$$

It is clear we can write (114) in the form

$$\frac{1}{2m} \sum_{j=1}^{f} \left(\frac{p_j}{a}\right)^2 = 1. \tag{114'}$$

Consequently the integral

$$\int \cdots \int d\left(\frac{p_1}{a}\right) d\left(\frac{p_2}{a}\right) \cdots d\left(\frac{p_f}{a}\right),$$

in which the lower limits are zero in each case and the upper limits subject only to (114') is the *same* as the integral

$$(\Phi_p)_{E=1} = \int \cdots \int dp_1 \, dp_2 \cdots dp_f,$$

in which the lower limits are zero and the upper ones subject only to (113). But the integral for which the energy E has the value a^2 is given by

$$(\Phi_p)_{E=a^2} = a^f \int \cdots \int d\left(\frac{p_1}{a}\right) \cdots d\left(\frac{p_f}{a}\right),$$

where the upper limits are subject to (114'). Therefore we conclude that

$$(\Phi_p)_E = E^{f/2}(\Phi_p)_{E=1}. \tag{115}$$

Φ_p must then vary directly as $E^{f/2}$, since $(\Phi_p)_{E=1}$ is a constant. This constant may be evaluated as follows. Let

$$\Phi_p = CE^{f/2}. \tag{116}$$

Going back to (111) we see that we can replace $d\phi_p$ by $d\Phi_p = f/2 \cdot CE^{f/2-1} dE$. Moreover if we integrate (111) between $E = 0$ and $E = \infty$ we get unity. That is

$$\frac{fC\tau^{f/3}}{2} \cdot \int_0^\infty e^{(\psi-H)/\Theta} E^{f/2-1} dE = 1. \tag{117}$$

We recall that

$$e^{\psi/\Theta} = \frac{1}{\displaystyle\int e^{-H/\Theta} d\phi} = \frac{1}{\tau^{f/3}(2\pi m\Theta)^{f/2}}. \tag{118}$$

Therefore (117) becomes

$$\frac{fC}{2(2\pi m\Theta)^{f/2}} \int_0^\infty e^{-E/\Theta} E^{f/2-1} dE = 1. \tag{119}$$

From the definition of the gamma function there results

$$C = \frac{(2\pi m)^{f/2}}{f/2 \cdot \Gamma(f/2)} = \frac{(2\pi m)^{f/2}}{\Gamma(f/2 + 1)}.$$ (120)

We may now express $\Delta N/N$ as follows

$$\frac{\Delta N}{N} = \frac{1}{(2\pi m\Theta)^{f/2}} \cdot \frac{f}{2} \cdot \frac{(2\pi m)^{f/2}}{\Gamma(f/2 + 1)} \cdot \int_{E}^{E+\Delta E} e^{-E/\Theta} E^{f/2-1} dE,$$

which reduces for ΔE sufficiently small compared with E to the form

$$\frac{\Delta N}{N} = \frac{e^{-E/\Theta}}{\Theta\Gamma(f/2)} \cdot \left(\frac{E}{\Theta}\right)^{f/2-1} \cdot \Delta E.$$ (121)

Incidentally the reader may check this final expression by observing that the summation of (121) over all E, gives unity in conformity with the fact that

$$\frac{\Sigma \Delta N}{N} = 1.$$

Let us now find the "most popular" value of E, i.e., that for which $\Delta N/\Delta E$ is a maximum. For this value of E there are in a *given* energy interval more elements of the ensemble than in any other interval of the same size. We differentiate $\Delta N/\Delta E$ with respect to E and on putting the result equal to zero obtain

$$E_{\mathrm{mp}} = \left(\frac{f}{2} - 1\right)\Theta.$$ (122)

If f is very large this is effectively $f/2 \cdot \Theta$ or the *canonical* average (106). For a system with a very large number of degrees of freedom the canonical average energy is also the "most popular" value of the energy. This again checks our previous conclusion that for f large we do not make a very great mistake in using the canonical average $\bar{E}$ for the energy of the system represented by a canonical ensemble.

There remains only the task of finding the number of systems having energy slightly different from E_{mp}. Thus, for example, suppose $E = 1.01 E_{\mathrm{mp}} = 1.01(f/2 - 1)\Theta$. It is left to the reader to carry out the straightforward arithmetical calculation showing that for 1 cm^3 of gas under standard conditions with $f = 3(2.7) \times 10^{19}$

$$\frac{\Delta N(E)}{\Delta N(E_{\mathrm{mp}})} \doteq e^{-1.8 \times 10^{15}}.$$

This shows that the chance of picking out in the canonical ensemble an element corresponding to energy differing by only 1 per cent from the most popular value is practically negligible. The corresponding fluctuation of the energy of the actual system represented by the ensemble from $\bar{E}$ is therefore also negligibly small. All this of course is predicated on the large value of f.

12. THE STATISTICAL MECHANICAL INTERPRETATION OF TEMPERATURE

We have now seen the possibility of representing thermodynamical quantities by means of averages over Gibbsian ensembles and have learned that the choice of ensemble, i.e., whether canonical or microcanonical, is largely a matter of mathematical convenience. In order to make the connection between statistical mechanics and thermodynamics more definite and convincing it is necessary to establish more precisely the statistical mechanical analogues of the fundamental thermodynamical state variables, temperature and entropy. As a matter of fact in Sec. 10 in the discussion of the Maxwell-Boltzmann distribution law we have had an intimation that the analogue of temperature is to be found in the characteristic ensemble parameter Θ. We now wish to place this association on a somewhat firmer basis by showing that Θ possesses certain important properties which are precisely those of the temperature in the thermodynamical sense. We recall that when two thermodynamical systems are in equilibrium the condition that they have the same temperature is that when they are put in thermal contact (and of course isolated from all other systems) the composite system thus formed will be in equilibrium at the same temperature as that of either system before contact. On the other hand two systems in equilibrium at different temperatures will not be in equilibrium when joined, though they will, of course, approach equilibrium with a change in the temperature of both.

Let the Hamiltonians of the two systems be H_A and H_B respectively. The phase probabilities in the canonical ensembles representing the two systems will then be respectively

$$P_A d\phi_A = e^{(\Psi_A - H_A)/\Theta} d\phi_A, \tag{123}$$

$$P_B d\phi_B = e^{(\Psi_B - H_B)/\Theta} d\phi_B, \tag{124}$$

where we have assumed the *same* parameter Θ for both ensembles. Now let the systems be joined. The Hamiltonian for the composite system will have the form

$$H = H_A + H_B + H_{AB}, \tag{125}$$

where the term H_{AB} refers to the energy of interaction of the two systems. We shall suppose that this energy is very small compared with
either H_A or H_B, though there are indeed practical cases in which this
is by no means true; these we shall rule out of our present discussion
and proceed to call H_{AB} zero, effectively.

Now $P_A d\phi_A$ denotes the probability of picking at random from
the ensemble corresponding to system A an element whose phase
lies in $d\phi_A$, and similarly for B. Let the phase space for A have $2k$
dimensions and that for B have $2l$ dimensions. Then the phase space
for the composite system will have $2k + 2l$ dimensions and the element
of volume in it will be denoted by $d\phi_A d\phi_B$. The probability of picking
at random from the ensemble of the composite system an element whose
A component has its phase in $d\phi_A$ and whose B component has at the
same time its phase in $d\phi_B$ is, from elementary probability considerations,

$$P_A P_B d\phi_A d\phi_B = e^{(\psi_A + \psi_B - H_A - H_B)/\Theta} d\phi_A d\phi_B. \tag{126}$$

In other words we think of the combination of the two systems as taking place in such a way that each element of the composite ensemble is
made up by joining two elements of the original ensembles for A and B
respectively. But the probability of picking out of the composite
ensemble an element with phase in $d\phi = d\phi_A d\phi_B$ of course is just

$$Pd\phi = e^{(\psi - H)/\Theta} d\phi. \tag{127}$$

Now $\psi = \psi_A + \psi_B$ since the ψ's are constants and no matter what
precise relation exists between $P_A P_B d\phi_A d\phi_B$ and $Pd\phi$, we must have
in both cases

$$\int P_A P_B d\phi_A d\phi_B = 1 = \int Pd\phi. \tag{128}$$

But from the further fact that $H = H_A + H_B$ in the ideal case of
negligible interaction it follows that actually

$$P_A P_B d\phi_A d\phi_B = Pd\phi, \tag{129}$$

which means that when the two original systems having common Θ
are joined the resulting system is described by an ensemble characterized by the same Θ. On the other hand if the ensemble for A had
been characterized by the parameter Θ_A and that for B by a *different*
parameter Θ_B, after joining we should have

$$P_A P_B d\phi_A d\phi_B = e^{(\psi_A - H_A)/\Theta_A} e^{(\psi_B - H_B)/\Theta_B} d\phi_A d\phi_B. \tag{130}$$

This would not correspond with $Pd\phi$ for any Θ and hence no canonical
ensemble could be formed for the resulting system, i.e., it could not

be a system in equilibrium in the theory of statistical mechanics. However we must suppose that after a sufficiently long time has elapsed the composite system will come to equilibrium by some kind of energy exchange between the two original systems. It can then be shown that the modulus Θ of the resulting ensemble has a value lying between Θ_A and Θ_B. Indeed by the use of the equipartition principle it develops that Θ is related to Θ_A and Θ_B in precisely the same way in which the final equilibrium temperature of a mixture of two gases is related to the original temperatures of the components.

It is clear that Θ possesses the chief properties that characterize the thermodynamical temperature T. The precise relation between Θ and T, i.e., the nature of the constant c in the relation

$$\Theta = cT,$$

can be obtained only from a comparison between an empirical thermo-dynamical law and the statistical mechanical analogue. If we use the equation of state (eq. 14 of Chapter III) for this purpose it is not difficult to show that $c = k$, i.e., that

$$\Theta = kT, \tag{131}$$

which indicates that the ensemble modulus Θ in the Gibbs statistical mechanics plays the same role as the canonical distribution modulus in the classical Maxwell-Boltzmann statistics (cf. Section 3 of Chapter IV).

13. THE STATISTICAL MECHANICAL INTERPRETATION OF ENTROPY

Closely associated with and fully as fundamental as the interpreta-tion of temperature in statistical mechanics is the meaning of entropy. The problem is to find a statistical quantity which possesses the properties associated with entropy in thermodynamics (Chapter III, Sec. 2). Following Gibbs we again begin with a canonical ensemble in which

$$e^{-\psi/\Theta} = \int e^{-H/\Theta} d\phi. \tag{83}$$

Now the Hamiltonian of the system is a function of the p's and q's which also involves certain parameters. These we shall label $\xi_1, \xi_2 \cdots \xi_j$. $\cdots$. Their number depends on the type of system and the number of degrees of freedom. In the simple harmonic oscillator, for example, there are two, viz., the mass and stiffness of the system. (Cf. Sec. 3 of Chapter IV for the introduction of these external parameters in the Maxwell-Boltzmann statistics.) Let us now see what happens when the ξ's and Θ are varied. This variation has no reference to change in time and does not entail changes in the p's and q's. Equation (83) then yields

$$e^{-\psi/\Theta}\left[-\frac{\delta\psi}{\Theta}+\frac{\psi}{\Theta^2}\cdot\delta\Theta\right]$$

$$=\frac{\delta\Theta}{\Theta^2}\cdot\int He^{-H/\Theta}d\phi-\frac{1}{\Theta}\Sigma\delta\xi_j\int\frac{\partial H}{\partial\xi_j}e^{-H/\Theta}d\phi. \quad (132)$$

Multiplication by $\Theta e^{\psi/\Theta}$ and the replacement of $\int He^{(\psi-H)/\Theta}\,d\phi$ by $\overline{H}$ yields

$$\delta\psi=\frac{(\psi-\overline{H})}{\Theta}\,\delta\Theta+\sum\overline{\left(\frac{\partial H}{\partial\xi_j}\right)}\,\delta\xi_j. \quad (133)$$

If we denote $(\psi-H)/\Theta$ by the new symbol η, so that $(\psi-\overline{H})/\Theta=\overline{\eta}$, we have from (133)

$$\delta\psi=\overline{\eta}\delta\Theta+\sum\overline{\left(\frac{\partial H}{\partial\xi_j}\right)}\,\delta\xi_j. \quad (134)$$

Now if in the defining equation for $\overline{\eta}$ we vary both coordinates and parameters, denoting such changes by differentials to distinguish them from changes in which parameter alterations alone are involved, the result is

$$d\psi-d\overline{H}=\overline{\eta}d\Theta+\Theta d\overline{\eta}. \quad (135)$$

But since ψ and Θ are independent of the coordinates

$$d\psi=\delta\psi\quad\text{and}\quad d\Theta=\delta\Theta.$$

Comparison of (134) and (135) then leads to

$$d\overline{E}=-\Theta d\overline{\eta}+\sum\overline{\left(\frac{\partial H}{\partial\xi_j}\right)}\,\delta\xi_j, \quad (136)$$

where we have replaced $d\overline{H}$ by its equivalent $d\overline{E}$, i.e., the change in the average energy. Now the last term in (136) represents the average change in the energy of the system due to the variation in the external parameters. Consequently it can be interpreted as the negative of the average *work* which the system does when the external parameters are varied. We shall denote it by $-\delta W$. Therefore (136) becomes

$$-\Theta d\overline{\eta}=d\overline{E}+\delta W. \quad (137)$$

If we introduce the relation (131) between Θ and T, this takes the form

$$-kT d\bar{\eta} = d\bar{E} + \delta W, \tag{138}$$

which looks very much like the familiar thermodynamical expression (eq. 4 in Chapter III)

$$T dS = dE + \delta W, \tag{139}$$

(where indeed we previously used ΔW in place of δW with no difference in physical meaning). If we decide to let (138) serve as the statistical interpretation of (139) we must identify dS with $-k d\bar{\eta}$ or set

$$S = -k\bar{\eta}, \tag{140}$$

with a possible additive constant independent of the coordinates and external parameters as well as Θ and ψ. This is Gibbs' statistical mechanical interpretation of the entropy of a system.

We ought to look into the analogy between $-\bar{\eta}$ and the entropy a little. For example we recall from Chapter III the statement of the second law of thermodynamics in the form that the entropy is a maximum for a closed system in equilibrium. Can we show that $-\bar{\eta}$ is larger for a canonical ensemble than for any other ensemble with the same number of elements and the same average energy? We shall call $\eta = (\psi - H)/\Theta = \log P$, the index of phase probability. Now let η for the non-canonical ensemble be denoted by η', where

$$\eta' = \eta + \Delta\eta, \tag{141}$$

and $\Delta\eta$ is an arbitrary function of the p's and q's. Because the number of elements and average energy are the same in both ensembles, we can write

$$\int e^{\eta+\Delta\eta} d\phi = \int e^{\eta} d\phi = 1, \tag{142}$$

and

$$\int H e^{\eta+\Delta\eta} d\phi = \int H e^{\eta} d\phi. \tag{143}$$

We seek to prove that $\overline{\eta'} > \bar{\eta}$. This corresponds to $-\bar{\eta} > -\overline{\eta'}$. Though the average $\overline{\eta'}$ is not a canonical average it is calculated over its ensemble in the usual way. Thus we wish to show that

$$\int (\eta + \Delta\eta) e^{\eta+\Delta\eta} d\phi > \int \eta e^{\eta} d\phi. \tag{144}$$

Now

$$\int (\eta + \Delta\eta)e^{\eta+\Delta\eta}\, d\phi = \int \left(\frac{\psi - H}{\Theta} + \Delta\eta\right)e^{\eta+\Delta\eta}d\phi$$

$$= \frac{\psi}{\Theta}\int e^{\eta+\Delta\eta}d\phi - \frac{1}{\Theta}\int He^{\eta+\Delta\eta}d\phi + \int \Delta\eta e^{\eta+\Delta\eta}\, d\phi. \quad (145)$$

By using (142) and (143), we can reduce (145) to

$$\int (\eta + \Delta\eta)e^{\eta+\Delta\eta}d\phi = \frac{\psi}{\Theta} - \frac{1}{\Theta}\int He^{\eta}d\phi + \int \Delta\eta e^{\eta+\Delta\eta}d\phi. \quad (146)$$

But for the same reason

$$\int \eta e^{\eta}d\phi = \frac{\psi}{\Theta} - \frac{1}{\Theta}\int He^{\eta}d\phi. \quad (147)$$

Therefore to prove (144) we must examine $\int \Delta\eta e^{\eta+\Delta\eta}\, d\phi$, which can also be written $\int (\Delta\eta e^{\Delta\eta} + 1 - e^{\Delta\eta})e^{\eta}d\phi$. The parenthetical term in the integrand is $(\Delta\eta - 1)e^{\Delta\eta} + 1$. If we plot this as a function of $\Delta\eta$, we see that it has only one minimum for real values of $\Delta\eta$. This has the value zero and occurs for $\Delta\eta = 0$. For all other values of $\Delta\eta$, the term in question is positive and greater than zero. Moreover e^{η} is always positive. Therefore

$$\int (\Delta\eta e^{\Delta\eta} + 1 - e^{\Delta\eta})e^{\eta}\, d\phi \geqq 0$$

(the equality sign corresponding to $\Delta\eta = 0$) for the whole range of integration. Therefore either $\Delta\eta$ vanishes, in which case the two ensembles are identical throughout, or

$$\int \Delta\eta e^{\eta+\Delta\eta}d\phi > 0$$

and (144) is substantiated. Hence

$$-\bar{\eta} > -\bar{\eta'}. \quad (148)$$

Consequently for a system not in equilibrium and represented by a non-canonical ensemble the entropy represented by $-\bar{\eta'}$ will tend to increase. It is clear that the statistical mechanical analogy $-k\bar{\eta}$ for entropy satisfies the "increasing" property of entropy in thermodynamics.

Further evidence of the suitability of $-\bar{\eta}$ to represent the entropy of a thermodynamical system will be found in the fact that $-\bar{\eta}$ is a maximum for a *uniform* distribution of the elements of the ensemble in phase space as compared with any other distribution of the same number of elements and corresponding to the same value of the average energy. The reader can readily show this by a slight modification of the method just used to demonstrate $-\bar{\eta} > -\bar{\eta}'$. In other words $-\bar{\eta}$ can be used as a measure of uniformity; the greater the value of $-\bar{\eta}$ for a given ensemble, the more nearly uniform is the distribution of elements. The canonical ensemble is the one which is most nearly uniform in distribution of all ensembles with given average energy and given number of elements. Obviously the appropriateness with which a canonical ensemble can be considered to represent a system in equilibrium depends in the last analysis on the extent to which any ensemble representing an actual dynamical system tends toward uniformity of distribution with the passage of time, independently of the initial distribution. This approach to uniformity cannot be logically demonstrated for an arbitrary initial distribution but proofs have been given for initial distributions which are not themselves so specialized as to be highly improbable.[11] We therefore feel safe in accepting the proposition that the Gibbsian analogue of the entropy for a closed system tends to increase and *practically* never decreases. We must recognize, of course, that it is subject to the same probability difficulties already envisaged in Sec. 3, Chapter IV in the discussion of the Maxwell-Boltzmann interpretation of entropy.

One last point remains for consideration: does $-k\bar{\eta}$ represent a state variable? From the definition

$$-k\bar{\eta} = -k \int \left(\frac{\psi - H}{\Theta} \right) e^{(\psi - H)/\Theta} d\phi$$

it follows that after the integration has been carried out the only quantities left on the right-hand side are the parameters, viz., the ξ_j, Θ and ψ and the physical volume occupied by the system being represented. The latter is involved in the integration limits for the q's. The limits for the p's are $+\infty$ and $-\infty$ effectively. $\Theta = kT$. Hence effectively $-k\bar{\eta}$ depends only on the volume and temperature and the other parameters which characterize the state. Therefore $-k\bar{\eta}$ represents a state variable and its association with entropy may be considered substantially verified.

---

[11] Cf. Gibbs, "Statistical Mechanics," Chapter XII. For a concrete illustration, Lindsay and Margenau, *op. cit.*, p. 245, may be consulted.

14. FREE ENERGY AND THE GIBBS PHASE INTEGRAL

We have so far said little about the parameter ψ which enters into the definition of the probability coefficient for a canonical ensemble. But eq. (134) written in the form

$$d\psi = \bar{\eta}d\Theta - \delta W,$$

with $\bar{\eta} = -S/k$ and $d\Theta = kdT$, is in precisely the form of eq. (10) of Chapter III, in which $d\psi$ (there represented as $d\Psi$) represents the change in the *free energy* of the system. Consequently we may safely treat ψ as the statistical mechanical analogue of the free energy. We have already commented on the importance of this thermodynamic function in the derivation of the equation of state (eq. 12 of Chapter III). It is interesting to observe that in the Gibbs statistical mechanics ψ is immediately given in terms of a certain integral. Thus from (83)

$$\psi = -\Theta \log \int e^{-H/\Theta} d\phi. \tag{149}$$

It is customary to refer to $\int e^{-H/\Theta} d\phi$ as the Gibbs *phase integral*, sometimes denoted by I. Its evaluation as a function of Θ and the external parameters of a system therefore leads at once to the equation of state. If we compare (149) with eq. (73) of Chapter IV we see that the Gibbs phase integral appears to bear some analogy to the function Z, which there we called the distribution or partition function. Indeed the connection looks even closer if we examine again the evaluation of Z for a system of free particles in Sec. 4 of Chapter IV. There except for a multiplicative constant we actually computed the phase integral. (NOTE: It must not be forgotten that ψ in statistical mechanics corresponds to Ψ in Chapter IV.)

As an illustration of the phase integral we shall calculate it for the special case of a system of n simple harmonic oscillators with masses m_j and stiffness coefficients k_j. The Hamiltonian is

$$H = \sum_{j=1}^{n} \left(\frac{p_j^2}{2m_j} + \frac{k_j q_j^2}{2} \right), \tag{150}$$

if we suppose that the oscillators are free of mutual interaction. We therefore have from (149)

$$\psi = -\Theta \log \int (2n) \int e^{-\Sigma(p_j^2/2m_j\Theta + k_j q_j^2/2\Theta)} h^{-n} dq_1 \cdots dq_n \, dp_1 \cdots dp_n, \tag{151}$$

with the limits of integration taken between $-\infty$ and $+\infty$ for each variable. In this expression we have written $d\phi = \dfrac{dq_1 \cdots dq_n \, dp_1 \cdots dp_n}{h^n}$, where h is a quantity having the dimensions of coordinate times momentum and is here put in to secure the proper dimensionality (cf. the discussion after eq. 83 in Sec. 9). Now

$$\int_{-\infty}^{+\infty} e^{-p_j^2/2m_j\Theta}dp_j = \sqrt{2\pi m_j\Theta}.$$

Consequently

$$\psi = -\,\Theta \log \Theta^n \prod_{j=1}^{n}\left(\frac{1}{h\nu_j}\right). \tag{152}$$

If the dependence of the frequencies ν_j on the volume of the system were known we could use (152) to determine the equation of state. However, we can at any rate get the expression for the entropy. From the equipartition of energy we know that

$$\bar{E} = n\Theta = nkT. \tag{153}$$

This could of course be computed directly from $\bar{H}$. Now from $\psi = \bar{E} - TS$, we get

$$S = \frac{\bar{E} - \psi}{T} = nk + k \log (kT)^n \prod_{j=1}^{n}\left(\frac{1}{h\nu_j}\right)$$

$$= nk + k \prod_{j=1}^{n}\left(\frac{kT}{h\nu_j}\right). \tag{154}$$

So far as the Gibbs statistical mechanics is concerned h is just a constant having the appropriate dimensions to make the fundamental expression (151) dimensionally correct. It is clear, however, that we can interpret h^n as the unit of "volume" in phase space. As such in classical theory it may have any numerical value. According to the quantum theory, however, h is a fundamental constant of nature, called the Planck constant of action, with the value (cf. Chapter VIII)

$$h = 6.55 \times 10^{-27} \text{ erg sec.}$$

The dimensions of $h\nu_j$ are then those of energy like kT.

In the classical theory of solids, a solid crystal is considered to be effectively a collection of harmonic oscillators. Consequently the formulas just derived have an application to an ideal crystalline solid.

In particular from (153) we can get the heat capacity at constant volume for such a solid. Thus

$$C_V = \frac{d\bar{E}}{dT} = nk. \tag{155}$$

Here n is the number of degrees of freedom of the crystal. If we think of each atom making up the crystalline solid as having three degrees of freedom and assume that the number of atoms per gram molecule is still Avogadro's number, it follows from (155) that the molar heat capacity of a monatomic crystal is $3(6.06) \times 10^{23} \times (1.37) \times 10^{-16}$ ergs/degree C. When reduced to calories degree C this figure becomes 5.96 cal/degree C. This is in rather good agreement with the experimental value for monatomic crystals at room temperature. The simple classical theory here presented fails indeed to account for the variation of the molar heat capacity with the temperature. For this the quantum theory seems to be demanded. (Cf. Chapter IX, Sec. 3.)

It should be possible to use eq. (149) for the free energy to attack theoretically the derivation of the equation of state of a real gas. Considerable progress has been made on this recently but the subject lies beyond the scope of the present book.[12]

15. ALTERNATIVE INTERPRETATION OF ENTROPY

It is well to recognize that $-\bar{\eta}$ is not the only statistical mechanical quantity which possesses the appropriate properties to serve as an analogue of entropy in thermodynamics. Consider the quantity

$$S = k \log \phi_{\bar{E}}, \tag{156}$$

where $\phi_{\bar{E}}$ is the total phase volume enclosed by the energy surface $H = \bar{E}$, and $\bar{E}$ is the average energy over a canonical ensemble. Let the energy of the dynamical system represented by the ensemble, namely $\bar{E}$, be changed slightly without altering the external parameters $\xi_1 \cdots \xi_n$. Physically this will correspond to a flow of heat into or out of the system. Then from (156) there will be a change in S of magnitude

$$dS = kd \log \phi_{\bar{E}} = \frac{k}{\phi_{\bar{E}}} \frac{\partial \phi_{\bar{E}}}{\partial \bar{E}} d\bar{E}, \tag{157}$$

where $\partial \phi_{\bar{E}}/\partial \bar{E}$ is the rate of change of $\phi_{\bar{E}}$ with respect to $\bar{E}$ while the

---

[12] An elaborate discussion will be found in Mayer and Mayer, "Statistical Mechanics," John Wiley & Sons, New York, 1940, pp. 277 ff.

ξ's remain fixed. From eq. (60) $\partial \phi_{\bar{E}}/\partial \bar{E} = \omega(\bar{E})$. Hence

$$dS = \frac{kd\bar{E}}{\phi_{\bar{E}}/\omega(\bar{E})}. \tag{158}$$

Now we have already shown (eq. 71) that $\phi_{\bar{E}}/\omega(\bar{E})$ is twice the average kinetic energy per degree of freedom taken over the microcanonical ensemble corresponding to total energy $\bar{E}$. If the system consists of free particles, as we shall here assume for convenience, this means that

$$\frac{\phi_{\bar{E}}}{\omega(\bar{E})} = \frac{2\bar{E}}{f}, \tag{159}$$

if f is the number of degrees of freedom. But for an aggregate of free particles, the equipartition theorem yields

$$\bar{E} = \frac{f\Theta}{2}. \tag{160}$$

Therefore (158) becomes

$$dS = \frac{kd\bar{E}}{\Theta} = \frac{d\bar{E}}{T}. \tag{161}$$

But since $d\bar{E}$ must here represent change in energy caused by the reversible flow of heat, this is the usual expression for the change in entropy in a reversible thermodynamical process.

Although the above discussion is not very rigorous and is indeed rather specialized the suggestion is, at any rate, that $k \log \phi_{\bar{E}}$ is a possible analogue of the entropy. We could proceed to apply to it the tests used on $-\bar{\eta}$. It will be simpler, however, to examine directly its relation to $-\bar{\eta}$. We shall restrict the discussion to an aggregate of free particles, i.e., an ideal gas.

We begin with

$$e^{-\bar{\eta}} = e^{-\psi/\Theta}e^{\bar{E}/\Theta}. \tag{162}$$

But for an ideal gas this becomes

$$e^{-\bar{\eta}} = e^{-\psi/\Theta}e^{f/2}.$$

We can dispose of the factor $e^{-\psi/\Theta}$ by recalling that

$$e^{-\psi/\Theta} = \int e^{-H/\Theta}\,d\phi, \tag{163}$$

where the integration is to be conducted over the whole phase space. Writing

$$d\phi = d\phi_q d\phi_p,$$

where $d\phi_q$ refers to that part of the elementary phase volume in which the q's enter and $d\phi_p$ the corresponding momentum part, we can further say that

$$e^{-\psi/\Theta} = \tau^{f/3} \int_{-\infty}^{+\infty} \cdots \int_{-\infty}^{+\infty} e^{-\Sigma p_j^2/2m} dp_1 \cdots dp_f, \qquad (164)$$

where τ is the physical volume occupied by the gas. The f-tuple integral in (164) is evaluated in the usual way. The result is

$$e^{-\psi/\Theta} = \tau^{f/3}(2\pi m\Theta)^{f/2}. \qquad (165)$$

The consequence is that

$$-\bar{\eta} = \log \tau^{f/3} + \frac{f}{2} \log 2\pi m\Theta + \frac{f}{2}. \qquad (166)$$

We now wish to compare this with $\log \phi_{\bar{E}}$. This may be written

$$\phi_{\bar{E}} = \tau^{f/3} \int_0^{\bar{E}} d\phi_p. \qquad (167)$$

The integral has already been evaluated in eqs. (116) and (120), and we can immediately write

$$\phi_{\bar{E}} = \frac{\tau^{f/3}(2\pi m)^{f/2}\bar{E}^{f/2}}{\Gamma(f/2 + 1)}. \qquad (168)$$

This leads to

$$\log \phi_{\bar{E}} = \log \tau^{f/3} + \frac{f}{2} \log 2\pi m\Theta + \frac{f}{2} \log \frac{f}{2} - \log \Gamma\left(\frac{f}{2} + 1\right).$$

Now the asymptotic expansion of $\log \Gamma\left(\frac{f}{2} + 1\right)$ for large positive f can be put into the form[13]

$$\log \Gamma\left(\frac{f}{2} + 1\right) = \left(\frac{f}{2} + \frac{1}{2}\right) \log \frac{f}{2} - \left(\frac{f}{2} + 1\right) + \log \sqrt{2\pi}$$

$$+ \text{ terms involving } \frac{f}{2} \text{ in the denominator.}$$

Neglecting terms in this expansion small compared with $f/2$ we see that $\log \phi_{\bar{E}}$ can be expressed in the form

$$\log \phi_{\bar{E}} = \log \tau^{f/3} + \frac{f}{2} \log 2\pi m\Theta - \log \sqrt{\pi f} + \frac{f}{2}. \qquad (169)$$

If now we compare $-\bar{\eta}$ in (166) with the asymptotic form of $\log \phi_{E}'$

[13] Whittaker and Watson, "Modern Analysis" fourth edition, Macmillan, 1928.

in (169) we see that they differ only in the term log $\sqrt{\pi f}$ which is very small compared with the other terms in f if f is large. Hence as f increases we have the asymptotic relation

$$-\bar{\eta} \sim \log \phi_{\bar{E}}. \qquad (170)$$

This indicates the important relation between the two definitions of entropy.

16. RÉSUMÉ

This concludes our survey of the statistical mechanics of Gibbs which will stand for a long time as a monument of the power of abstract thought over physical problems. At the risk of a certain amount of redundance it will be desirable to sum up its features as contrasted to those of the Maxwell-Boltzmann method of statistical distributions.

We recall in the first place that the statistical distribution method operates throughout with the actual system being discussed. Thus, for example, we have a certain set of independent particles with a certain property, e.g., energy, and inquire about the most probable distribution of the particles with respect to this property. This most probable distribution is, of course, arbitrarily defined, but the definition in terms of the number of ways of realizing each state of the system, is at any rate plausible. This process leads to the so-called *canonical* distribution. We seek to identify the parameters entering into the distribution, i.e., ψ, Θ, and log P_c or log w, with observed properties of the system being described. This is done by showing that relations satisfied by these quantities are mathematically of the same form as the important thermodynamical relations among the state variables of the system in the thermodynamical mode of description. This provides one statistical interpretation of the macroscopic, thermodynamical properties of physical systems. The scheme has been criticized from several points of view, notably because of the use of Stirling's formula in its mathematical development to evaluate $N!$ no matter what the value of N is. This has led to an alternative formulation, namely the method of Darwin and Fowler, which we shall discuss in the following chapter.

The method of Gibbs does not operate with the actual system being discussed. Rather it builds an abstract ensemble to represent the behavior of the system. The subsequent analysis is carried out wholly with the ensemble and the connection with the properties of the actual system is made solely through the fundamental postulate of Sec. 6. Thus averages taken over the ensemble are conceived to represent observed values of the corresponding quantities for the actual system.

This places extreme importance on the choice of ensemble. Gibbs's choice of the canonical ensemble (he made little use of the micro-canonical ensemble) must be considered a stroke of genius. Operating with it, he was able to provide an analogy for all the thermodynamics which was known at his time. It is interesting to observe that he made no effort to build a *model mechanism* for the physical system under consideration. The canonical ensemble is in no sense a model. It is an abstract fiction, having no physical existence. Of course, it is true that to calculate averages over a canonical ensemble, one needs the Hamiltonian function of the system being described; this marks Gibbs's scheme as lying wholly within the framework of classical mechanics. The Maxwell-Boltzmann method is not subject to this particular restriction as it can envisage the distribution of any set of entities whatever. In one sense, therefore, the Maxwell-Boltzmann method is more general than that of Gibbs. On the other hand the Maxwell-Boltzmann statistics is more specialized in the sense that it operates only with free particles and thus neglects the possibility of their mutual interactions. The attempt to apply the Maxwell-Boltzmann statistics to a real gas, for example, necessitates the introduction of mechanical concepts and the postulation of forces lying outside the framework of the method itself. Indeed it involves essentially the application of some kind of kinetic theory. The method of Gibbs, on the contrary, is general enough to include all sorts of dynamical systems within its scope.

The comparison between the two types of statistical method will hardly be complete, however, without an exposition of the Darwin and Fowler modification of the Maxwell-Boltzmann scheme. This will form the content of the following chapter.

PROBLEMS

1. Apply Euler's theorem on homogeneous functions to deduce eq. (22).

2. Write the expression for the kinetic energy in terms of spherical, cylindrical and paraboloidal coordinates. Evaluate the component conjugate momenta in each case and comment on their physical significance.

3. Prove that the canonical equations are invariant in form with respect to an arbitrary point transformation of generalized coordinates.

4. A particle revolves in a circle about a fixed axis. Plot the representative curve in phase space.

5. A particle moves along a straight line in a uniform field of force. Plot the representative curve in phase space under the assumption that the particle is not allowed to exceed a certain maximum velocity.

6. A particle moves along a straight line in a field of force directed toward a fixed point on the line and varying inversely as the square of the distance from the point. Plot the representative curve in phase space under the assumption that the particle is confined to a segment of length a on either side of the fixed point. Assume that the total energy is negative.

7. In the case of the simple harmonic oscillator form the integral $\oint pdq$, which is supposed to be taken over a whole phase curve. This is called the phase integral. What allowed energies of the oscillator correspond to equating the phase integral to nh, where h is Planck's constant of action and n is integral? Do the same problem for the simple rotator mentioned in Problem 4 above.

8. Find the expression for the average energy over the canonical ensemble corresponding to a simple rotator. Do the same for a microcanonical ensemble.

9. Discuss the phase space for inverse square central field motion in terms of spherical coordinates. N.B. This is, of course, four-dimensional, but since in central field motion p_θ is constant, one can adequately represent the situation by a three-dimensional phase space, by employing r, θ, and p_r as coordinates. Plot the surface of constant energy in this space. Indicate the phase curve on this surface.

10. Use Gibbs's method to show how Liouville's theorem may be used to prove the invariance of the element of volume in phase space with respect to an arbitrary point transformation.

11. A particle moves in an inverse square central force field in an elliptical orbit with the force center at one focus. Find the expression for the probability that the particle will be found with its radius vector lying in the interval r, $r + dr$.

12. Prove that the canonical average of the energy of the simple harmonic oscillator is equal to the modulus Θ by evaluating

$$\frac{\int_{-\infty}^{+\infty} \int (p^2/2m + kq^2/2)e^{-(p^2/2m + kq^2/2)/\Theta}\, dp\, dq}{\int_{-\infty}^{+\infty} \int e^{-(p^2/2m + kq^2/2)/\Theta}\, dp\, dq}.$$

13. Calculate the root-mean-square deviation of the energy from the canonical mean for an aggregate of N simple harmonic oscillators.

14. Evaluate the momentum space volume Φ_p in eq. (112) directly by the use of the gamma function $\Gamma(n) = \int_0^\infty x^{n-1}e^{-x}dx$ and the beta function $B(m,\ n) = \int_0^1 x^{m-1}(1 - x)^{n-1}dx$. (Cf. E. B. Wilson, "Advanced Calculus," p. 378. Ginn and Co., 1912.)

15. Evaluate $\dfrac{\Delta N(E)}{\Delta N(E_{\mathrm{mp}})}$ (Sec. 11) for a system consisting of a single particle with three degrees of freedom where $E = 1.01\ E_{\mathrm{mp}}$. Do the same for a system of 100 particles.

16. Prove that $-\bar{\eta}$ (Sec. 13) is a maximum for a uniform distribution of the elements of an ensemble in phase space as compared with any other distribution of the same number of elements and corresponding to the same value of the average energy.

CHAPTER VII

STATISTICAL MECHANICS BY THE METHOD OF DARWIN AND FOWLER

1. FUNDAMENTAL CONCEPTS

The basic statistical concept in Gibbs's statistical mechanics is the *ensemble*. This is abandoned in the more recently developed method of Darwin and Fowler [1] and we must understand clearly the significance of the change. Gibbs considers a system of f degrees of freedom and proceeds to construct an ensemble whose elements are exact copies of the system in all its possible phases. On the other hand, the Darwin-Fowler method visualizes the system in question as made up of a large number of independent constituent systems, e.g., N in number. In their notation the N constituents together form an *assembly* of systems. At any instant the state of the assembly depends on the states of its constituent systems and quantities representing properties of the assembly are averaged over all possible states of the assembly. For a concrete example, suppose that a perfect gas consisting of N free mass particles is to be described statistically. Each particle will be considered a constituent system of the assembly, the latter representing the gas as a whole. The state of the gas depends on the state of the constituent particles and since each particle is capable of existing in various states characterized by different position, momentum, energy, etc., the corresponding states of the gas, i.e., the assembly, are very varied.

It is evidently necessary to make clearer what we shall mean by a *state*. Let us suppose that the property in which we are interested is the energy. The state of the assembly would be ideally specified by stating the precise energy value of each constituent system. Since in practical applications the constituent systems are very numerous and since in general they are indistinguishable, e.g., all particles of the same nature, this mode of specification is impracticable. We therefore fall back on the specification of the *number* of constituent systems in each allowed energy interval. Effectively the situation is like that envisaged in Sec. 1 of Chapter IV, where we considered the distribu-

---

[1] R. H. Fowler, "Statistical Mechanics," second edition, 1936. Cambridge University Press. The original joint papers date from 1922.

tion of N indistinguishable objects among μ boxes. The N objects constitute the assembly and the μ boxes are possible or allowed energy values. As far as classical statistics is concerned these energy boxes may be of arbitrarily small size and continuously distributed. According to the quantum mechanical point of view, however, the allowed energy values may be discrete, corresponding to a lower limit to the size of the boxes. Since we shall shortly have occasion to apply statistics to problems treated by the quantum theory we shall take from the start the general point of view.

It is well to emphasize that, like the Maxwell-Boltzmann method, the Darwin-Fowler statistics in the form presented here operates with independent constituent systems. It is only for these that one can talk of the number of systems in each allowed energy interval, etc. Any attempt to generalize the method to apply to interacting constituent systems would appear to necessitate the introduction of Gibbsian ensembles (cf. Sec. 6 of this chapter).

As in Chapter IV we shall assume that the individual possible energy states or boxes have certain *a priori probabilities* or *elementary weights* associated with them which we shall designate as $g_0, g_1 \cdots g_j \cdots$. We generalize the earlier discussion by refraining from setting a limit to the number of possible states. In the discussion of quantum statistics (Chapter VIII) it will develop that the elementary weights of the energy states of a quantum mechanical system are always integers. On the other hand, in classical statistics the elementary weight associated with the element $d\phi$ in phase space is $d\phi/h^n$, where h^n merely represents the *unit* volume in phase space and h is Planck's action constant. The inclusion of the divisor h^n is to secure the necessary non-dimensionality in the weight. (Cf. Sec. 14, Chapter VI.)

We are now ready to write the expression for the probability or, as we shall now call it, the weight to be associated with that state of the assembly in which, of the N constituent systems, N_0 are in the energy state E_0, N_1 in E_1, $\cdots N_j$ in E_j, etc. This follows immediately from eq. (6) of Chapter IV with appropriate change in terminology. If the weight in question is denoted by W, we have

$$W = \frac{N! \prod_j g_j^{N_j}}{\prod_j N_j!}, \tag{1}$$

where

$$\sum_j N_j = N, \tag{2}$$

the fixed total number of constituent systems in the assembly, and

$$\sum_j E_j N_j = E, \qquad (3)$$

the fixed total energy of the assembly.

Now we want our statistics to give us the *average* number of constituent systems in any particular energy state, say that corresponding to E_r, subject to the conditions (2) and (3). Evidently to get this number, which we shall denote by $\overline{N}_r$, we must first multiply N_r by the weight W and sum over all sets of numbers $N_0, N_1 \cdots N_j \cdots$ satisfying conditions (2) and (3). Then we must divide the result by the sum of all the W's consistent with (2) and (3). In abbreviated symbolical form

$$\overline{N}_r = \frac{\Sigma N_r W}{\Sigma W}. \qquad (4)$$

To grasp the significance of the method it is essential to understand the meaning of the sums in the expression for $\overline{N}_r$. Going back to (1) we see that a value of W corresponds to each mode of distribution of the N constituent systems over the energy states. To get ΣW we must add all these various values of W for *all possible* modes of distribution consistent with (2) and (3). This gives the denominator in (4). The numerator is obtained likewise, only before summing we multiply each value of W by the N_r which is appropriate to *that* value. The remaining problem now is the mathematical evaluation of these summations to express the value of $\overline{N}_r$ as a function of the elementary weights and the energy E_r associated with the rth state. We shall discuss this in the next section.

At this place, however, we ought to notice the difference between the method of procedure here and that followed in Chapter IV in the treatment of statistical distributions. There we made W (or its equivalent P_μ^N) a maximum subject to conditions equivalent to (2) and (3). This resulted in the so-called canonical distribution (eq. (27) of Chapter IV); it was assumed that the number of systems associated with a particular energy value in this distribution would correspond to the observed number when the system was in a state of equilibrium. We then used this number to compute average values, e.g., the total energy under various assumptions as to the possible energy values. The Darwin-Fowler method proceeds differently; average values, e.g., $\overline{N}_r$, are calculated *directly* without the necessity for maximizing W. We shall find to be sure, that these average values will agree with the corresponding distribution formulas of the Maxwell-Boltzmann statistics as well as the averages calculated on the basis of canonical ensembles in Gibbs' statistical mechanics. Nevertheless the variation in the mathematical machinery used provides an interesting check on the other ways of looking at the problem and certain questionable approximations, e.g., the wide use of Stirling's formula for $N!$ in the analysis of Chapter IV can be avoided. In this way our confidence in the statistical point of view will be strengthened. Moreover the method of Darwin and Fowler provides a very natural introduction to quantum statistics, used for most contemporary problems in statistical physics.

2. EVALUATION OF AVERAGES

Our next problem is the purely mathematical one of evaluating the sums in (4). First consider

$$\Sigma W = \sum \frac{N! \, g_0^{N_0} g_1^{N_1} \cdots g_r^{N_r} \cdots}{N_0! \, N_1! \cdots N_r! \cdots}. \tag{5}$$

We attack this by means of the multinomial expansion. First recall the binomial expansion

$$(z_0 + z_1)^N = \sum \frac{N!}{N_0! \, N_1!} z_0^{N_0} z_1^{N_1}, \tag{6}$$

where $N_0 + N_1 = N$ and the sum is taken over all N_0 and N_1 satisfying this restriction. By a simple generalization

$$(z_0 + z_1 + z_2 + \cdots + z_r + \cdots)^N$$
$$= \sum \frac{N!}{N_0! \, N_1! \cdots N_r! \cdots} \cdot z_0^{N_0} \cdots z_r^{N_r} \cdots, \tag{7}$$

where the summation is taken over all $N_0, N_1 \cdots N_r, \cdots$, etc., satisfying the condition $\Sigma N_j = N$. The connection between (7) and (5) is obvious, but we have still to introduce the g's and the condition $\Sigma N_j E_j = E$. We do this by taking the expansion

$$(g_0 z^{E_0} + g_1 z^{E_1} + \cdots + g_r z^{E_r} + \cdots)^N$$
$$= \sum \frac{N!}{N_0! \, N_1! \cdots N_r! \cdots} \cdot g_0^{N_0} g_1^{N_1} \cdots g_r^{N_r} \cdots z^{\Sigma N_j E_j} \tag{8}$$

If no further restriction is placed on the N_j beyond that implied in eq. (2) the sum on the right of (8) contains *all* powers of z given by $z^{\Sigma N_j E_j}$. If now we wish to restrict the N_j further by the condition (3), where E is a constant, the only terms in the sum on the right of (8) which interest us are those in which z is raised to the power E. The sum of the coefficients of all these terms is then our ΣW. It follows that ΣW is equal to the coefficient of z^E in the polynomial expansion in eq. (8). If we can find some way of evaluating this coefficient we shall have found the desired expression for ΣW without employing Stirling's formula.

Consider the contour integral in the complex plane

$$\int_C z^n dz,$$

where z is the complex variable $x + iy = r(\cos\theta + i\sin\theta)$ and the path of integration C is a circle of radius r about the origin. Moreover n is an *integer*. This integral may be evaluated by means of real integrals by transforming to the equivalent polar coordinates. Thus $dz = r(-\sin\theta + i\cos\theta)d\theta$, whence

$$\int_C z^n dz = ir^{n+1}\int_0^{2\pi}(\cos\theta + i\sin\theta)^{n+1}d\theta.$$

By utilizing De Moivre's theorem

$$(\cos\theta + i\sin\theta)^n = \cos n\theta + i\sin n\theta, \tag{9}$$

we have

$$\int_C z^n dz = ir^{n+1}\int_0^{2\pi}[\cos(n+1)\theta + i\sin(n+1)\theta]d\theta.$$

But

$$\int_0^{2\pi}\cos(n+1)\theta d\theta = \int_0^{2\pi}\sin(n+1)\theta d\theta = 0 \text{ for } n \neq -1,$$

while

$$\int_0^{2\pi}\cos(n+1)\theta d\theta = 2\pi \text{ for } n = -1 \text{ and } \int_0^{2\pi}\sin(n+1)\theta d\theta$$

$= 0$ for $n = -1$. Hence we reach the general conclusion that

$$\int_C z^n dz = 2\pi i \text{ for } n = -1,$$
$$= 0 \quad \text{for } n \neq -1. \tag{10}$$

It follows that if we integrate $(\Sigma g_j z^{E_j})^N$ about C and divide by $2\pi i$ we shall obtain the coefficient of z^{-1} in the expansion. This of course assumes that all the exponents in the expansion are integral. To assure this all we need do is to choose our unit of energy so small that effectively $\Sigma N_j E_j$ can always be represented to a sufficiently high degree of accuracy as an integer. We want, however, the coefficient of z^E. We must therefore integrate $(\Sigma g_j z^{E_j})^N/z^{E+1}$ about C to get the coefficient of z^E in the expansion $(\Sigma g_j z^{E_j})^N$. Let us call the sum in the parenthesis for convenience, Z, viz.,

$$Z = \Sigma g_j z^{E_j}. \tag{11}$$

We shall follow Darwin and Fowler in referring to this as the " partition function." [2] In this notation, then

$$\Sigma W = \frac{1}{2\pi i} \int_C \frac{Z^N dz}{z^{E+1}}. \tag{12}$$

We must next find the numerator in the expression for $\overline{N_r}$. On multiplying the summand of (5) by N_r and then cancelling it in numerator and denominator, we obtain

$$\Sigma N_r W = N \sum \frac{(N-1)!\, g_0^{N_0} g_1^{N_1} \cdots g_r^{N_r} \cdots}{N_0!\, N_1! \cdots (N_r-1)!\, N_{r+1}! \cdots}, \tag{13}$$

where the summation is still to be conducted over all $N_0, N_1 \cdots N_r \cdots$ consistent with conditions (2) and (3). Let us now introduce a new set of numbers $M_0, M_1, \cdots M_r, \cdots$ defined by

$$M_0 = N_0,\; M_1 = N_1, \cdots M_r = N_r - 1,\; M_{r+1} = N_{r+1}, \cdots.$$

Then $\Sigma N_r W$ may be written

$$\Sigma N_r W = N g_r \sum \frac{(N-1)!\, g_0^{M_0} g_1^{M_1} \cdots g_r^{M_r} \cdots}{M_0!\, M_1! \cdots M_r! \cdots}, \tag{14}$$

where the summation is now conducted over all $M_0, \cdots M_r \cdots$ consistent with the conditions $\Sigma M_j = N - 1$ and $\Sigma M_j E_j = E - E_r$. The previous analysis now indicates that $\Sigma N_r W$ is $N g_r$ times the coefficient of z^{E-E_r} in the expansion of $(\Sigma g_j z^{E_j})^{N-1}$. Hence

$$\Sigma N_r W = \frac{N g_r}{2\pi i} \int_C \frac{Z^{N-1} dz}{z^{E-E_r+1}}, \tag{15}$$

and the average quantity we desire is

$$\overline{N_r} = \frac{N \int_C \left(\dfrac{g_r z^{E_r}}{Z}\right) \cdot \dfrac{Z^N dz}{z^{E+1}}}{\int_C \dfrac{Z^N dz}{z^{E+1}}}. \tag{16}$$

The evaluation of the integrals in the numerator and denominator of

---

[2] In Fowler, *op. cit.*, p. 38, $f(z)$ is used to denote the partition function.

N_r is carried out by the method of *steepest descents*, which will now be described.[3]

We consider the function

$$\phi(z) = \frac{Z(z)}{z^{E/N}} = \frac{\Sigma g_j z^{E_j}}{z^{\Sigma N_j E_j / N}},\tag{17}$$

which can be written in the alternative form

$$\phi(z) = \frac{(g_0 + g_1 z^{E_1 - E_0} + g_2 z^{E_2 - E_0} + \cdots + g_r z^{E_r - E_0} + \cdots)}{z^{(N_0/N - 1)E_0 + N_1/N \cdot E_1 + \cdots + N_r/N \cdot E_r + \cdots}}.$$

It is clear that we can split $\phi(z)$ into two sets of terms, one a series of negative powers of z and the other a series of positive powers. Thus

$$\phi(z) = \sum_{j=0}^{j=n} g_j / z^{k_j} + \sum_{i=n+1}^{\infty} g_i z^{l_i}.\tag{18}$$

We recall that the g's are all positive integers as are the exponents k_j and l_i. It will be noted that we can always arrange our zero energy level so that all the E_j are positive and increase monotonically with j. Consider the behavior of $\phi(z)$ on the real axis. At $z = 0$, $\phi(z)$ is certainly infinite owing to the presence of the first term in (18). At $z = 1$, $\phi(z)$ is again infinite because the second term diverges for $z = 1$ (being $\sum_{i=n+1}^{\infty} g_i$.) Let us now differentiate $\phi(z)$. We get

$$\frac{d\phi(z)}{dz} = -\sum \frac{k_j g_j}{z^{k_j + 1}} + \sum l_i g_i z^{l_i - 1}.\tag{19}$$

Now as z goes from 0 to 1, both terms on the right side of (19) increase monotonically. This is shown diagrammatically in Fig. 7·1 where A is a schematic representation of the plot of $\Sigma l_i g_i z^{l_i - 1}$ for real values of z between 0 and 1, while B represents $-\Sigma k_j g_j / z^{k_j + 1}$ in the same interval. A schematic plot of $\phi(z)$ is also included. There is only *one* value of z between 0 and 1 for which $d\phi(z)/dz = 0$, and here $\phi(z)$ will have a *minimum*. Let us call this value $z = \zeta$. Going back to (17) we have then

$$\left(\frac{dZ/dz}{z^{E/N}} - \frac{EZ/N}{z^{E/N+1}} \right)_{z=\zeta} = 0,$$

or

$$E = \frac{N\zeta (dZ/dz)_\zeta}{Z(\zeta)} = N\zeta \frac{d \log Z(\zeta)}{d\zeta},\tag{20}$$

which acts as a defining equation for ζ.

---

[3] The method was apparently first described by P. Debye, *Math. Ann.*, **67**, 535 (1909); *Münch. Sitzungsberichte*, **40** (1910). See also E. T. Copson, "Theory of Functions of a Complex Variable," p. 330. Oxford, 1935.

Now consider the circle in the complex plane with center at the origin passing through the point $z = \zeta$. This circle is represented by the equation $z = \zeta e^{i\alpha}$, where α is the angle about the origin measured from the real axis. We seek the behavior of $[\phi(z)]^N = [Z(z)]^N/z^E$ on this circle, where

$$[Z(z)]^N = [\Sigma g_j \zeta^{E_j} e^{i\alpha E_j}]^N. \tag{21}$$

If we write out the sum in the bracket in (21) it will have both a real and imaginary part. The absolute value of this resulting complex expression becomes

$$|Z(z)| = \sqrt{\Sigma g_j^2 \zeta^{2E_j} + \Sigma g_j g_k \zeta^{E_j+E_k} \cos \alpha \, (E_j - E_k)}.$$

For $\alpha \neq 0$, $|Z(z)|$ is less than its value for $\alpha = 0$, unless for all the values of E_j there exists the relation

$$\alpha(E_j - E_k) = 2\pi n \tag{22}$$

for all j and k, n being any integer.   Consequently if the condition (22) is *not* fulfilled, the abso-
lute value of $Z(z)$ will be greater at $z = \zeta$ than for any other point on the circle $z = \zeta e^{i\alpha}$. Therefore if N is large, $[Z(z)]^N$ will have a strong maximum at this point. For this reason $z = \zeta$ is known as a " saddle " point, since whereas it corre- sponds to a *minimum on* the real axis, as we go away in either direction from the real axis the function falls away very steeply, the steepness increasing as N increases. We shall suppose that N is so large that the value of $[Z(z)]^N$ and hence the value of $[\phi(z)]^N$ at any point on the circle save the saddle point is *negligible*. If this circle is chosen for the

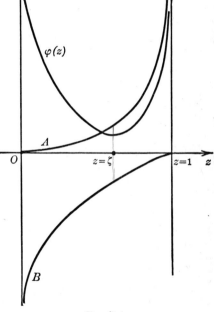

FIG. 7·1

contour C, the value of the integral in the numerator of (16) becomes effectively

$$N \int_C \left(\frac{g_r z^{E_r}}{Z} \right) \frac{Z^N dz}{z^{E+1}} \doteq \frac{N g_r \zeta^{E_r}}{Z(\zeta)} \int_C \frac{Z^N}{z^{E+1}} dz, \tag{23}$$

since the value of z^{E_r}/Z will have no appreciable effect on the integral save for $z = \zeta$. This enables us to express the average value $\overline{N_r}$ at once in the form

$$\overline{N_r} = \frac{N g_r \zeta^{E_r}}{Z(\zeta)}, \tag{24}$$

without the necessity of calculating $\displaystyle\int_C \frac{Z^N}{z^{E+1}}\, dz$. It should be noted that strictly speaking what we have said above about the saddle point corresponding to much larger values of $[Z(z)]^N$ on the real axis than for points just off the axis also applies as well to *other* points on the real axis for $0 < z < 1$. However from function theory it follows that the result of the integration is independent of the precise contour around the origin. Hence we are at liberty to pick that contour for which the integration is simplest. This proves to be the case for the contour passing through the saddle point. It is usually assumed that the descent from the saddle point is steepest (cf. Fowler, *op. cit.*, p. 36) and indeed this seems qualitatively to be the case, though we shall not endeavor to give a proof of it here. The steepness will naturally improve the accuracy of the evaluation of $\overline{N_r}$ by means of contour integration.

We have still to examine what happens when eq. (22) is satisfied. It will be noted that this will be true only if all the differences $E_j - E_k$ have an integral common factor, say l. For then (22) will hold for $\alpha/2\pi = 1/l,\ 2/l \cdots (l-1)/l$. Consequently instead of only one maximum point on the contour circle there will be l such points. The result is to multiply the integral in (23) by l, but since numerator and denominator are multiplied by the same quantity, the value of $\overline{N_r}$ given in (24) is not affected.

The contour integral for ΣW will be of importance in the subsequent analysis and we shall therefore evaluate it here. Let us expand $\log [\phi(z)]^N$ in a Taylor series about the point $z = \zeta$ and along the circular contour. We have

$$\log [\phi(z)]^N = N \log \phi(z) =$$

$$N\left\{\log \phi(\zeta) + (z-\zeta)\left[\frac{d \log \phi(z)}{dz}\right]_\zeta + \frac{(z-\zeta)^2}{2!} \cdot \left[\frac{d^2 \log \phi(z)}{dz^2}\right]_\zeta + \cdots\right\}. \tag{25}$$

But at $z = \zeta$, $\phi(z)$ has its minimum and therefore the coefficient of $z - \zeta$ vanishes. Moreover if $z - \zeta$ is small enough we can replace it by $ia\zeta$ to a sufficiently good approximation. Hence we have

$$\log [\phi(z)]^N = N \left\{ \log \phi(\zeta) - \frac{1}{2}\zeta^2\alpha^2 \frac{d^2\phi(\zeta)}{d\zeta^2} \Big/ \phi(\zeta) + \cdots \right\}$$

or

$$[\phi(z)]^N = [\phi(\zeta)]^N e^{-\frac{N}{2}\zeta^2\alpha^2 \frac{d^2\phi(\zeta)}{d\zeta^2} / \phi(\zeta)}. \tag{26}$$

Incidentally this serves to exemplify the large rate of decrease of $[\phi(z)]^N$ for N very large as one passes from $z = \zeta$ to some nearby value.

We now have, writing $dz = iz \, d\alpha$,

$$\frac{1}{2\pi i} \int_C \frac{Z^N}{z^{E+1}} dz = \frac{[\phi(\zeta)]^N}{2\pi} \int_{-\infty}^{+\infty} e^{-\frac{N}{2}\zeta^2\alpha^2 \frac{d^2\phi(\zeta)}{d\zeta^2} / \phi(\zeta)} \cdot d\alpha, \tag{27}$$

where we have availed ourselves of the possibility of conducting the integration about any convenient path which passes through $z = \zeta$ (where $\alpha = 0$) since the integrand is extremely small save at this point. The limits are chosen as $+\infty$ and $-\infty$ for simplicity also. The result of the integration is

$$\frac{1}{2\pi i} \int_C \frac{Z^N}{z^{E+1}} dz = \frac{[\phi(\zeta)]^N}{\sqrt{2\pi N\zeta^2 \frac{d^2\phi(\zeta)}{d\zeta^2} / \phi(\zeta)}}$$

$$= \frac{[Z(\zeta)]^N \zeta^{-E}}{\sqrt{2\pi N\zeta^2 \frac{d^2\phi(\zeta)}{d\zeta^2} / \phi(\zeta)}}. \tag{28}$$

Let us return to the formula (24) which gives the average number of systems in the assembly in the energy state E_r. It is the distribution law. Evidently if we sum $\bar{N}_r$ over all r we must get N. This condition indeed is satisfied by (24) since

$$\sum_r \bar{N}_r = \frac{N \sum_r g_r \zeta^{E_r}}{\sum_r g_r \zeta^{E_r}} = N. \tag{29}$$

The presence of the parameter ζ and the partition function $Z(\zeta)$ makes the distribution law appear a little strange, especially as it was said above that the Darwin-Fowler method leads to essentially the same result as the canonical distribution in the Maxwell-Boltzmann statistics. However we recall that the latter involves the parameter Θ

which we have found it necessary to interpret as kT in order to establish connection with experimental results. If we now set

$$\zeta = e^{-1/\Theta} = e^{-1/kT}, \tag{30}$$

(24) becomes

$$\overline{N_r} = \frac{N g_r e^{-E_r/kT}}{\Sigma g_r e^{-E_r/kT}}, \tag{31}$$

in precise agreement with the canonical distribution (27) or (27′) of Chapter IV (making allowance for changes in notation). We shall shortly present independent reasons for making the assumption (30). To do this we shall find it necessary to discuss assemblies consisting of more than one kind of system.

3. ASSEMBLY OF TWO KINDS OF SYSTEMS

In place of an assembly consisting of systems all of which are of the same type, let us imagine an assembly in which there are two kinds of systems. The analysis can be readily generalized to any number of types, but we shall find it convenient for the sake of simplicity of notation to confine our attention to two.

Let now the number of systems of the two kinds be N_1 and N_2 respectively, where

$$N_1 + N_2 = N. \tag{32}$$

Of the N_1 systems of the first type, let $N_{10}, N_{11}, N_{12}, \cdots, N_{1r}, \cdots$ be the numbers in the energy states $E_{10}, E_{11}, \cdots, E_{1r}, \cdots$ respectively. Of the N_2 systems of the second type, let $N_{20}, N_{21}, N_{22}, \cdots, N_{2r}, \cdots$ reside in the energy states $E_{20}, E_{21}, \cdots, E_{2r}, \cdots$ respectively. Note the necessary change in notation from Sec. 2 in order to denote adequately the two types of systems. The *a priori* weights attached to the energy states of the first type of system are now $g_{10}, g_{11}, g_{12}, \cdots$, $g_{1r}, \cdots$ and those for the second type of system $g_{20}, g_{21}, \cdots, g_{2r}, \cdots$.

Clearly we have the relations

$$\sum_j N_{1j} = N_1; \quad \sum_j N_{2j} = N_2;$$

$$\sum_j N_{1j} E_{1j} + \sum_j N_{2j} E_{2j} = E. \tag{33}$$

Here E is the total energy of the assembly. The eqs. (33) replace the two equations (2) and (3).

Our first task is to express the weight to be associated with the state of the assembly in which N_{10} systems of the first type are in the energy state E_{10}, N_{11} in E_{11}, $\cdots$, N_{20} in E_{20}, etc.   From the analysis of Sec. 1 this weight is expressible in the form

$$\frac{N_1! \prod_j g_{1j}^{N_{1j}}}{\prod_j N_{1j}!} \cdot \frac{N_2! \prod_j g_{2j}^{N_{2j}}}{\prod_j N_{2j}!} . \tag{34}$$

The *average* number of systems of the first kind in the energy state E_{1r} is then $\overline{N_{1r}}$ and its value is given by

$$\overline{N_{1r}} = \frac{\Sigma N_{1r} W}{\Sigma W} . \tag{35}$$

The procedure for the evaluation of $\overline{N_{1r}}$ follows that employed in Sec. 2.   Thus we use the polynomial expansions:

$$(\Sigma g_{1j} z^{E_{1j}})^{N_1} = \sum \frac{N_1! \prod_j g_{1j}^{N_{1j}}}{\prod_j N_{1j}!} z^{\Sigma N_{1j} E_{1j}}, \tag{36}$$

$$(\Sigma g_{2j} z^{E_{2j}})^{N_2} = \sum \frac{N_2! \prod_j g_{2j}^{N_{2j}}}{\prod_j N_{2j}!} z^{\Sigma N_{2j} E_{2j}}. \tag{37}$$

The product of (36) and (37) is

$$(\Sigma g_{1j} z^{E_{1j}})^{N_1} (\Sigma g_{2j} z^{E_{2j}})^{N_2} =$$

$$\sum \frac{N_1! \prod_j g_{1j}^{N_{1j}}}{\prod_j N_{1j}!} \cdot \frac{N_2! \prod_j g_{2j}^{N_{2j}}}{\prod_j N_{2j}!} z^{\Sigma(N_{1j} E_{1j} + N_{2j} E_{2j})}. \tag{38}$$

By precisely the same reasoning as in Sec. 2, it follows that the denominator in the expression for $\overline{N_r}$, viz., ΣW, is the coefficient of z^E in the expansion (38).   Moreover the numerator can be handled in similar fashion.   Let us write

$$\Sigma g_{1j} z^{E_{1j}} = Z_1; \quad \Sigma g_{2j} z^{E_{2j}} = Z_2. \tag{39}$$

The result is that

$$\overline{N_{1r}} = \frac{\displaystyle\int_C \frac{N_1 g_{1r}}{Z_1} z^{E_{1r}} \cdot \frac{Z_1^{N_1} Z_2^{N_2}}{z^{E+1}} \, dz}{\displaystyle\int_C \frac{Z_1^{N_1} Z_2^{N_2}}{z^{E+1}} \, dz} . \tag{40}$$

The application of the method of steepest descents with

$$[\Phi(z)]^N = \frac{Z_1^{N_1} Z_2^{N_2}}{z^E}, \tag{41}$$

yields finally

$$\overline{N_{1r}} = \frac{N_1}{Z_1(\zeta)} g_{1r} \zeta^{E_{1r}}, \tag{42}$$

where ζ is the value of z which makes $\Phi(z)$ a minimum on the real axis. Similarly

$$\overline{N_{2r}} = \frac{N_2}{Z_2(\zeta)} g_{2r} \zeta^{E_{2r}}, \tag{42'}$$

with the same ζ, since there is again only *one* minimum for $\Phi(z)$ on the real axis between 0 and 1.   Since

$$\frac{d\Phi(z)}{dz} = 0 \text{ for } z = \zeta,$$

we get the relation

$$E = N_1 \zeta \frac{d}{d\zeta} \log Z_1 + N_2 \zeta \frac{d}{d\zeta} \log Z_2. \tag{43}$$

Each term on the right of (43) is of the same form as the expression for E in an assembly of systems all of the same kind, viz., eq. (20). This leads to the expectation that each term in (43) may be looked upon as the *average* energy of the type of system it represents.   This can be verified as follows.   From the definition of average we have

$$\overline{E_1} = \frac{\Sigma W \left(\sum_j N_{1j} E_{1j} \right)}{\Sigma W}. \tag{44}$$

The evaluation of the numerator is carried out by differentiating both sides of eq. (36) with respect to z and multiplying the result by z. Thus

$$z \frac{d}{dz} Z_1^{N_1} = \sum \frac{N_1! \prod_j g_{1j}^{N_{1j}} \left(\sum_j N_{1j} E_{1j} \right) \cdot z^{\sum N_{1j} E_1}}{\prod_j N_{1j}!}. \tag{45}$$

Multiply further by $Z_2^{N_2}$ and get

$$Z_2^{N_2} z \frac{d}{dz} Z_1^{N_1} = \sum \frac{N_1! \prod_j g_{1j}^{N_{1j}} N_2! \prod_j g_{2j}^{N_{2j}} \left(\sum_j N_{1j} E_{1j} \right) z^{\sum (N_{1j} E_{1j} + N_{2j} E_{2j})}}{\prod_j N_{1j}! \prod_j N_{2j}!}. \tag{46}$$

The coefficient of z^E in the expansion on the right is precisely the numerator of E_1. Hence we again apply the contour integration and have

$$\overline{E_1} = \frac{\displaystyle\int_C Z_2^{N_2} z \frac{d}{dz} Z_1^{N_1}/z^{E+1} \cdot dz}{\displaystyle\int_C Z_1^{N_1} Z_2^{N_2}/z^{E+1} \cdot dz}$$

$$= \frac{\displaystyle\int_C dz/z^{E+1} \cdot N_1 Z_2^{N_2} Z_1^{N_1} z \frac{d}{dz} \log Z_1}{\displaystyle\int_C Z_1^{N_1} Z_2^{N_2}/z^{E+1} \cdot dz}. \tag{47}$$

The method of steepest descents applied to (47) then yields

$$\overline{E_1} = N_1 \zeta \frac{d}{d\zeta} \log Z_1(\zeta), \tag{48}$$

which provides the confirmation of our surmise above that the total energy is the sum of the *average* energies of the component assemblies of different kinds of systems.

We are now ready to give some reasons for the association of ζ with the absolute temperature of the assembly as assumed in eq. (30), viz., $\zeta = e^{-1/kT}$. Suppose we consider first an assembly consisting of N_1 systems of only one kind. The average number of such systems in the rth energy state is then given by (42) (with $\zeta = \zeta_1$)

$$\overline{N_{1r}} = \frac{N_1}{Z_1(\zeta_1)} \cdot g_{1r} \cdot \zeta_1^{E_{1r}}, \tag{49}$$

where ζ_1 is given by

$$E_1 = N_1 \zeta_1 \frac{d}{d\zeta_1} \log Z_1, \tag{50}$$

the condition that ζ_1 shall provide the minimum value of $\phi_1(z) = Z_1(z)/z^{E_1/N_1}$ along the real axis. Consider next an assembly of N_2 systems of a second kind in which the corresponding average distribution is given by

$$\overline{N_{2r}} = \frac{N_2}{Z_2(\zeta_2)} \cdot g_{2r} \cdot \zeta_2^{E_{2r}}, \tag{51}$$

with ζ_2 corresponding to the minimum value of $\phi_2(z) = Z_2(z)/z^{E_2/N_2}$ on the real axis. Note, of course, that in general it is unnecessary that $\zeta_1 = \zeta_2$. However if the two assemblies are brought together and form a single assembly in equilibrium, the values $\overline{N_{1r}}$ and $\overline{N_{2r}}$ above given will necessarily be special cases of

$$\overline{N_{\alpha r}} = \frac{N_\alpha g_{\alpha r} \zeta^{-E_{\alpha r}}}{Z_\alpha(\zeta)}, \tag{52}$$

in which $\alpha = 1$ and 2 respectively for the two types of systems and ζ is one constant which is the same for both as long as they are in equilibrium. Hence when two assemblies in contact are in equilibrium, they must have associated with them the same value of ζ. This at once suggests the possible connection of ζ with the temperature, since thermodynamically speaking it is the temperature which is the same for thermodynamic systems in equilibrium. It must also be remarked that from definition ζ must be a positive quantity.

We should be more specific. Consider an assembly of linear simple harmonic oscillators. We shall suppose there are two types, one with frequency ν_1 and the other with frequency ν_2. Let the numbers of the two types be N_1 and N_2 respectively. Now the study of quantum mechanics reveals (cf. Chapter VIII) that the possible energy states of a harmonic oscillator do not form a continuous series but are discretely distributed. In fact we have

$$E_{1j} = (j + \tfrac{1}{2})h\nu_1; \quad E_{2j} = (j + \tfrac{1}{2})h\nu_2. \tag{53}$$

At the same time the *a priori* weight factors are all unity. Thus

$$g_{1j} = g_{2j} = 1, \quad \text{for all } j. \tag{54}$$

Consequently the partition function $Z_1(\zeta)$ becomes

$$Z_1(\zeta) = \sum_j g_{1j}\zeta^{-E_{1j}} = \zeta^{-h\nu_1/2}\sum_j \zeta^{-jh\nu_1}.$$

Since $\sum_j \zeta^{-jh\nu_1} = 1/(1 - \zeta^{-h\nu_1})$ if j runs to infinity, we have

$$Z_1(\zeta) = \frac{\zeta^{-h\nu_1/2}}{1 - \zeta^{-h\nu_1}}, \tag{55}$$

and similarly

$$Z_2(\zeta) = \frac{\zeta^{-h\nu_2/2}}{1 - \zeta^{-h\nu_2}}. \tag{56}$$

The fundamental distribution formula (52) with the appropriate substitutions then yields for the average number of oscillators of the two types in the rth energy state,

$$\overline{N_{1r}} = N_1(1 - \zeta^{-h\nu_1})\zeta^{-rh\nu_1},$$

$$\overline{N_{2r}} = N_2(1 - \zeta^{-h\nu_2})\zeta^{-rh\nu_2}. \tag{57}$$

The average energy values are given by substitution into eq. (50) with $\zeta_1 = \zeta$. The result is

$$\overline{E_1} = N_1 \left(\frac{h\nu_1}{2} + \frac{h\nu_1}{\zeta^{-h\nu_1} - 1} \right). \tag{58}$$

$$\overline{E_2} = N_2 \left(\frac{h\nu_2}{2} + \frac{h\nu_2}{\zeta^{-h\nu_2} - 1} \right). \tag{59}$$

Now $\overline{E_1}$ includes both the kinetic and potential energies, which in classical mechanics are each equal on the average to $kT/2$ per particle (equipartition of energy). When ν_1 and ν_2 approach zero we should expect the results of quantum theory to approach those of classical theory. Hence in the limit

$$\lim_{\nu_1 \to 0} \frac{\overline{E_1}}{N_1} = kT = \lim_{\nu_2 \to 0} \frac{\overline{E_2}}{N_2}. \tag{60}$$

Now from (58) and (59)

$$\lim_{\nu_1 \to 0} \frac{\overline{E_1}}{N_1} = -\frac{1}{\log \zeta}. \tag{61}$$

This follows from

$$\zeta^{-h\nu_1} = e^{-h\nu_1 \log \zeta} = 1 - h\nu_1 \log \zeta + \cdots. \tag{62}$$

By comparison of (60) with (61) we get

$$\zeta = e^{-1/kT}, \tag{63}$$

as the indicated expression for ζ. In the next section we shall give still another demonstration of this relation. For the moment let us note that the above discussion need not be confined to a linear harmonic oscillator; the two- and three-dimensional cases are also easily handled. The reader may show that for the two-dimensional oscillator, for which $E_j = (j + 1)h\nu$ from quantum mechanics and $g_j = j + 1$, the partition function becomes

$$Z(\zeta) = \frac{\zeta^{h\nu}}{(1 - \zeta^{h\nu})^2}, \tag{64}$$

and the average energy becomes

$$\overline{E} = N \left(h\nu + \frac{2h\nu}{\zeta^{-h\nu} - 1} \right). \tag{65}$$

Here we have for convenience omitted the subscript denoting the type of system in question. This leads to precisely the same connection between ζ and T that we found in the one-dimensional case. For now

$$\lim_{\nu \to 0} \frac{\overline{E}}{N} = -\frac{2}{\log \zeta},$$

but since the oscillator has two degrees of freedom, in the limit of vanishing frequency its energy becomes $2kT$, and (63) is again obtained.

For the three-dimensional oscillator, quantum mechanical reasoning [4] indicates $E_j = (j + 3/2)h\nu$ and $g_j = 1/2 \cdot (j + 1)(j + 2)$. The result for the average energy is

$$\overline{E} = N\left(\frac{3h\nu}{2} + \frac{3h\nu}{\zeta^{-h\nu} - 1}\right), \tag{66}$$

and again (63) is found to be satisfied.

The reader will find some interest in comparing the average energy for each type of harmonic oscillator obtained in the present discussion with the canonical distribution formulas in Chapter IV. Thus expressing $\overline{E}$ in (65) in terms of T, the two-dimensional oscillator average energy is

$$\overline{E} = N\left(h\nu + \frac{2h\nu}{e^{h\nu/kT} - 1}\right), \tag{67}$$

which is precisely the form of eq. (47) in Chapter IV with $\Theta = kT$. It must be realized, of course, that $\overline{E}$ in (47) corresponds to our $\overline{E}/N$ in (67). The physical significance of average energy expressions like (67) will appear more clearly when we study the quantum statistics of radiation in the next chapter.

4. STATISTICS OF AN IDEAL GAS

Consider an assembly of N particles each of mass m and with negligible mutual interaction forces. The particles are confined in a vessel of volume τ. This can be represented symbolically by assuming that the potential energy for any particle is $V(x, y, z) = 0$ everywhere inside the vessel but rises abruptly to infinity at the walls and maintains this value everywhere outside, implying that no particle is able to escape from the vessel. In applying the Darwin-Fowler method to such an assembly the essential matter is the evaluation of the partition function Z (eq. 11). The energy values E_j no

---

[4] Cf. for example, L. Pauling and E. B. Wilson, "Introduction to Quantum Mechanics," McGraw-Hill, New York, 1935, p. 100.

longer form a discrete set but are continuously distributed. We have indeed

$$E = \frac{1}{2m} (p_x^2 + p_y^2 + p_z^2) + V(x, y, z). \tag{68}$$

If we suppose that the phase space of the assembly is divided into cells with phase volume Δ_j, where

$$\Delta_j = \Delta p_{xj} \, \Delta p_{yj} \, \Delta p_{zj} \, \Delta x_j \, \Delta y_j \, \Delta z_j, \tag{69}$$

and assign one set of momentum and coordinate values to each cell, we can write

$$E_j = \frac{1}{2m} (p_{xj}^2 + p_{yj}^2 + p_{zj}^2) + V(x_j, y_j, z_j). \tag{70}$$

From Sec. 1 the elementary weights are given by

$$g_j = \frac{\Delta_j}{h^3}. \tag{71}$$

The partition function for this cell distribution becomes

$$Z' = \frac{1}{h^3} \cdot \Sigma \Delta_j z^{(p_{xj}^2 + p_{yj}^2 + p_{zj}^2)/2m + V(x_j, y_j, z_j)}. \tag{72}$$

As the cells decrease in size and increase in number the sum above goes into an integral over the phase space, viz.,

$$Z = \frac{1}{h^3} \int\int\int\int\int\int z^{(p_x^2 + p_y^2 + p_z^2)/2m + V(x, y, z)} \, dp_x \, dp_y \, dp_z \, dx \, dy \, dz, \tag{73}$$

where, of course, it is essential not to confuse the z which is the basic independent variable in Z with the space coordinate z. The volume integration is to be conducted over the whole physical volume τ and the momentum integration from $-\infty$ to $+\infty$ for each component. This expression can be materially simplified by noting that

$$\int\int\int z^{V(x, y, z)} \, dx \, dy \, dz = \tau, \tag{74}$$

since $V = 0$ everywhere inside the vessel. Therefore

$$Z = \frac{\tau}{h^3} \int\int\int z^{(p_x^2 + p_y^2 + p_z^2)/2m} \, dp_x \, dp_y \, dp_z. \tag{75}$$

If we utilize the fact that

$$a^{bx^2} = e^{-bx^2 \log 1/a},$$

we can express the partition function in the form

$$Z = \frac{\tau}{h^3} \cdot \int\int\int_{-\infty}^{+\infty} e^{-(p_x^2 + p_y^2 + p_z^2)/2m \cdot \log 1/z}\, dp_x\, dp_y\, dp_z, \tag{76}$$

which at once yields

$$Z = \frac{\tau}{h^3} \cdot \left(\frac{2\pi m}{\log 1/z}\right)^{3/2}. \tag{77}$$

In the interpretation of this expression it must be recalled that $z < 1$. We can now use the fundamental formula (24) to obtain the average number of particles in the phase element $dp_x dp_y dp_z\, dx\, dy\, dz$. This number is ΔN, where

$$\Delta N = \frac{N \cdot \dfrac{dp_x\, dp_y\, dp_z\, dx\, dy\, dz}{h^3} \cdot \zeta^{(p_x^2 + p_y^2 + p_z^2)/2m}}{\dfrac{\tau}{h^3} \cdot \left(\dfrac{2\pi m}{\log 1/\zeta}\right)^{3/2}}. \tag{78}$$

Therefore the probability of finding a particle within this phase element is

$$P = \frac{\Delta N}{N} = \frac{(\log 1/\zeta)^{3/2}}{(2\pi m)^{3/2}\tau} \cdot \zeta^{(p_x^2 + p_y^2 + p_z^2)/2m} \cdot dp_x\, dp_y\, dp_z\, dx\, dy\, dz. \tag{79}$$

The probability that a particle shall have its momentum components included in the interval p_x, $p_x + dp_x$, with no restriction on its position in the vessel, etc., is then

$$P' = \int\int\int P\, dx\, dy\, dz = \frac{(\log 1/\zeta)^{3/2}}{(2\pi m)^{3/2}} \zeta^{(p_x^2 + p_y^2 + p_z^2)/2m}\, dp_x\, dp_y\, dp_z. \tag{80}$$

Placing $p_x = mv_x$, etc. and $\zeta = e^{-1/kT}$ from (63), we obtain P' in the form of the Maxwellian velocity distribution already discussed in Chapter V (cf. eq. 51 of that chapter) and again by the Gibbs method in Sec. 10 of Chapter VI, viz.,

$$P' = \left(\frac{m}{2\pi kT}\right)^{3/2} e^{-m(v_x^2 + v_y^2 + v_z^2)/2kT}\, dv_x\, dv_y\, dv_z. \tag{81}$$

Again we see that the connection between ζ and T in the form $\zeta = e^{-1/kT}$ is definitely indicated. Still another way of looking at the same matter is provided by the classical equipartition principle, which in the present instance takes the form

$$\bar{E} = \frac{3NkT}{2}. \tag{82}$$

Let us calculate $\overline{E}$ on the Darwin-Fowler method and see what form ζ must have to satisfy the equipartition principle. We have

$$\overline{E} = N\zeta \, \frac{d}{d\zeta} \log Z(\zeta). \tag{83}$$

If the reader substitutes for Z the value given in (77) and performs the indicated operations he will come out with

$$\overline{E} = \frac{3}{2} N \left(\log \frac{1}{\zeta} \right)^{-1}. \tag{84}$$

Equating this to $3/2 \cdot NkT$ gives again

$$\zeta = e^{-1/kT}, \tag{85}$$

which completes our validation of the connection between the Darwin-Fowler parameter ζ and the absolute temperature.

The reader will probably have noted the close connection between the partition function (77) and the so-called distribution function obtained in Sec. 4, Chapter IV (eq. 83) for an ideal gas on the Maxwell-Boltzmann statistics. By allowing for the difference in notation for the physical volume the two expressions are in complete agreement. It is true that the general defining expression for Z in Maxwell-Boltzmann statistics in eq. (53), Chapter IV, appears not to agree with eq. (11) of the present chapter. The reason is to be found in the different definitions of the g_j in the two methods. In the Maxwell-Boltzmann statistics the g_j are genuine mathematical *a priori* probabilities which are proper fractions, while in the Darwin-Fowler method the g_j are elementary weights which are integers. This explains the appearance of the factor μ in the earlier definition of Z. Actually there is complete agreement between the two points of view and further evidence of this will appear as we proceed.

5. THE CONCEPT OF ENTROPY

We must now see how the idea of entropy fits into the Darwin-Fowler statistical method. Somewhere in the theory we must find a quantity which for an isolated system tends to increase and which moreover is a maximum for a system in equilibrium. This quantity must finally enter into equations which are formally equivalent to the relations of thermodynamics.

The reader will recall from Chapter VI (Sec. 13) that Gibbs introduced $-k\overline{\eta} = k(\overline{E} - \psi)/\Theta$ as the statistical mechanical analogue of entropy. This quantity was found to possess the necessary qualifications stated in the preceding paragraph. It has indeed the interesting property that it can be defined for non-canonical as well as canonical distributions and hence applies to both equilibrium and non-equilibrium states. In a certain sense therefore it *overpredicts* experience, since in thermodynamics the entropy is defined for equilibrium states only. Since the Darwin-Fowler method confines itself to the calculation of averages over actual assemblies of systems, where these averages are then interpreted as the measured values of properties of the assemblies in states of *equilibrium*, we should expect that the Darwin-Fowler definition of entropy will apply only to equilibrium configurations. This has the possible advantage that it does not transcend experience like the Gibbs theory. On the other hand it has the disadvantage that no matter what precise definition is chosen, we cannot hope to show that the value of the entropy increases with the passage of time. All we can hope to do is to show that there is an increase in entropy when two assemblies in equilibrium are combined to form a new assembly.

In view of the close fundamental connection between the Darwin-Fowler method and the classical Maxwell-Boltzmann statistics we expect that the definition of entropy in the former will follow the example set by the latter. It is natural to replace the " statistical probability " w (eq. 49, Chapter IV) by the expression ΣW, the sum of weights entering into the denominator of eq. (4) of the present chapter. As before we shall divide ΣW by $N!$ and finally define

$$S = k \log \Sigma W - k \log N!, \tag{86}$$

where k is, as usual, the Boltzmann gas constant. The analytical expression for ΣW in terms of a contour integral has already been given in eq. (12), Sec. 2, and the value in terms of the parameters of the assembly has been calculated in eq. (28), which we set down here again for reference

$$\Sigma W = [Z(\zeta)]^N \zeta^{-E} \sqrt{\phi(\zeta)/2\pi N \zeta^2 \phi''(\zeta)},$$

where

$$\phi(\zeta) = \frac{Z(\zeta)}{\zeta^{E/N}},$$

and $\phi''(\zeta)$ denotes the second derivative with respect to ζ. If we take the logarithm of ΣW, we obtain

$$\log \Sigma W = N \log Z(\zeta) - E \log \zeta + \tfrac{1}{2} \log [\phi(\zeta)/2\pi N \zeta^2 \phi''(\zeta)]. \tag{87}$$

Let us look into the magnitude of the last term. Substitution of the expression for $\phi(\zeta)$ given above yields for this term

$$\tfrac{1}{2} \log Z(\zeta) - \frac{E}{2N} \log \zeta - \tfrac{1}{2} \log 2\pi N - \log \zeta + \frac{E}{2N} \log \zeta$$

$$- \tfrac{1}{2} \log \left[Z''(\zeta) + \frac{E}{N}\left(\frac{E}{N}+1\right) Z\zeta^{-2} - \frac{2E}{N} Z'\zeta^{-1} \right]. \quad (88)$$

The first, second, fourth, and fifth terms in (88) are very small compared with the first two terms in (87). Now we write further

$$Z'(\zeta) = \Sigma E_j g_j \zeta^{E_j-1}; \quad Z''(\zeta) = \Sigma E_j(E_j - 1)g_j\zeta^{E_j-2}$$

whence the bracket term in (88) becomes

$$- \tfrac{1}{2} \log \zeta^{-2}\left[\Sigma E_j^2 g_j\zeta^{E_j} + \frac{E}{N}\left(1 + \frac{E}{N}\right)Z - \left(1 + \frac{2E}{N}\right)\Sigma E_j g_j\zeta^{E_j} \right].$$

We can further write

$$\Sigma E_j^2 g_j\zeta^{E_j} = \overline{E^2}Z,$$

where $\overline{E^2}$ is a kind of mean-square energy value, while

$$\Sigma E_j g_j\zeta^{E_j} = \overline{E}Z,$$

where $\overline{E} = E/N$. Consequently the bracket term becomes

$$- \tfrac{1}{2} \log [\overline{E^2} - \overline{E}^2]Z + \log \zeta.$$

Now certainly $\overline{E^2} - \overline{E}^2$ is of the order of magnitude of $\overline{E}^2$ or smaller. In neglecting the bracket we shall then be neglecting terms of the order of $\log \overline{E}$ and $\log Z$ which are small compared with $N \log Z$. The upshot is that, if we disregard the constant term $-\tfrac{1}{2} \log 2\pi N$ (which since it is a constant will play no role in entropy changes and which in any case is small compared with the terms retained as long as N is large), we can get a very good approximation to $\log \Sigma W$ by retaining only the first two terms in (87) and writing therefore

$$\log \Sigma W = N \log Z(\zeta) - E \log \zeta. \quad (89)$$

This should be compared with (63) in Chapter IV.

Let us suppose that we have two assemblies composed of different types of systems and imagine that the two assemblies are joined to form a single one. From Sec. 3 we are justified in replacing the partition function Z by $Z_1^{N_1/N}Z_2^{N_2/N}$, where Z_1 and Z_2 are the partition functions for the individual assemblies before the combination. Hence $\log \Sigma W$ now becomes

$$\log \Sigma W = N_1 \log Z_1(\zeta) + N_2 \log Z_2(\zeta) - E \log \zeta. \qquad (90)$$

Here, of course, we also have

$$E = E_1 + E_2,$$

where E_1 and E_2 represent the energies of the individual, isolated assemblies.

Before combination the entropies of the individual assemblies are respectively

$$S_1 = k[N_1 \log Z_1(\zeta_1) - E_1 \log \zeta_1 - \log N_1!],$$
$$S_2 = k[N_2 \log Z_2(\zeta_2) - E_2 \log \zeta_2 - \log N_2!], \qquad (91)$$

where we have used different values of ζ since the temperatures of the assemblies need not be the same. Let us find the condition laid on ζ_1 in order that S_1 shall be a minimum. This is clearly

$$\frac{\partial S_1}{\partial \zeta_1} = k\left[\frac{N_1}{Z_1(\zeta_1)}\frac{dZ_1(\zeta_1)}{d\zeta_1} - \frac{E_1}{\zeta_1}\right] = 0, \qquad (92)$$

which yields the energy value

$$\frac{N_1\zeta_1}{Z_1(\zeta_1)} \cdot \frac{dZ_1(\zeta_1)}{d\zeta_1}, \qquad (93)$$

which is just the energy value for equilibrium, as already determined previously in eqs. (20) and (48). Hence S_1 has a stationary value for the value of ζ for which the first assembly is in equilibrium with total energy E_1. That this stationary value is a minimum is clear from the form of S_1. In fact (91) allows us to write

$$S_1 = k \log \frac{[Z_1(\zeta_1)]^{N_1}}{N_1!\zeta_1^{E_1}} = k \log \frac{[\phi(\zeta_1)]^{N_1}}{N_1!}. \qquad (94)$$

But we know from the method of steepest descents in Sec. 2 that $\phi(z)$ has a *minimum* on the real axis for the value $z = \zeta_1$. This assures the minimum property of S_1. In similar fashion we can show that S_2 has a minimum for the value of ζ for which the second assembly is in equilibrium with total energy E_2.

Now let the two assemblies be joined to form a single assembly and let ζ correspond to the temperature of the combined assembly. We then have for the entropy

$$S = k[N_1 \log Z_1(\zeta) + N_2 \log Z_2(\zeta)$$
$$- (E_1 + E_2) \log \zeta - \log N_1! - \log N_2!]. \qquad (95)$$

This can be written as the sum of S_1 (ζ) and S_2 (ζ), i.e., the sum of the entropies of the two isolated assemblies at the same temperature, where, of course

$$S_1(\zeta) = k[N_1 \log Z_1(\zeta) - E_1 \log \zeta - \log N_1!]$$
$$S_2(\zeta) = k[N_2 \log Z_2(\zeta) - E_2 \log \zeta - \log N_2!]. \qquad (96)$$

Now we have just shown that $S_1(\zeta)$ has a minimum for $\zeta = \zeta_1$ corresponding to (93) and $S_2(\zeta)$ a minimum for $\zeta = \zeta_2$. Therefore unless $\zeta_1 = \zeta_2 = \zeta$ it follows that

$$S_1(\zeta_1) < S_1(\zeta); \quad S_2(\zeta_2) < S_2(\zeta). \qquad (97)$$

Consequently except for this special case

$$S(\zeta) = S_1(\zeta) + S_2(\zeta) > S_1(\zeta_1) + S_2'(\zeta_2). \qquad (98)$$

This shows that the entropy after the combination of the two assemblies is greater than the sum of the individual entropies previously. Of course, if the two assemblies are already in equilibrium at the *same* temperature, the total entropy is unchanged, in agreement with the usual thermodynamical result.

The final step is to show that the Darwin-Fowler entropy $S = k \log \Sigma W - k \log N!$ satisfies the fundamental thermodynamical relation (the first law)

$$dE + \Delta A = T dS, \qquad (99)$$

where we here temporarily denote the element of work done by the assembly by ΔA to avoid confusion in notation.

For simplicity let us assume that the assembly consists of systems of only one kind. The possible energy states E_j will be functions of n external parameters which we shall denote by $\xi_1 \cdots \xi_n$, e.g., the volume of the region occupied by the assembly. If no external influence is brought to bear on the assembly, the ξ's remain unaltered and with them the E_j values. Since the partition function Z depends on the energy states, it likewise is a function of the ξ's. Thus the total energy is given by

$$E = \frac{N\zeta}{Z} \frac{dZ(\zeta, \xi_1, \cdots \xi_n)}{d\zeta}, \qquad (100)$$

and the change in energy associated with change in the temperature parameter ς and changes $d\xi_1, \cdots d\xi_n$ in the external parameters can be conveniently written in the form

$$dE = N\left[\frac{\partial \log Z}{\partial \varsigma}d\varsigma + \varsigma\frac{\partial^2 \log Z}{\partial \varsigma^2}d\varsigma\right]$$

$$+ N\varsigma\sum_{j=1}^{n}\frac{\partial^2 \log Z}{\partial \varsigma d\xi_j}d\xi_j. \tag{101}$$

We calculate ΔA by noting that $-\dfrac{\partial E_i}{\partial \xi_j}$ is the force associated with the change in E_i due to unit change in ξ_j. Thus $-\dfrac{\partial E_i}{\partial \xi_j}d\xi_j$ is the work done by a system of the assembly in the state E_i when ξ_j changes by $d\xi_j$. The total work done by such a system when the changes $d\xi_1, d\xi_2, \cdots d\xi_n$ take place is then

$$-\sum_{j=1}^{n}\frac{\partial E_i}{\partial \xi_j}d\xi_j.$$

Now on the average there are

$$\overline{N_i} = \frac{Ng_i\varsigma^{E_i}}{Z(\varsigma)} \tag{102}$$

systems in the assembly in the energy state E_i. Hence the total contribution of these to the work done is

$$-\frac{Ng_i\varsigma^{E_i}}{Z(\varsigma)}\sum_{j=1}^{n}\frac{\partial E_i}{\partial \xi_j}d\xi_j, \tag{103}$$

and the work done by the systems in all states becomes

$$-\frac{N}{Z(\varsigma)}\sum_i g_i\varsigma^{E_i}\sum_{j=1}^{n}\frac{\partial E_i}{\partial \xi_j}d\xi_j = \Delta A. \tag{104}$$

Now from the definition of the partition function it follows that

$$\sum_{j=1}^{n}\frac{\partial}{\partial \xi_j}\log Z(\varsigma, \xi_1, \cdots \xi_n)d\xi_j$$

$$= \frac{1}{Z}\sum_{j=1}^{n}\frac{\partial Z}{\partial \xi_j}d\xi_j = \frac{1}{Z}\sum_{j=1}^{n}\sum_i g_i\varsigma^{E_i}\log\varsigma\frac{\partial E_i}{\partial \xi_j}d\xi_j. \tag{105}$$

Hence by comparison with (104) we obtain

$$\Delta A = -\frac{N}{\log \zeta} \sum_{j=1}^{n} \frac{\partial}{\partial \xi_j} (\log Z) d\xi_j. \qquad (106)$$

Therefore

$$\Delta A + dE = N \left[\frac{\partial \log Z}{\partial \zeta} d\zeta + \zeta \frac{\partial^2 \log Z}{\partial \zeta^2} d\zeta + \zeta \sum_{j=1}^{n} \frac{\partial^2 \log Z}{\partial \zeta \partial \xi_j} d\xi_j \right.$$
$$\left. - \frac{1}{\log \zeta} \sum_{j=1}^{n} \frac{\partial}{\partial \xi_j} (\log Z) d\xi_j \right]. \qquad (107)$$

Now let us go back to the Darwin-Fowler entropy definition (86) and write

$$S = kN \log Z - kN\zeta \log \zeta \frac{\partial \log Z}{d\zeta} - k \log N!. \qquad (108)$$

The change in S corresponding to changes $d\zeta$ and $d\xi_1, \cdots d\xi_n$ then becomes

$$dS = kN \frac{\partial \log Z}{\partial \zeta} d\zeta - kN \log \zeta \frac{\partial \log Z}{\partial \zeta} d\zeta$$
$$- kN \frac{\partial \log Z}{\partial \zeta} d\zeta - kN\zeta \log \zeta \frac{\partial^2 \log Z}{\partial \zeta^2} d\zeta$$
$$- kN \sum_{j=1}^{n} \frac{\partial \log Z}{\partial \xi_j} d\xi_j - kN\zeta \log \zeta \cdot \sum_{j=1}^{n} \frac{\partial^2 \log Z}{\partial \zeta \partial \xi_j} d\xi_j. \qquad (109)$$

Reduction of (109) and comparison with (107) yields finally

$$- \frac{dS}{k \log \zeta} = \Delta A + dE. \qquad (110)$$

But since $\log \zeta = -1/kT$, this is equivalent to (99), further validating the Darwin-Fowler definition of entropy.

A simple illustration of the preceding considerations is provided by the ideal gas of Sec. 4. The substitution of the partition function (77) into the entropy expression (108) immediately leads to

$$S = kN \log \left[\frac{\tau}{h^3 N} (2\pi m k T)^{3/2} \right] + \frac{E}{T} + kN, \qquad (111)$$

which is identical with (87) of Chapter IV. If we form the total differential, treating τ, the volume, as the sole external parameter, we obtain

$$TdS = \frac{kNT}{\tau}\,d\tau + \tfrac{3}{2}\,kNdT - \frac{E}{T}\,dT + dE. \qquad (112)$$

But we recall from (82) that E, which represents the average total energy, for an ideal gas is $\dfrac{3NkT}{2}$ and from this

$$TdS = \frac{kNT}{\tau}\,d\tau + dE. \qquad (113)$$

From the equation of state of the ideal gas, however, $p\tau = NkT$; therefore $kNT/\tau = p$ and $pd\tau = dA$ and Eq. (113) becomes equivalent to (99).

6. THE PARTITION FUNCTION AND GIBBS'S PHASE INTEGRAL

The reader will have observed the close connection between the analysis in the preceding section and that in Sec. 3, Chapter IV. There we were still using w for the statistical probability but the analogy between this and ΣW is very close. The question arises as to the connection between the Darwin-Fowler partition function and entropy and Gibbs's statistical mechanics. In the first place we note the interesting mathematical similarity between the partition function

$$Z = \Sigma g_j e^{-E_j/kT}$$

and the Gibbs phase integral

$$I = e^{-\psi/\Theta} = \int e^{-H/\Theta}d\phi.$$

In fact for a system composed of free particles, in evaluating Z we actually effectively computed I. It is well to note, however, that the two differ in their logical basis. In the Gibbs phase integral H is the Hamiltonian function for a dynamical system described by an ensemble of elements distributed throughout phase space. The various values of H for different parts of phase space are not different values of the energy of a particular component system; they refer to the fictitious elements of the ensemble. In the partition function, on the other hand, the E_j are the possible energy values of a component system forming a constituent of a whole assembly of systems. We recall that it is the assembly of component systems in the Darwin-Fowler method which corresponds to the actual system described by the ensemble in the Gibbs method. Hence we expect that the formal analogy between I and Z will be of validity only for systems which can be described by a Gibbsian ensemble constructed for a *single* constituent of the system without bothering to construct an ensemble for the *whole* system. We found (cf. Sec. 10, Chapter VI) this to be possible for a system of *free* particles. For a system of interacting particles, however, this procedure could not be carried out and here the analogy between I and Z could not be logically maintained. This naturally will not prevent the replacement of the summation in Z by an equivalent integration whenever this proves to be mathematically more convenient. Moreover it is quite conceivable that the simple Darwin-Fowler method may be generalized to deal with systems in which the constituents interact with each other and for which in the partition function the E_j will refer to possible energy values of the *whole* assembly. As a matter of fact Darwin and Fowler do use such partition functions occasionally. Their theoretical justification will presumably rest ultimately on an appeal to the Gibbsian ensemble concept.

In the next chapter we shall consider in detail the modification introduced into statistics by the advent of quantum mechanics. There we shall find it convenient to use as a framework the method of Darwin-Fowler or its equivalent, the classical method of Chapter IV. This must not be interpreted to mean, however, that it is impossible to develop quantum statistics by a generalization of the method of Gibbs. The close connection between the partition function and the Gibbs phase integral which we have just stressed suggests the possibility of translating the Gibbs statistical mechanics into the quantum mechanical terminology. This will involve the replacement of the concept of the motion of ensembles in phase space by that of the existence of definite and often discrete quantum states which alone specify the possible motions of physical systems. Integration of quantities over phase space will be replaced by summations over the discrete quantum states. In certain cases, e.g., at high temperatures, the quantum states may be crowded together so closely that for practical purposes the summations may be replaced by integrals. In these limiting cases one therefore expects that quantum statistics will lead to the same result as classical statistics.[5]

---

[5] For further discussion of this point, cf. Mayer and Mayer, "Statistical Mechanics," pp. 123 ff, 218 ff, 240. (John Wiley & Sons, 1940.)

PROBLEMS

1. Consider an assembly of N systems in which each system is a rotator about a fixed axis. Let there be n types of rotators with frequencies $\nu_1, \nu_2 \cdots \nu_n$ and the numbers of each type $N_1 \cdots N_n$. Use the energy values given by the classical Bohr quantum theory. Find $\overline{N_{jr}}$ and $\overline{E}_j$.

2. Solve Problem 1 for the case in which the rotators have two degrees of freedom. For the energy values, cf. Lindsay and Margenau, " Foundations of Physics," p. 433.

3. Find the partition function and the average energy for an assembly of N two-dimensional harmonic oscillators.

4. Solve Problem 3 for the case of N three-dimensional oscillators.

5. Find the expression for the entropy of an assembly of N simple harmonic oscillators of the same frequency in terms of the total energy and the temperature. Solve the same problem for an assembly composed of n types of oscillators with frequencies $\nu_1, \nu_2 \cdots \nu_n$.

6. Find the expression for the specific heat at constant volume for an assembly of N simple harmonic oscillators of the same frequency.

7. Find the expression for the specific heat at constant volume for an assembly of N simple fixed axis rotators with frequencies $\nu_1, \nu_2 \cdots \nu_n$. (Cf. Problem 1.)

CHAPTER VIII

FUNDAMENTALS OF QUANTUM STATISTICS

1. REVIEW OF QUANTUM MECHANICS

The Darwin-Fowler method of developing statistical mechanics is well adapted to handle the modification in classical statistics brought about by the introduction of the quantum theory. Before we embark on the description of quantum statistics, however, it will be desirable to review briefly the fundamental principles of quantum mechanics.[1]

Quantum mechanics like its classical prototype deals with physical systems described by means of coordinates and conjugate momenta: we shall still be dealing with the q_j and p_j and the number of degrees of freedom of the system under discussion will still be denoted by f. The various properties of the system such as its total momentum, energy, angular momentum, are called *observables*, and it is the task of quantum mechanics to predict the allowed numerical values of these observables as well as their average values. In the first part of this program it differs decidedly from classical mechanics since in the latter all real values of observables are possible. In the second part of the program it reminds us of the fundamental problem of statistical mechanics. But the concept of the state of a physical system in quantum mechanics is very different from that in classical mechanics. In classical mechanics we know the state of a system if we have given the instantaneous values of the q's and the p's which characterize it, in other words, its phase. In quantum mechanics, on the other hand, the state is characterized by a certain function of the coordinates, known usually as a state function or ϕ function,[2] the only restrictions

---

[1] A more extensive survey, well adapted to the purposes of the present work, will be found in Chapter IX of Lindsay and Margenau's "Foundations of Physics." For the professional treatises on the subject the reader may consult Dirac's "Principles of Quantum Mechanics," Oxford Univ. Press, second edition, 1935; or, as more suitable for the general reader, Kemble's "Fundamental Principles of Quantum Mechanics," McGraw-Hill, 1937.

[2] The ϕ function is also often called a "wave" function. The reader must be careful to distinguish between the state function of quantum mechanics and the state variables of thermodynamics (Chapter III).

on which are that it must be single-valued and quadratically inte-grable, i.e., $\int \phi^* \phi d\tau$ exists, where ϕ^* is the complex conjugate of ϕ and $d\tau$ is the element of volume in configuration space, that is, the space of the q's. This purely abstract characterization must, of course, be supplemented by the statement that quantum mechanics provides a way of assigning proper state functions to systems and ways of using the ϕ functions to calculate possible and average values of observables.

The process indicated is carried out by assigning to each observable an *operator*, e.g., for the component momentum in the x direction p_x, the differential operator $\dfrac{h}{2\pi i} \dfrac{\partial}{\partial x}$ is chosen, where h is Planck's constant, and for the energy, the Hamiltonian operator, which is the Hamilton-ian function with each momentum component in it replaced by its appropriate operator. One of the fundamental assumptions of quan-tum mechanics then is that the *only possible* values of an observable p for a particular system are the characteristic values of the equation

$$P\phi = p\phi, \tag{1}$$

where the left-hand side consists of the result of operating on the ϕ function with the operator P characteristic of the observable p and the right side is simply the numerical value of the observable multiplied into the ϕ function. In general it is found that only for certain values of p in (1) is it possible to obtain solutions for ϕ which satisfy the fundamental restrictions mentioned above. These are the possible values of the observable and the corresponding ϕ functions, usually denoted now as ψ functions, are the corresponding state functions for the observable. Thus if ψ_k is the state function corresponding to the value p_k of the observable,

$$P\psi_k = p_k\psi_k \tag{2}$$

is an identity with ψ_k satisfying all the fundamental conditions imposed on state functions. It is customary to refer to the values p_k as the *eigenvalues* of the observable and the corresponding functions ψ_k as the *eigenfunctions* or *eigenstates* of the observable. For atomic problems the most important form of equation (1) is that for which the observable is the energy. It then becomes the Schrödinger equation

$$H\phi = E\phi, \tag{3}$$

in which H is the Hamiltonian operator and E the numerical value of the energy. The eigenfunctions ψ_k are functions of the configurational and spin coordinates of the system but they are also characterized by certain parameters, called quantum numbers. These are usually represented by n (principal quantum number), l (azimuthal quantum number), m (magnetic quantum number) and s (spin quantum number). The eigenvalues E are of course characterized by different values of n, l, m, s.

As a simple illustration the harmonic oscillator may be cited. Here the Hamiltonian operator is

$$H = \frac{1}{2m} \left(\frac{h}{2\pi i} \frac{\partial}{\partial x} \right)^2 + \frac{k}{2} x^2,$$

and eq. (3) becomes, with ψ in place of ϕ to conform to popular usage,

$$\frac{d^2\psi}{dx^2} + \frac{8\pi^2 m}{h^2} \left(E - \frac{1}{2} kx^2 \right) \psi = 0. \tag{4}$$

The eigenvalues of E turn out to be

$$E_n = (n + \tfrac{1}{2})h\nu, \tag{5}$$

with ν = frequency of the oscillator $= \dfrac{1}{2\pi} \sqrt{k/m}$. The eigenfunctions are

$$\psi_n = c_n H_n \left(\sqrt{\frac{k}{h\nu}} \, x \right) e^{-kx^2/2h\nu}, \tag{6}$$

where $H_n \left(\sqrt{\dfrac{k}{h\nu}} \, x \right)$ is the so-called Hermite polynomial of order n, the most compact representation of which is

$$H_n(\xi) = (-1)^n \, e^{\xi^2} \frac{d^n(e^{-\xi^2})}{d\xi^n}. \tag{7}$$

The final fundamental postulate of quantum mechanics says that when a system is in the state characterized by ϕ, the expected average of an observable p from a series of measurements is given by

$$\bar{p} = \frac{\displaystyle\int \phi^* P \phi \, d\tau}{\displaystyle\int \phi^* \phi \, d\tau}. \tag{8}$$

Here as usual $P\phi$ is to be interpreted as the result of operating on ϕ with the operator P and it must be recalled that ϕ need not be an eigenstate of the system for the observable p. The most direct significance of the state function ϕ is found in the quantum mechanical theorem that $\phi^*(\lambda_1 \cdots \lambda_f)\phi(\lambda_1 \cdots \lambda_f)$ measures the probability that the system in the state ϕ will have its coordinates $q_1 \cdots q_f$ equal to $\lambda_1 \cdots \lambda_f$ respectively. More strictly $\phi^*(\lambda_1 \cdots \lambda_f)\phi(\lambda_1 \cdots \lambda_f)dq_1 \cdots dq_f$ is the probability that the system will have its coordinates in the range $dq_1 \cdots dq_f$ in the neighborhood of the values $\lambda_1 \cdots \lambda_f$. In order that the system shall not be found at this place it is essential that $\phi^*\phi$ vanish there.

In order to understand quantum statistics it is necessary to consider N identical, indistinguishable physical systems forming an assembly in the Darwin-Fowler sense. Since the systems are identical the Hamiltonian has the same form for all, though each will be a function of the coordinates of the particular system in question. If *all* the coordinates of the jth system including the spin coordinates[3] are represented for simplicity by q_j, and if each system is considered isolated from all the others, we shall have for the description of the energy behavior of the assembly the N Schrödinger equations

$$H_1\psi_i(q_1) = E_i\psi_i(q_1),$$

$$H_2\psi_j(q_2) = E_j\psi_j(q_2), \qquad (9)$$

$$\cdots \cdots \cdots \cdots$$

$$H_N\psi_k(q_N) = E_k\psi_k(q_N),$$

where the sequences of the eigenvalues E_i, $E_j \cdots$ are really the same set in every case. The same is also true of the eigenfunctions $\psi_i, \psi_j \cdots$, except that each is a function of the coordinates of a single system.

If now we think of the assembly as a *single* system without however contemplating the mutual force interactions between the individual constituent systems, i.e., still envisage them as relatively far apart, the resultant Schrödinger equation will be

$$(H_1 + H_2 + \cdots + H_N)\psi(q_1, \cdots q_N) = E\psi(q_1, \cdots q_N), \quad (10)$$

where $\psi(q_1, \cdots q_N)$ is the eigenfunction for the assembly and E the corresponding eigenvalue. On examination eq. (10) is seen to be satisfied by

$$\psi = \psi_i(q_1)\psi_j(q_2) \cdots \psi_k(q_N), \qquad (11)$$

with

$$E = E_i + E_j + \cdots + E_k. \qquad (12)$$

This may be interpreted as meaning that ψ is the eigenstate of the assembly in which the first system is in eigenstate ψ_i corresponding to

---

[3] Cf. Lindsay and Margenau, *op. cit.*, p. 478.

eigenvalue E_i, etc., and E as the total energy of the assembly is the sum of the eigenvalues of the individual systems. Suppose we interchange *two* systems of the assembly so that system 1 now has energy E_j and system 2, energy E_i. The total energy E is unchanged but ψ becomes

$$\psi' = \psi_i(q_2)\psi_j(q_1) \cdots \psi_k(q_N), \tag{13}$$

which in general is a different function from ψ in (11). Thus we have a different eigenfunction for the assembly corresponding to the same eigenvalue. This corresponds to what is called *degeneracy* in the state of the assembly. The degree of the degeneracy is the number of different eigenfunctions with the same eigenvalue. Clearly in the present case this number is $N!$, since there are $N!$ ways of permuting the N sets of coordinates of the individual systems. If we denote any one of the functions obtained by such a permutation by Ψ_P, it follows from the *linearity* of the equation (10) that the linear combination

$$\Psi = \Sigma a_P \Psi_P \tag{14}$$

is also an eigenfunction of the assembly corresponding to the energy E (assuming that the coefficients a_P are so chosen that Ψ is normalized,[4] i.e., $\int \Psi^* \Psi d\tau = 1$).

We now introduce the Pauli exclusion principle which cuts the number of possible Ψ functions in (14) to *one* by means of the following postulate:

If the individual systems are elementary charged particles (in particular electrons or protons) the only combinations of the form (14) realized in nature are *antisymmetrical* with respect to an interchange of the coordinates of two systems, i.e., such an interchange produces a change in sign without changing the value. Of all possible combinations of the form (14) there is only one which is antisymmetrical and this may be written in the form of the determinant

$$\Psi = c \begin{vmatrix} \psi_i(q_1)\psi_i(q_2) & \cdots & \psi_i(q_N) \\ \psi_j(q_1)\psi_j(q_2) & \cdots & \psi_j(q_N) \\ \cdots & \cdots & \cdots \\ \cdots & \cdots & \cdots \\ \psi_k(q_1)\psi_k(q_2) & \cdots & \psi_k(q_N) \end{vmatrix}, \tag{15}$$

where c is a constant. An interchange of two q's is equivalent to an

[4] Cf. Lindsay and Margenau, *op. cit.*, p. 413.

interchange of two columns of the determinant and this leads merely to a change of sign. It is an interesting consequence of the Pauli principle, that if two of the charged particles are in the same state, i.e., if $i = j$, for example, two rows of the determinant become equal and the determinant vanishes with the concomitant vanishing of Ψ. This may be interpreted to mean that it is impossible for two such charged particles in an assembly to be in *identical* states. This is often presented as the statement of Pauli's principle. It is to be noted that the principle allows two elementary charged particles to be characterized by the same n, l, and m values provided the spin quantum numbers are different. There are only two possible values of the latter and their difference is interpreted physically as an opposition or antiparallelism of the direction of spin. It often happens that the numerical value of the energy depends very slightly on the spin and in that case the Pauli principle allows us to think of *two* elementary charged particles in practically the same energy state, their spins being opposed.

Suppose in (15) we interchange *two pairs* of q's, i.e., q_1 with q_2 and q_2 with q_3. Since each interchange involves a change of sign with no change in magnitude, the two interchanges will leave the sign unaltered. The state function Ψ is *symmetrical* with respect to interchange of two pairs of elementary charged particles. If then each individual system of the assembly consists of a pair of such charged particles or indeed any even number of them, the wave function of the assembly must be such that an interchange of two systems leaves it completely unaltered. To represent such an assembly of composite systems we need a *symmetrical* state function in place of the antisymmetrical one in (15). If the ψ's in (15) are still interpreted as representing the eigenfunctions of these composite systems we can easily get such a symmetrical function from (15) by changing all the minus signs in the determinant expansion to plus. It can be shown indeed that the symmetrical eigenfunction thus obtained is the only possible symmetrical one. An illustration of a composite system of this type is provided by the deuteron, the nucleus of the hydrogen isotope of mass 2. Many neutral atoms are also of similar character.

2. DISTRIBUTIONS IN QUANTUM STATISTICS

We are now ready to apply the quantum mechanical ideas of the preceding section to statistics and statistical distributions. We have just seen that the state of an assembly of elementary charged particles is given by the one antisymmetrical linear combination of eigenfunctions for the individual systems corresponding to the particles. How does this affect the statistical weight attached to the assembly, i.e., (1) of Chapter VII? For convenience we rewrite this here, viz.,

$$W = \frac{N!\, g_0^{N_0} g_1^{N_1} \cdots g_r^{N_r}}{N_0!\, N_1! \cdots N_r! \cdots}. \tag{16}$$

But this is just the total number of independent state functions which can be formed by taking the product of all the functions for the individual systems with all possible permutations of coordinates. To see this, note that a product of the kind in question is like (11), i.e.,

$$\psi_i(q_1)\psi_j(q_2) \cdots \psi_k(q_N).$$

There are $N!$ possible products of this kind obtained by permuting the $q_1 \cdots q_N$ in the individual ψ functions. If the *individual* energy states, however, are themselves degenerate and the degree of degeneracy of the ith state is g_i, etc., so that there are g_i independent state functions corresponding to the ith energy value, the number $N!$ must be multiplied by the g's where, moreover, each g is raised to the power of the number of systems in the corresponding state. This alone would give us for the number of state functions required

$$N!\, g_0^{N_0} g_1^{N_1} \cdots g_r^{N_r} \cdots . \tag{17}$$

With N_0 systems in the zeroth state, N_1 in the first state, etc., a product like (11) becomes, for example,

$$\psi_0(q_1)\, \psi_0(q_2) \cdots \psi_0(q_{N_0})\psi_1(q_{N_0+1})\psi_1(q_{N_0+2}) \cdots \psi_1(q_{N_1+N_0}) \cdots \cdots$$

Now the $N_0!$ permutations of the $q_1, q_2, \cdots q_{N_0}$ among the first N_0 factors do not produce new and different states. As a result (17) must be divided by

$$N_0!\, N_1! \cdots N_r! \cdots$$

in order to get the actual number of independent state functions representing the state of the assembly for a given value, E, of the energy. If it were not for the Pauli exclusion principle we should expect to use the statistical weight (16) in our statistical calculations for quantized systems. However, the principle insists that actually the numbers $N_0, N_1 \cdots N_r \cdots$ cannot exceed unity for any assembly realized in nature, and that for any set of values satisfying this criterion $W = 1$; otherwise W must vanish. It is clear then, that the exclusion principle forces us to abandon (16) as an expression for the statistical weight. The new situation may be expressed in the following way.

For an assembly represented by an antisymmetrical wave function the statistical weight W has the following values

$$W = 1 \text{ for } N_r = 0, 1 \text{ (any } r),$$

$$W = 0 \text{ for all other values of } N_r. \tag{18}$$

With this we can now proceed to derive the corresponding distribution law. The average number of systems in the rth state is (cf. eq. (4) of Chapter VII)

$$\overline{N_r} = \frac{\Sigma N_r W}{\Sigma W}. \tag{19}$$

We shall first calculate the denominator which we recall is the sum of all weights of the assembly subject only to the conditions (2) and (3) of Chapter VII. We can avoid the analytical complexity introduced by these conditions by noting that ΣW may be expressed as the coefficient of $x^N z^E$ in the expansion

$$M = \sum_{N_0, N_1 \cdots N_r \cdots} W x^{\Sigma N_i} z^{\Sigma N_j E_j}, \tag{20}$$

where in the summation the N's may be *any* positive integers and are no longer restricted by the conditions mentioned. Now M may be rewritten

$$M = \sum_{N_0, N_1 \cdots N_r \cdots} \prod_j W x^{N_i} z^{N_j E_j}. \tag{21}$$

In the evaluation of the product, if in any factor N_j is different from 0 or 1 the whole expression vanishes since $W = 0$ unless N_j is equal to 0 or 1. Consequently (21) is the sum of all products of the form

$$\prod_j x^{N_i} z^{N_j E_j},$$

where $N_j = 0$ or 1. This sum itself, however, is most simply written as a product, namely

$$M = (1 + xz^{E_0})(1 + xz^{E_1})(1 + xz^{E_2}) \cdots$$

$$= \prod_j (1 + xz^{E_j}). \tag{22}$$

Thus the extreme terms in the sum represent respectively that in which every $N_j = 0$ and that in which every $N_j = 1$. All other possible combinations are represented in the intermediate terms.

In Sec. 2, Chapter VII we showed that the coefficient of z^E in the expansion

$$\sum \frac{N!\, g_0^{N_0} g_1^{N_1} \cdots g_r^{N_r} \cdots}{N_0!\, N_1 \cdots N_r! \cdots} z^{\Sigma N_j E_j} = Z^N$$

is

$$\frac{1}{2\pi i} \int_C \frac{Z^N}{z^{E+1}}\, dz.$$

Hence by the use of the same reasoning the coefficient of $x^N z^E$ in the expansion (20) for M will be given by

$$\left(\frac{1}{2\pi i}\right)^2 \int_C \int_{C'} \frac{M\, dx\, dz}{x^{N+1} z^{E+1}}, \qquad (23)$$

where C and C' are closed contours about the origin in the complex plane and both x and z are considered to be complex variables.

We next get the expression for the numerator in $\bar{N}_r$. Let us calculate $1/\log z \cdot \dfrac{\partial M}{\partial E_r}$. From (21) differentiation yields

$$\frac{1}{\log z} \frac{\partial M}{\partial E_r} = \sum_{N_0 N_1 \cdots N_r \cdots} N_r \prod_j W x^{N_j} z^{N_j E_j}. \qquad (24)$$

But $\Sigma N_r W$ is just the coefficient of $x^N z^E$ in the expansion on the right of (24) and therefore the coefficient of the same power in $\dfrac{1}{\log z} \dfrac{\partial M}{\partial E_r}$. Consequently

$$\Sigma N_r W = \left(\frac{1}{2\pi i}\right)^2 \int_C \int_{C'} \frac{1}{\log z} \cdot \frac{\partial M}{\partial E_r} \frac{dx}{x^{N+1}} \frac{dz}{z^{E+1}}. \qquad (25)$$

We can put the term $\dfrac{1}{\log z} \cdot \dfrac{\partial M}{\partial E_r}$ into somewhat more suitable form by writing

$$M = \prod_j \left[1 + x\, (e^{\log z})^{E_j}\right] \qquad (26)$$

whence

$$\frac{1}{\log z} \cdot \frac{\partial M}{\partial E_r} = \frac{M x z^{E_r}}{1 + x z^{E_r}} = M x \frac{\partial}{\partial x} \log\,(1 + x z^{E_r}). \qquad (27)$$

The method of steepest descents may now be applied to the integral in (25) by treating the integrations with respect to z and x separately. Let the saddle point along the real axis for x correspond to[5] $x = \mu$ and

---

[5] The reader should be careful not to confuse the μ of this chapter with that of Chapter IV.

the saddle point along the real axis for z correspond to $z = \zeta$. Then since the function in the integrand can be shown to satisfy the requirements of the method we can write at once

$$\bar{N}_r = \mu \frac{\partial}{\partial \mu} \log (1 + \mu \zeta^{E_r}) = \frac{\zeta^{E_r}}{1/\mu + \zeta^{E_r}}. \tag{28}$$

This is the distribution formula for an assembly of elementary charged particles. If we identify ζ with $e^{-1/kT}$, as in the classical case of Chapter VII, (28) becomes

$$\bar{N}_r = \frac{e^{-E_r/kT}}{1/\mu + e^{-E_r/kT}} = \frac{1}{1/\mu \cdot e^{E_r/kT} + 1}. \tag{29}$$

Assemblies with this distribution law are said to obey the *Fermi-Dirac statistics*. This should then apply to an assembly of electrons. We note at once the difference from the classical statistical distribution law (31) of Chapter VII. The quantity μ appears as a new statistical parameter in addition to ζ. Its significance will be discussed shortly.

Before investigating the application of (29) we ought to notice that there is another possible quantum statistical distribution law. This will hold for an assembly whose eigenfunction is *symmetrical*. Here the weight to be attached to the assembly is also equal to unity for there is still *only one* symmetrical state function associated with the assembly, but now all values of N_r are possible since the symmetrical function does not vanish no matter how many individual systems are in the same state. Thus we write in place of (18)

$$W = 1, \text{ all } N_r. \tag{30}$$

In eq. (21) we must therefore now remove the restriction that N_j can have only the values 0 or 1 in order to avoid a vanishing product. Thus M can now be written as the sum of all products of the form

$$\prod_j x^{N_j} z^{N_j E_j},$$

in which N_j may take on any values; but this itself may be expressed in the form of a product of sums, viz.,

$$M = (1 + xz^{E_0} + x^2 z^{2E_0} + \cdots)(1 + xz^{E_1} + x^2 z^{2E_1} + \cdots) \cdots$$

$$= \prod_j \sum_{n=0}^{\infty} x^n z^{nE_j}. \tag{31}$$

Consequently since x and z are both less than unity in absolute value

$$M = \prod_j \left(\frac{1}{1 - xz^{E_j}} \right). \qquad (32)$$

The evaluation of $\overline{N_r}$ proceeds precisely as in the preceding case with

$$\frac{1}{\log z} \frac{\partial M}{\partial E_r} = \frac{Mxz^{E_r}}{1 - xz^{E_r}} = - Mx \frac{\partial}{\partial x} \log(1 - xz^{E_r}) \qquad (33)$$

The result is

$$\overline{N_r} = \frac{\mu \zeta^{E_r}}{(1 - \mu \zeta^{E_r})} = \frac{\zeta^{E_r}}{(1/\mu - \zeta^{E_r})}. \qquad (34)$$

This is the distribution law for what is usually termed the *Bose-Einstein statistics*. With the usual substitution for ζ it becomes

$$\overline{N_r} = \frac{1}{1/\mu \cdot e^{E_r/kT} - 1}. \qquad (35)$$

The only mathematical difference between (35) and (29) is the sign before the 1 in the denominator. This leads to a very fundamental difference in the physical meaning, however, as will appear shortly.

It is instructive to observe that the expression for $\overline{N_r}$ in the classical case of Sec. 2, Chapter VII (eq. 24 or 31) can also be obtained directly by the method of this section. For we can write

$$M = \sum_{N_0, N_1 \cdots N_r, \cdots} N! \frac{\prod_k g_k^{N_k}}{\prod_k N_k!} x^{\Sigma N_i} z^{\Sigma N_j E_j}$$

in the form

$$M = N! \Sigma \prod_j \frac{g_j^{N_j}}{N_j!} x^{N_j} z^{N_j E_j}. \qquad (36)$$

Furthermore the sum of all the products indicated in (36) may be expressed as the product of sums, viz.

$$M = N! \prod_j \sum_{n=0}^{\infty} \frac{g_j^n}{n!} x^n z^{nE_j} = N! \prod_j e^{g_j x z^{E_j}}. \qquad (37)$$

As before we form

$$\frac{1}{\log z} \frac{\partial M}{\partial E_r} = M g_r x z^{E_r},$$

and finally get

$$\overline{N_r} = \mu g_r \zeta^{E_r} = \mu g_r e^{-E_r/kT}. \qquad (38)$$

This is in the form of the distribution formula (24) in Chapter VII if we set

$$\mu = \frac{N}{Z(\zeta)}. \tag{39}$$

This helps to make clear the physical significance of the distribution parameter μ in the general quantum statistical case. It must be so chosen that $\Sigma \overline{N_r} = N$, the total number of systems in the assembly. This will serve to fix it in terms of N and ζ. The evaluation of μ will be carried out in the following sections. Independent justification of the association of ζ with temperature in the quantum statistical case will also be given.

3. ALTERNATIVE TREATMENT OF QUANTUM STATISTICAL DISTRIBUTIONS

Before proceeding to apply the distribution formulas (29) and (35) for the Fermi-Dirac and Bose-Einstein quantum statistics to the properties of gases and solids it will be worth while to present an alternative method of derivation. We shall here revert to the method of Chapter IV and shall not hesitate to use Stirling's formula. Moreover we shall derive the distribution laws for all three types of statistics.

We wish to distribute an assembly of N objects, e.g., material particles, into energy states in such a way that in the states between E_j and $E_j + dE_j$ there are N_j particles, etc. To make the discussion more pictorial we visualize the energy interval as a region in phase space, a kind of energy shell containing all values from E_j to $E_j + dE_j$. In classical statistics this shell is conceived to contain a *continuous* range of energy values but in quantum statistics it is necessary to give it a structure and to suppose that it consists of *cells* associated with each one of which there is a definite possible state of a particle of the assembly. Let us suppose there are n_j of these cells in the jth energy shell. We shall shortly derive an expression for the dependence of n_j on E_j and dE_j.

We proceed first to distribute the particles in accordance with a suggestion of Brillouin.[6] Each *cell* is assigned a *capacity* dependent on the number of particles in it. In particular for a cell with p occupants the capacity is assumed to be $1 - pa$, where a is a real parameter which may assume different values, to be discussed later. The weight attributed to the jth shell is the number of ways of assigning N_j particles to the n_j cells in the shell subject to the above capacity limitation.

[6] L. Brillouin, "Les Statistiques Quantiques," Vol. 1, pp. 167 ff., Paris, 1930.

The first particle may be placed in n_j ways, but the second in only $n_j - a$ ways, since the cell already occupied has now a capacity of only $1 - a$. The number of ways of assigning all N_j particles will be denoted by w_j, where

$$w_j = n_j(n_j - a)(n_j - 2a) \cdots (n_j - (N_j - 1)a) = \frac{a^{N_i}(n_j/a)!}{(n_j/a - N_j)!}. \quad (40)$$

It is, of course, assumed that $n_j - (N_j - 1)a > 0$ and that algebraic meaning can be associated with $(n_j/a)!$ etc. The weight corresponding to a distribution of the whole assembly in which there are N_0 particles in the energy shell about E_0, N_1 in the energy shell about E_1, etc. (with $\Sigma N_j = N$, and $\Sigma N_j E_j = E = $ constant) is then the number of ways of assignment of the N particles to the shells multiplied by the number of arrangements among the cells in every shell. The total weight then becomes

$$w = \frac{N!}{\displaystyle\prod_j N_j!} \cdot \prod_j \frac{a^{N_i}(n_j/a)!}{(n_j/a - N_j)!}. \quad (41)$$

We now follow the procedure of Sec. 2 of Chapter IV and inquire for the distribution corresponding to maximum w subject to the usual conditions on the total number of particles and the total energy. Using Stirling's formula and making some reductions, we have

$$\log w = N \log N - N - \Sigma N_j \log N_j + 1/a \cdot \Sigma n_j \log \frac{n_j}{n_j - aN_j}$$

$$+ \Sigma N_j \log (n_j - aN_j). \quad (42)$$

We now set $\delta \log w = 0$ subject to the conditions mentioned and get

$$\Sigma \delta N_j \log \left(\frac{n_j - aN_j}{N_j} \right) = 0 \quad (43)$$

subject to

$$\Sigma \delta N_j = \Sigma E_j \delta N_j = 0. \quad (44)$$

Introducing the undetermined multipliers γ_1 and γ_2 and proceeding precisely as in Sec. 2 of Chapter IV we are finally led to

$$\frac{N_j}{n_j} = \frac{1}{a + e^{-\gamma_1} e^{-\gamma_2 E_j}}. \quad (45)$$

N_j/n_j is the average number of particles per cell in the jth shell for the distribution corresponding to maximum w, i.e., that which we termed the canonical distribution in classical Maxwell-Boltzmann statistics.

Coupled with a knowledge of n_j, eq. (45) constitutes the quantum statistical distribution formula analogous to the classical formula (25) of Chapter IV. If we set

$$\gamma_2 = -\frac{1}{kT} \tag{46}$$

the distribution formula becomes

$$N_j/n_j = \frac{1}{a + e^{-\gamma_1}e^{E_j/kT}}. \tag{47}$$

We naturally seek a connection between (47) and the distribution laws (29), (35) and (38) already derived in the previous section by the Darwin-Fowler method. Let us first look at the matter from the purely formal mathematical standpoint. If $a = 0$, (47) becomes

$$N_j = n_j e^{\gamma_1}e^{-E_j/kT}. \tag{48}$$

Here N_j has precisely the same dependence on E_j as $\bar{N}_r$ on E_r in eq. (38). It evidently is the *classical* distribution law. The two formulas become identical if we identify μg_j in (38) with $e^{\gamma_1}n_j$ in (48). What physical significance can we attach to the choice $a = 0$? It clearly corresponds to a constant capacity of unity for every cell independent of the number of particles in it. But this is just the classical assumption that every cell has the same a priori probability. The weight g_j is then simply the number of cells available with energy E_j and corresponds to n_j. The parameter μ will finally be associated with e^{γ_1}.

In looking for a connection between (47) and the quantum statistical formulas (29) and (35) we are naturally led to try the assumptions $a = +1$ and $a = -1$. The form of N_j/n_j in (47) with $a = 1$ then looks much like that of $\bar{N}_r$ in (29) and there is a similar resemblance between (47) for $a = -1$ and (35), particularly if we agree to let e^{γ_1} stand for μ. Unfortunately we should naturally wish to associate N_j in the one case with $\bar{N}_r$ in the other, whereas the appearance of n_j in (47) appears as a sort of stumbling block. This difficulty is cleared up when we reflect that the $\bar{N}_r$ and the N_j do not after all refer to the same thing. The rth energy state in the Darwin-Fowler method of Sec. 2 is a genuine microscopic energy level to which the specific energy value E_r is assigned. In the Fermi-Dirac statistics only zero or one particle may exist in this state. On the other hand in the alternative treatment of the present section N_j is the number of particles in a whole range or shell of energy values ranging from E_j to $E_j + dE_j$ and n_j represents the number of possible or allowed energy states in this range. Consequently the E_r values in (29) refer strictly to the energies associated with the various *cells* in a particular shell in the Brillouin method, while the E_j value in (47) refers to the average energy over a whole shell of states. If we like we may think of (29) as defining a microscopic distribution and (47) as defining a macroscopic distribution. That the distinction does not appear to be necessary in the case of classical statistics where, as we have just seen in the preceding paragraph, we are able at once to identify formula (48) with (38), is not so surprising when we consider that in classical statistics there is no real necessity for subdividing energy shells into discrete cells; there is indeed no prescribed lower limit to the size of the energy interval and no reason why we should not identify E_r in the one case with E_j in the other. A similar statement holds for the identification of g_j with n_j. However we are naturally more interested in the quantum statistical case. With the distinction between the two alternative points of view held clearly in mind while we realize that there is no essential inconsistency involved, we can proceed to use whichever form of distribution formula seems more convenient. For the present we shall continue our discussion on the basis of eq. (47).

It is desirable, however, to pay a little attention to the physical significance which can be attached to the choices $a = +1$ and -1 in the Brillouin point of view. The assignment $a = 1$ implies that the capacity of a cell is unity when no particle is in it but drops to zero as soon as one particle enters. Consequently on this choice a cell may hold at most one particle; there are only two possibilities, one or zero. The connection between this and the Pauli exclusion principle, which led to the Fermi-Dirac statistics from quantum mechanics, is clear. If on the other hand $a = -1$, the capacity of a cell with p occupants is $1 + p$, i.e., the capacity of the cell increases with the number of occupants. The connection with the Bose-Einstein statistical assumption expressed in (30) is not indeed so clear as in the corresponding case of $a = 1$ and the Fermi-Dirac statistics. Nevertheless there appears to be no essential inconsistency between the two points of view. Moreover we are not restricted to the values of $a = +1$ and -1. For example, $0 < a < 1$ would imply a loosening of the Fermi restriction though at the same time allowing less freedom of occupancy of cells than the classical theory. Certain analytical difficulties with fractional a would indeed appear to arise from the fact that w_j in (40) must be integral. Closer inspection shows that these can be overcome, though we shall not pursue this possibility here.[7]

[7] Cf. R. B. Lindsay, *Phil. Mag.* [7] **17**, 264 (1934); also D. S. Kothari, *Phil. Mag.* **18**, 192 (1934).

The next step in the exploitation of the distribution formula (47) is to establish the connection between the parameter γ_2 and the temperature in a straightforward fashion. We shall use the elementary statistical-thermodynamical analogy (cf. eq. 68, Chapter IV)

$$kd \log w = \frac{dE}{T}, \tag{49}$$

where dE is the change in internal energy due to flow of energy, e.g., heat (not change in internal parameters). Since (49) holds for equilibrium states only we must use the maximum $\log w$, i.e., that corresponding to the distribution law (45). The change in $\log w$ associated with changes dN_j in the number of particles in the jth shell due to the inflow of heat is

$$d \log w = \Sigma dN_j \log \left(\frac{n_j - aN_j}{N_j} \right). \tag{50}$$

But $\log \dfrac{n_j - aN_j}{N_j} = - \gamma_1 - \gamma_2 E_j.$ Hence

$$d \log w = - \Sigma(\gamma_1 + \gamma_2 E_j)dN_j = - \gamma_2 \Sigma E_j dN_j = - \gamma_2 dE. \tag{51}$$

We note that though the number of particles does not change when heat is added, the total energy changes by $\Sigma E_j dN_j$ since the effect of the energy flow is to alter the number of particles in the higher energy shells. Hence the analogy (49) leads to

$$\gamma_2 = - \frac{1}{kT}$$

in agreement with our assumption (46).

We shall conclude this section by a brief reference to the more conventional method of discussing the Fermi-Dirac and Bose-Einstein distribution formulas in order to point out certain differences with the Brillouin method just described.

Let us first consider the Fermi-Dirac case. The problem to be solved is still the distribution of N identical objects in energy shells with N_j in the jth cell and the number of available cells in the jth cell being equal to n_j. It is assumed that no more than one object can be put into any cell. The number of ways in which N_j objects can be placed in n_j cells so that no cell contains more than one object is equal to the number of ways in which the n_j cells can be divided into two groups with N_j in one group (those which contain one object) and

$n_j - N_j$ in the other group (those which contain no object). From Chapter II this number is

$$\frac{n_j!}{N_j! \, (n_j - N_j)!}.$$

Consequently the total number of ways of distributing all N objects is

$$\prod_j \frac{n_j}{N_j! \, (n_j - N_j)!}. \tag{41'}$$

On this view this should be the statistical probability or weight associated with the distribution. It will be noted at once that it is not exactly the value (41) obtained above for $a = 1$. Rather, it is equal to $w/N!$.

We proceed next to the Bose-Einstein distribution by a similar direct method. We now wish to distribute N_j objects among n_j energy cells in such a way that no restriction is placed on the number of objects in any cell. This is clearly the number of combinations of n_j things N_j at a time with all possible repetitions allowed. From the algebraic theory of combinations, this number is equal to the number of combinations of $n_j + N_j - 1$ objects N_j at a time *without* repetitions. Consequently the required total statistical probability or weight becomes

$$\prod_j \frac{(N_j + n_j - 1)!}{N_j! \, (n_j - 1)!}. \tag{41''}$$

Now if in eq. (40) we let $a = -1$, which should correspond to the Bose-Einstein distribution in accordance with our previous assumptions, the value of w becomes

$$w = N! \prod_j \frac{(N_j + n_j - 1)!}{N_j! \, (n_j - 1)!},$$

which again is just $N!$ times the value (41″) obtained by direct counting.

The question arises: What is to be done about the factor $N!$ which occurs in the Brillouin method of computing the statistical weights but is absent in the direct counting scheme? It will be recalled that this same factor occurs in the expression for w in the classical Maxwell-Boltzmann statistics in Chapter IV. There we found its presence of no particular moment as far as the distribution function is concerned. It proved indeed embarrassing in connection with the statistical definition and evaluation of the entropy and free energy; we found it necessary to use $w/N!$ as an "effective statistical probability" in the definition of entropy. If we use the Brillouin expression (41) for w the same situation will prevail in quantum statistics. We could, of course, redefine the statistical probability to bring it into agreement with (41') and (41'') and this will be the more logical course if we consider the quantum statistical distributions to be the fundamental ones.[8] However we shall find it simpler to continue to use the Brillouin w and define entropy in terms of $w/N!$. All applications will then be perfectly consistent.

4. EVALUATION OF n_j FOR AN ASSEMBLY OF FREE PARTICLES

Before we can apply formula (47) to concrete cases we must have n_j or the number of cells in the jth energy shell. This is the same as the number of possible energy values lying in the interval E_j to $E_j + dE_j$. Its value clearly depends on the nature of the assembly. The method of evaluation will be quantum mechanical which is reasonable since we are talking about quantum statistics. We shall confine our attention to an assembly of free particles all having the same mass, the statistical analogue of an ideal gas. The problem is to determine the allowed energy values of the assembly. Since the particles are assumed to exert no forces on each other, these values can be readily calculated by direct summation from the energy eigenvalues for a single particle confined to a closed vessel. Suppose for convenience the vessel is a rectangular parallelepiped with dimensions l_1, l_2, l_3. The Hamiltonian for the particle is $(p_x^2 + p_y^2 + p_z^2)/2m$ since, as the potential energy is constant it may conveniently be taken equal to zero. The corresponding quantum mechanical operator becomes (cf. Sec. 1)

$$- \frac{h^2}{8\pi^2 m} \left(\frac{\partial^2}{\partial x^2} + \frac{\partial^2}{\partial y^2} + \frac{\partial^2}{\partial z^2} \right) = - \frac{h^2}{8\pi^2 m} \nabla^2.$$

The appropriate Schrödinger equation then becomes

$$\nabla^2 \psi + \frac{8\pi^2 m}{h^2} E\psi = 0. \tag{52}$$

This may be solved by separation of the variables, i.e., by writing $\psi(x, y, z)$ in the form of the product of three functions $\psi_x(x), \psi_y(y), \psi_z(z)$ depending respectively on x, y, and z alone. Thus

$$\psi = \psi_x \psi_y \psi_z. \tag{53}$$

[8] This, for example, is the view of Mayer and Mayer, "Statistical Mechanics," pp. 111 ff. For another discussion of the problem see Brillouin, *op. cit.*, Vol. 1, pp. 171 ff.

Equation (52) becomes consequently

$$\frac{1}{\psi_x} \cdot \frac{d^2\psi_x}{dx^2} + \frac{1}{\psi_y} \cdot \frac{d^2\psi_y}{dy^2} + \frac{1}{\psi_z} \cdot \frac{d^2\psi_z}{dz^2} = -\kappa^2, \tag{54}$$

where $8\pi^2 mE/h^2$ has been replaced by κ^2. Let us write $\kappa^2 = \kappa_1^2 + \kappa_2^2 + \kappa_3^2$. Then we merely have to solve the individual ordinary differential equations

$$\frac{d^2\psi_x}{dx^2} + \kappa_1^2\,\psi_x = 0; \quad \frac{d^2\psi_y}{dy^2} + \kappa_2^2\,\psi_y = 0; \quad \frac{d^2\psi_z}{dz^2} + \kappa_3^2\,\psi_z = 0. \tag{55}$$

The solutions are

$$\begin{aligned}
\psi_x &= A_x e^{i\kappa_1 x} + B_x e^{-i\kappa_1 x} \\
\psi_y &= A_y e^{i\kappa_2 y} + B_y e^{-i\kappa_2 y} \\
\psi_z &= A_z e^{i\kappa_3 z} + B_z e^{-i\kappa_3 z}.
\end{aligned} \tag{56}$$

These solutions are subject to the boundary conditions

$$\begin{aligned}
\psi_x &= 0 \text{ at } x = 0, l_1, \\
\psi_y &= 0 \text{ at } y = 0, l_2, \\
\psi_z &= 0 \text{ at } z = 0, l_3,
\end{aligned} \tag{57}$$

if we suppose that the container is placed with one corner at the origin and has the coordinate planes for three of its faces. These boundary conditions express the fact that the particle is confined to the vessel, i.e., there is no probability of its ever being found at or outside the walls. The conditions (57) lead at once to

$$\sin \kappa_1 l_1 = 0; \quad \sin \kappa_2 l_2 = 0; \quad \sin \kappa_3 l_3 = 0,$$

or expressed more explicitly

$$\kappa_1 = \frac{n_1\pi}{l_1}; \quad \kappa_2 = \frac{n_2\pi}{l_2}; \quad \kappa_3 = \frac{n_3\pi}{l_3}. \tag{58}$$

where n_1, n_2, and n_3 are any integers, positive or negative but not zero. The energy eigenvalues of the free particle in the vessel therefore are

$$E_{(n_1, n_2, n_3)} = \frac{h^2}{8m}\left(\frac{n_1^2}{l_1^2} + \frac{n_2^2}{l_2^2} + \frac{n_3^3}{l_3^2}\right). \tag{59}$$

Corresponding to every set of integers n_1, n_2, n_3, eq. (59) gives a possible energy value. The corresponding eigenfunction is

$$\psi = C \sin \frac{n_1\pi x}{l_1} \cdot \sin \frac{n_2\pi y}{l_2} \cdot \sin \frac{n_3\pi z}{l_3}, \tag{60}$$

where C is a constant determined from the normalization condition

expressing the fact that the probability of finding the particle somewhere in the vessel is unity. This takes the form

$$\int_0^{l_3} \int_0^{l_2} \int_0^{l_1} |\psi|^2 \, dx \, dy \, dz = 1. \tag{61}$$

Application of this yields

$$C = \sqrt{\frac{8}{l_1 l_2 l_3}} = 2\sqrt{\frac{2}{\tau}}, \tag{62}$$

where τ is the volume of the vessel. Inspection of (59) now discloses
that because of the small value of $h^2/8m$ in absolute units, if τ is large,
i.e. the vessel of macroscopic size, 1 cm^3 or larger, the energy eigenvalues are very close together. In fact they may for practical pur-

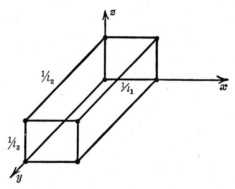

FIG. 8·1.

poses be considered effectively continuous.[9] In any case our problem
is to determine from (59) the number of values of $E_{(n_1, n_2, n_3)}$ lying in
the interval E_j to $E_j + dE_j$. For this purpose we set up a three-
dimensional rectangular lattice (Fig. 8·1) in which the sides of the unit
cell in the three coordinate directions are $1/l_1$, $1/l_2$, and $1/l_3$ respectively. Every point in the lattice is given by the three integers n_1, n_2, n_3
and the distance of the point from the origin is

$$r_{(n_1, n_2, n_3)} = \sqrt{\frac{n_1^2}{l_1^2} + \frac{n_2^2}{l_2^2} + \frac{n_3^2}{l_3^2}}. \tag{63}$$

With each point in the lattice there is associated an allowed energy
eigenvalue $E_{(n_1, n_2, n_3)}$ by (59). Since change in sign of n_1, n_2, n_3, or
any one of them, does not produce a new energy value nor a new
independent state function we limit the lattice points under considera-

[9] Cf. Lindsay and Margenau, *op. cit.*, pp. 428 ff, for a discussion of this subject

tion to the first octant of the lattice space, i.e., that for which n_1, n_2, n_3 are positive integers. The number of eigenvalues lying in the energy interval cited is then equal to the number of lattice points lying between the octant of the sphere of radius r_j corresponding to E_j and the octant of the sphere of radius $r_j + dr_j$ corresponding to $E_j + dE_j$. Now each lattice point can also be associated with a lattice cell like that shown in Fig. 8·1. Consequently the number of lattice points in the spherical shell octant just mentioned will also be equal to the number of lattice cells contained in it and this in turn will be given by the volume of the shell octant divided by the volume of the unit cell, namely $1/l_1 l_2 l_3 = 1/\tau$. Obviously the approximation involved in the last statement improves as τ becomes larger. In insisting that τ be macroscopic in size we are insuring a very good approximation. The volume of the octant in question in the lattice space is

$$\frac{4\pi}{8}\, r_j^2 dr_j.$$

But from (59) and (63)

$$r_j = \frac{2}{h}\sqrt{2mE_j}, \quad dr_j = \frac{1}{h}\cdot\sqrt{\frac{2m}{E_j}}\, dE_j, \tag{64}$$

and therefore the number of energy values required, which is just the n_j value we have been looking for, is

$$n_j = \frac{2\pi\tau}{h^3}\cdot (2m)^{3/2} E_j^{1/2}\, dE_j. \tag{65}$$

The quantum statistical distribution formula (47) then takes the form

$$N_j = \frac{4\pi m\tau/h^3 \cdot \sqrt{2mE_j}\, dE_j}{a + e^{-\gamma_1}e^{E_j/kT}}. \tag{66}$$

Once more we emphasize that in this formula $a = +1$ corresponds to the Fermi-Dirac statistics and $a = -1$ to the Bose-Einstein statistics. For particles with a spin quantum number $\frac{1}{2}$ in which the energy is practically the same for both spin directions (cf. the remarks near the end of Sec. 1) it is necessary to multiply the right side of (66) by 2 to get the correct value of N_j. For in this case we can effectively have two particles (with opposite spins) for each numerical value of the energy. This will be true with free electrons. For molecules without a spin, (66) should apply as it stands. On the other hand [10] for molecules with nuclear spin quantum number s, N_j must be multiplied by $2s + 1$.

[10] Cf. Mayer and Mayer, *op. cit.*, pp. 135 f.

5. QUANTUM STATISTICS OF A WEAKLY DEGENERATE GAS

We have still the task of evaluating the statistical parameter γ_1 in the distribution expression (66). This can be done by utilizing the condition $\Sigma N_j = N$, the total number of particles in the aggregate. In this connection considerable interest attaches in the first place to the special case $a = 0$. Then (66) should reduce effectively to the Maxwellian distribution of classical statistics. From the way we have expressed n_j we must write ΣN_j as an integral and have [11]

$$\frac{4\pi m\tau}{h^3} e^{\gamma_1}\sqrt{2m} \int_0^\infty \sqrt{E}\, e^{-E/kT}\, dE = N. \tag{67}$$

The integral in (67) is a well-known one and is equal to $\dfrac{kT}{2}\sqrt{\pi kT}$. Hence the parameter γ_1 is given by

$$e^{\gamma_1} = \frac{Nh^3}{\tau} \cdot \frac{1}{(2\pi mkT)^{3/2}}. \tag{68}$$

Substitution into N_j, now rewritten as dN for greater consistency, gives

$$dN = \frac{4\pi m N}{(2\pi mkT)^{3/2}} \sqrt{2mE}\, e^{-E/kT}\, dE \tag{69}$$

for the number of particles in the assembly having energies lying in the interval from E to $E + dE$. This can be readily transformed to give the distribution in terms of velocity by writing $E = mv^2/2$. The result is

$$dN = 4\pi N \left(\frac{m}{2\pi kT}\right)^{3/2} v^2 e^{-mv^2/2kT} dv, \tag{70}$$

which, with allowances for difference in notation, is identical with the Maxwellian distribution in eq. (53) of Chapter V. This at any rate indicates that the general distribution formula (47) includes the classical distribution as a special case, viz., that for $a = 0$.

We must now consider the general case where $-1 \le a \le +1$, with $a = +1$ (Fermi-Dirac) and $a = -1$ (Bose-Einstein) as the interesting

---

[11] This is really a matter of convenience justified by the fact already emphasized that the differences between successive eigenvalues are very small compared with the eigenvalues themselves. To handle the matter by means of a summation would involve using (59) directly, leading to a rather difficult problem in algebra.

limiting cases. The evaluation of e^{γ_1} proceeds as before, the condition $\Sigma N_j = N$ now taking the form

$$\frac{2\pi\tau}{h^3}(2m)^{3/2}\int_0^\infty \frac{\sqrt{E}dE}{a + e^{-\gamma_1}e^{E/kT}} = N. \tag{71}$$

There is a certain convenience in introducing the transformation $E/kT = u$. Then (71) becomes

$$\frac{2\pi\tau}{h^3}(2mkT)^{3/2}\int_0^\infty \frac{\sqrt{u}du}{e^{-\gamma_1}e^u + a} = N. \tag{72}$$

We shall set $-\gamma_1 = \gamma$ and confine our attention for the rest of this section to the case in which $\gamma > 1$ but is not sufficiently large for us to be justified in neglecting a compared with $e^\gamma e^u$. Now we can transform the integral in (72) in the following fashion, letting $a = \pm b$, where b is always positive, though a may be positive or negative. For the Fermi-Dirac and Bose-Einstein statistics $b = 1$. For other intermediate brands of statistics $0 < b < 1$. We shall carry through the general case. The integral in (72) then becomes

$$\int_0^\infty \frac{\sqrt{u}du}{e^\gamma e^u + a} = \frac{1}{b}\int_0^\infty \frac{\sqrt{u}du}{\pm 1 + e^{(\gamma - \log b) + u}}.$$

Call $e^{\gamma - \log b} = e^\alpha$. The foregoing integral is a special form of the integral

$$U(\rho,\alpha) = \int_0^\infty \frac{u^\rho du}{e^{\alpha+u} \pm 1},$$

with $\alpha > 1$ and ρ rational and positive. Since we can expand the denominator of the integrand in the form

$$\frac{1}{e^{\alpha+u}(1 \pm e^{-(\alpha+u)})} = e^{-(\alpha+u)}[1 \mp e^{-(\alpha+u)} + e^{-2(\alpha+u)} \cdots]$$

it follows that

$$U(\rho, \alpha) = \int_0^\infty u^\rho \sum_{j=1}^\infty (\mp 1)^{j-1}e^{-j(\alpha+u)}du. \tag{73}$$

Introduce the transformation $ju = t$ and utilize the fact that

$$\int_0^\infty u^\rho e^{-ju}du = \frac{1}{j^{\rho+1}}\int_0^\infty t^\rho e^{-t}dt = \frac{\Gamma(\rho+1)}{j^{\rho+1}}. \tag{74}$$

The result is the convergent expansion

$$U(\rho, \alpha) = \left(e^{-\alpha} \mp \frac{e^{-2\alpha}}{2^{\rho+1}} + \frac{e^{-3\alpha}}{3^{\rho+1}} \mp \cdots \right) \Gamma(\rho + 1). \quad (75)$$

In the particular case of (72) $\rho = 1/2$. Recalling that $\Gamma(3/2) = \sqrt{\pi}/2$, we finally have

$$N = \frac{\tau}{h^3} \frac{(2\pi mkT)^{3/2}}{b} \left(e^{-\alpha} \mp \frac{e^{-2\alpha}}{2^{3/2}} + \cdots + (\mp 1)^n \frac{e^{-(n+1)\alpha}}{(n+1)^{3/2}} + \cdots \right). \quad (76)$$

From this the *first* approximation to α is obtained in the form

$$e^{-\alpha} = \frac{h^3 Nb}{\tau (2\pi mkT)^{3/2}}. \quad (77)$$

It is interesting to observe that if we set $b = 1$, this is just the expression for e^{γ_1} in the classical statistics distribution formula. The *second* approximation to $e^{-\alpha}$ is

$$e^{-\alpha} = \frac{h^3 Nb}{\tau (2\pi mkT)^{3/2}} \left[1 \pm \frac{h^3 Nb}{2^{3/2} \tau (2\pi mkT)^{3/2}} \right]. \quad (78)$$

This approximation introduces a distinction between positive and negative a. In (78) the plus sign corresponds to positive a, while the minus sign corresponds to negative a. In the limiting cases in which $a = \pm 1$ we have $b = 1$. The value of e^{γ_1} for the Fermi-Dirac and Bose-Einstein statistics respectively is given to the second approximation (recalling that now $e^{\gamma_1} = e^{-\alpha}$) by

$$e^{\gamma_1}{}_{\text{Fermi-Dirac}} = \frac{h^3 N}{\tau (2\pi mkT)^{3/2}} \left[1 + \frac{h^3 N}{2^{3/2} \tau (2\pi mkT)^{3/2}} \right], \quad (79)$$

$$e^{\gamma_1}{}_{\text{Bose-Einstein}} = \frac{h^3 N}{\tau (2\pi mkT)^{3/2}} \left[1 - \frac{h^3 N}{2^{3/2} \tau (2\pi mkT)^{3/2}} \right]. \quad (80)$$

For 1 cm^3 of hydrogen at room temperature, the expression $h^3 N / \tau (2\pi mkT)^{3/2}$ has a numerical value of the order of 10^{-4}. Hence α is considerably greater than unity and the approximation in (78) is a very good one in this case. For reasons which will appear more clearly in the next section a gas for which this is true is said to be *weakly degenerate*. For the present we shall use the term *degeneracy* as an indication of the deviation of the properties of a gas treated quantum statistically from those of an ideal gas treated by classical statistics. The measure of the degeneracy is the value of e^{γ_1}. For hydrogen under the conditions just mentioned the degeneracy is indeed so weak that e^{γ_1} reduces for all practical purposes to the value for an ideal gas in classical statistics. As the temperature is lowered, e^{γ_1} increases and the degeneracy becomes greater. However for hydrogen even at its critical point e^{γ_1} is of the order of only 10^{-2}.

The distinction between quantum and classical statistics will be further brought out by a calculation of the total average energy of the gas as a function of the temperature. This is given by

$$E = \Sigma N_j E_j = \frac{2\pi\tau}{h^3} \cdot kT \cdot (2mkT)^{3/2} \int_0^\infty \frac{u^{3/2}du}{a + e^{-\gamma_1}e^u}. \qquad (81)$$

We again make use of the integral $U(\rho, \alpha)$ in eq. (75) with $\rho = 3/2$, and can finally write

$$E = \frac{3\tau}{2h^3} \cdot \frac{kT(2\pi mkT)^{3/2}}{b} \cdot$$
$$\left(e^{-\alpha} \mp \frac{e^{-2\alpha}}{2^{5/2}} + \cdots + (\mp 1)^n \frac{e^{-(n+1)\alpha}}{(n+1)^{5/2}} + \cdots \right), \qquad (82)$$

where the upper sign refers to positive a and the lower sign to negative a. Combining this with the expression for N in (76) gives

$$E = \tfrac{3}{2} NkT \cdot \frac{\left(e^{-\alpha} \mp \dfrac{e^{-2\alpha}}{2^{5/2}} + \cdots + (\mp 1)^n \dfrac{e^{-(n+1)\alpha}}{(n+1)^{5/2}} + \cdots \right)}{\left(e^{-\alpha} \mp \dfrac{e^{-2\alpha}}{2^{3/2}} + \cdots + (\mp 1)^n \dfrac{e^{-(n+1)\alpha}}{(n+1)^{3/2}} + \cdots \right)}. \qquad (83)$$

If $e^{-\alpha}$ is sufficiently small we can approximate this successfully by

$$E = \tfrac{3}{2}NkT\left[1 \pm \frac{e^{-\alpha}}{2^{5/2}} - e^{-2\alpha}\left(\frac{2}{3^{5/2}} + \frac{1}{2^4} \right) \cdots \right], \qquad (84)$$

where the upper sign now refers to positive a and the lower sign to negative a. If we set for brevity

$$K = \frac{h^3 N}{\tau(2\pi mkT)^{3/2}}, \qquad (85)$$

(78) with $b = 1$ becomes

$$e^{-\alpha} = K\left(1 \pm \frac{K}{2^{3/2}} \right). \qquad (86)$$

We can then substitute into (84) and obtain for the approximate expressions of the energy on the Fermi-Dirac and Bose-Einstein statistics respectively

$$E_{\text{F-D}} = \tfrac{3}{2}NkT\left[1 + \frac{K}{2^{5/2}} - \frac{2K^2}{3^{5/2}} + \cdots\right] \tag{87}$$

$$E_{\text{B-E}} = \tfrac{3}{2}NkT\left[1 - \frac{K}{2^{5/2}} - \frac{2K^2}{3^{5/2}} + \cdots\right]. \tag{88}$$

These may be considered as correct approximations as far as terms of order K^2 are concerned. It is plain that for a weakly degenerate gas the energy differs but slightly from the classical value.

We now wish to obtain the equation of state of a weakly degenerate gas. This involves getting the entropy and free energy. For the entropy we have agreed (Sec. 3) to use the definition

$$S = k \log \frac{w}{N!}. \tag{89}$$

By inserting the value of N_j/n_j given in eq. (45) into the expression for $\log w$ in eq. (42), we are led to

$$S = k\left[E/kT - \gamma_1 N + \frac{1}{a}\sum_j n_j \log\left(1 + ae^{\gamma_1}e^{-E_j/kT}\right)\right]. \tag{90}$$

From (65), replacing the summation by an equivalent integration, we have

$$\frac{1}{a}\sum_j n_j \log\left(1 + ae^{\gamma_1}e^{-E_j/kT}\right)$$

$$= \frac{2\pi\tau}{ah^3}(2m)^{3/2}\int_0^\infty \sqrt{E}\,\log\left(1 + ae^{\gamma_1}e^{-E/kT}\right)\,dE.$$

Partial integration of the integral leads finally to

$$S = -k\gamma_1 N + \frac{5}{3}\cdot\frac{E}{T}. \tag{91}$$

The free energy is

$$\Psi = E - TS = k\gamma_1 NT - \tfrac{2}{3}E. \tag{92}$$

The equation of state then becomes (eq. 12, Chapter III)

$$p = -\left(\frac{\partial\Psi}{\partial\tau}\right)_T = -NkT\frac{\partial\gamma_1}{\partial\tau} + \frac{2}{3}\frac{\partial E}{\partial\tau}. \tag{93}$$

From (78) with $b = 1$, we can evaluate γ_1 (recalling that $e^{-\alpha} = e^{\gamma_1}$)

and from (84) we can get $\dfrac{\partial E}{\partial \tau}$, being careful to keep terms of appropriate order in each case. The final result is

$$p = \frac{2}{3}\frac{E}{\tau}. \tag{94}$$

It is worth noting that this result, which we have already derived in the classical kinetic theory (eq. 12 of Chapter V) holds for both brands of quantum statistics. It is therefore a very general formula.

The equation of state for a weakly degenerate gas in the two brands of statistics then appears in the approximate form

$$p\tau = NkT\left(1 + \frac{K}{2^{5/2}} - \frac{2K^2}{3^{5/2}} + \cdots\right) \cdots \quad \text{Fermi-Dirac} \tag{95}$$

$$p\tau = NkT\left(1 - \frac{K}{2^{5/2}} - \frac{2K^2}{3^{5/2}} + \cdots\right) \cdots \quad \text{Bose-Einstein} \tag{96}$$

As a consequence of these equations, a weakly degenerate Bose-Einstein gas is more compressible than an ideal gas, while a weakly degenerate Fermi-Dirac gas is less compressible than an ideal gas. Actually the differences are so slight that they are entirely masked in real gases by the departures from ideality owing to the forces between the particles. These are of course neglected in eqs. (95) and (96). It is only at very low temperatures that the terms in K and K^2 become appreciable and here the intermolecular forces become particularly significant.

6. WEAKLY DEGENERATE GAS BY THE DARWIN-FOWLER METHOD

It will be worth while to consider how the problem of Sec. 5 can be attacked from the standpoint of Sec. 2. For this purpose we need expressions for N and E analogous to eqs. (71) and (81) in Sec. 5. We also need an expression for the entropy.

We proceed by analogy with the development in Chapter VII. There the sum of all the weights, ΣW, was shown to be equal to the contour integral

$$\Sigma W = \frac{1}{2\pi i}\int_C \frac{Z^N dz}{z^{E+1}},$$

where $Z = \Sigma g_j z^{E_j}$ is the partition function. The expression for the energy in terms of the parameter ζ (later associated with the temperature by $\zeta = e^{-1/kT}$) was obtained by expressing the fact that $Z/z^{E/N}$

has a minimum at $z = \zeta$ on the real axis. This led to eq. (20) of Chapter VII. What is the analogous equation in the case of quantum statistics? In eq. (23) of this chapter the sum of weights is given by the double contour integral

$$\Sigma W = \left(\frac{1}{2\pi i}\right)^2 \int_C \int_{C'} \frac{M \, dx \, dz}{x^{N+1} z^{E+1}}.$$

We expect to find the connection between E and ζ in this case by expressing the fact that $(M/z^E)^{1/N}$ has a minimum at $z = \zeta$ on the real axis. This demands that

$$\frac{\partial}{\partial z}\left(\frac{M^{1/N}}{z^{E/N}}\right) = 0 \quad \text{at } z = \zeta. \tag{97}$$

The differentiation yields

$$E = \zeta \frac{\partial}{\partial \zeta}\left[\log M(\mu, \zeta)\right]. \tag{98}$$

If we introduce from eq. (22) the Fermi-Dirac expression for M, which now takes the form

$$M(\mu, \zeta) = \prod_j (1 + \mu \zeta^{E_j})^{n_j}, \quad \text{(Fermi-Dirac)} \tag{99}$$

the energy expression (98) can be written

$$E_{\text{F-D}} = \zeta \frac{\partial}{\partial \zeta} \sum_j n_j \log(1 + \mu \zeta^{E_j}). \tag{100}$$

The parameter μ is the value of the complex variable x along the real axis where $(M/x^N)^{1/N}$ has a minimum. The condition for this is

$$\frac{\partial}{\partial x}(M/x^N)^{1/N} = 0 \quad \text{at } x = \mu. \tag{101}$$

When the differentiation is performed the result is

$$N_{\text{F-D}} = \mu \frac{\partial}{\partial \mu} \sum_j n_j \log(1 + \mu \zeta^{E_j}), \tag{102}$$

where again we are of course employing the Fermi-Dirac M. The reader will observe that $M(\zeta)$ in (99) is not quite the same M which we used in eq. (22). We have incorporated in it the exponent n_j, the number of cells associated with the energy shell E_j. The reason for this step should be clear from the discussion in Sec. 3 where we compared the Darwin-Fowler distribution formulas with those obtained by the alternative method. The E_j which we are using throughout our present development refers to a whole shell of values and not a single energy state. To it must therefore be attached the weight n_j.

The expressions for E and N in the Bose-Einstein statistics are obtained by the same reasoning as (100) and (102). The only difference is the function M, which is now

$$M(\zeta) = \prod_j \left(\frac{1}{1 - \mu \zeta^{E_j}}\right)^{n_j} \quad \text{(Bose-Einstein)}. \qquad (103)$$

The results are

$$E_{\text{B-E}} = -\zeta \frac{\partial}{\partial \zeta} \sum_j n_j \log(1 - \mu \zeta^{E_j}) , \qquad (104)$$

$$N_{\text{B-E}} = -\mu \frac{\partial}{\partial \mu} \sum_j n_j \log(1 - \mu \zeta^{E_j}). \qquad (105)$$

Let us go back and evaluate (102), using for this purpose the expression for n_j already obtained in (65) and replacing, as usual, the summation over j by an integration over the energy. We also set $\zeta = e^{-1/kT}$. Then (102) becomes

$$N_{\text{F-D}} = \mu \frac{\partial}{\partial \mu} \int_0^\infty \frac{2\pi\tau}{h^3} (2m)^{3/2} \log(1 + \mu e^{-E/kT}) \sqrt{E} \, dE. \qquad (106)$$

Differentiation under the integral sign is here allowed and the result is

$$N_{\text{F-D}} = \frac{2\pi\tau}{h^3} (2m)^{3/2} \int_0^\infty \frac{\sqrt{E} \, dE}{1 + 1/\mu \cdot e^{E/kT}}. \qquad (107)$$

But this is precisely our eq. (71) with $a = +1$ with $1/\mu$ in place of $e^{-\gamma_1}$. In similar fashion

$$E_{\text{F-D}} = \zeta \frac{\partial}{\partial \zeta} \int_0^\infty \frac{2\pi\tau}{h^3} (2m)^{3/2} \log(1 + \mu \zeta^E) \sqrt{E} \, dE.$$

The differentiation leads to

$$E_{\text{F-D}} = \frac{2\pi\tau}{h^3} (2m)^{3/2} \int_0^\infty \frac{E^{3/2} \, dE}{1 + 1/\mu \cdot e^{E/kT}}. \qquad (108)$$

With the transformation $u = E/kT$, this is identical with our previous eq. (81) when $a = +1$.

The reader may proceed to show that similar results are obtained with the Bose-Einstein statistics. It is clear that the straightforward application of the Darwin-Fowler quantum statistical formulas leads to all the results of Secs. 3, 4, and 5. We should, however, examine the entropy. In Chapter VII, (eq. 86), we saw that in the Darwin and Fowler method the entropy is defined as

$$S = k \log \Sigma\, W - k \log N!.$$

This was found in the case of classical statistics to lead to

$$S = kN \log Z(\varsigma) - kE \log \varsigma - k \log N!. \tag{109}$$

What is the corresponding expression in quantum statistics? This will presumably be obtained by replacing the partition function Z by its quantum statistical analogue. Actually to be rigorous one would have to evaluate the multiple contour integral (23) by a generalization of the method of steepest descents used in getting the expression for the similar simple integral $1/2\pi i \cdot \int_C \frac{Z^N}{z^{E+1}}\, dz$ of Chapter VII.

This has been done by Fowler.[12] We shall not repeat it here but merely point out that

$$k \log \left(\frac{1}{2\pi i}\right)^2 \int_C \int_{C'} \frac{M(x, z)dx\, dz}{x^{N+1}z^{E+1}}$$

$$= k \log M(\mu, \varsigma) - kN \log \mu - kE \log \varsigma \tag{110}$$

to the same approximation which led to (109). The reader who has followed through the evaluation of (28) in Chapter VII will see the plausibility of (110) though for the rigorous demonstration Fowler must be consulted. Incidentally (110) shows that the quantum statistical analogue of the partition function Z is

$$Z_{\text{qm}} = \frac{[M(\mu, \varsigma)]^{1/N}}{\mu}. \tag{111}$$

If now we apply (110) to the Fermi-Dirac statistics we get, using (99) and $\mu = e^{\gamma_1}$

$$S = k \sum_j n_j \left(1 + e^{\gamma_1} e^{-E_j/kT}\right) - kN\gamma_1 + \frac{E}{T}, \tag{112}$$

which is exactly eq. (90) with $a = +1$. The reader can proceed to derive the corresponding expression for the entropy on the Bose-Einstein statistics and again obtain agreement with eq. (90), this time with $a = -1$, of course.

[12] "Statistical Mechanics," second edition, pp. 47 ff.

7. FERMI-DIRAC STATISTICS OF A STRONGLY DEGENERATE GAS

We shall now return to the general quantum statistical distribution law (47) and consider the case of Fermi-Dirac statistics ($a = +1$) when γ_1 is positive and e^{γ_1} so large that for a considerable range of values of E_j, we have $1 \gg e^{-\gamma_1} e^{E_j/kT}$. In line with the discussion in Sec. 5 we shall refer to this as a case of strong degeneracy, since it necessarily implies a considerable deviation of N_j/n_j from the classical distribution formula (48).

As before we evaluate e^{γ_1} by utilizing the expression for N in terms of γ_1 and T, i.e., eq. (72). For $a = 1$ this becomes

$$N = \frac{2\pi\tau}{h^3} (2mkT)^{3/2} \int_0^\infty \frac{\sqrt{u}\,du}{1 + e^{-\gamma_1}e^u}. \tag{113}$$

The integral in (113) is a special case of the integral

$$U'(\rho, \gamma_1) = \int_0^\infty \frac{u^\rho du}{1 + e^{-\gamma_1}e^u}, \tag{114}$$

where $\gamma_1 \gg 1$ and ρ is rational and positive. Let us introduce the transformation $\gamma_1 y = -\gamma_1 + u$ and obtain

$$U'(\rho, \gamma_1) = \gamma_1^{\rho+1} \int_{-1}^\infty \frac{(1 + y)^\rho dy}{1 + e^{\gamma_1 y}}. \tag{115}$$

This may further be written

$$U'(\rho,\gamma_1) = \gamma_1^{\rho+1} \left[\int_0^1 \frac{(1 - y)^\rho dy}{1 + e^{-\gamma_1 y}} + \int_0^\infty \frac{(1 + y)^\rho dy}{1 + e^{\gamma_1 y}} \right].$$

The first integral on the right becomes

$$\frac{1}{(\rho + 1)} - \int_0^1 \frac{(1 - y)^\rho dy}{1 + e^{\gamma_1 y}},$$

whence

$$U'(\rho, \gamma_1) = \gamma_1^{\rho+1} \left[\frac{1}{(\rho+1)} - \int_0^1 \frac{(1 - y)^\rho dy}{1 + e^{\gamma_1 y}} + \int_0^\infty \frac{(1 + y)^\rho dy}{1 + e^{\gamma_1 y}} \right]. \tag{116}$$

Now since $\gamma_1 \gg 1$, $1 + e^{\gamma_1 y}$ is so large that the integration from 1 to ∞ adds very little to the value of the second integral in the bracket. Consequently, we can write to a good approximation

$$U'(\rho, \gamma_1) = \gamma_1^{\rho+1} \left[\frac{1}{(\rho + 1)} + \int_0^1 \frac{\{(1 + y)^\rho - (1 - y)^\rho\}}{1 + e^{\gamma_1 y}} dy \right]. \tag{117}$$

Since $y < 1$ we can expand the numerator in the integrand by the ordinary binomial expansion and obtain for the integral

$$2 \int_0^1 \frac{dy}{1 + e^{\gamma_1 y}} \sum_{j=0} \binom{\rho}{2j+1} y^{2j+1}. \tag{118}$$

The binomial coefficients are written in the form $\binom{\rho}{2j+1}$ as in eq. (7), Chapter II. The integral in (118) can further be written as a double sum by the expansion of $1/(1 + e^{\gamma_1 y})$, viz.,

$$2 \sum_{k,j} (-1)^k \binom{\rho}{2j+1} \int_0^1 e^{-(k+1)\gamma_1 y} y^{2j+1} dy. \tag{119}$$

The next step is to let $t = (k+1)\gamma_1 y$, whence the above integral becomes

$$2 \sum_{k,j} (-1)^k \binom{\rho}{2j+1} \int_0^1 \frac{e^{-t} t^{2j+1} dt}{[(k+1)\gamma_1]^{2j+2}}. \tag{120}$$

This suggests the gamma function, save that the integration limits are from 0 to 1. However we again use the fact that γ_1 is very large to assure us that for any j the $\int_1^\infty \frac{e^{-t} t^{2j+1} dt}{[(k+1)\gamma_1]^{2j+2}}$ is negligible compared with the integral in (120). Hence we can safely alter the upper limit in (120) to ∞ and write

$$2 \sum_{k,j} (-1)^k \frac{\binom{\rho}{2j+1}}{[(k+1)\gamma_1]^{2j+2}} \int_0^\infty e^{-t} t^{2j+1} dt$$

$$= 2 \sum_{k,j} (-1)^k \frac{\binom{\rho}{2j+1}}{[(k+1)\gamma_1]^{2j+2}} \Gamma(2j+2). \tag{121}$$

Finally we have for $U'(\rho, \gamma_1)$

$$U'(\rho, \gamma_1) = \gamma_1^{\rho+1} \left[1/(\rho+1) + 2 \sum_{j=0} \frac{c_{2j+2} \binom{\rho}{2j+1} \Gamma(2j+2)}{\gamma_1^{2j+2}} \right], \tag{122}$$

where we have set

$$\sum_k \frac{(-1)^k}{(k+1)^{2j+2}} = c_{2j+2}. \tag{123}$$

Using (122) in connection with (113) enables us to write

$$N = \frac{2\pi\tau}{h^3} (2mkT)^{3/2} \cdot \gamma_1^{3/2} \left[\frac{2}{3} + 2 \sum_{j=0} \frac{c_{2j+2} \binom{1/2}{2j+1} \Gamma(2j+2)}{\gamma_1^{2j+2}} \right]. \tag{124}$$

For most applications it will be sufficient to confine our attention to the first term in the summation in the bracket in (124) and write

$$N = \frac{2\pi\tau}{h^3} (2mkT)^{3/2} \gamma_1^{3/2} \left[\frac{2}{3} + \frac{c_2}{\gamma_1^2} \right]. \tag{125}$$

Now

$$c_2 = \sum_k \frac{(-1)^k}{(k+1)^2} = 1 - \frac{1}{2^2} + \frac{1}{3^2} - \frac{1}{4^2} \cdots = \frac{\pi^2}{12}. \tag{126}$$

Consequently to this approximation, the equation connecting N and γ_1 becomes

$$N = \frac{4\pi\tau}{3h^3} (2mkT)^{3/2} \gamma_1^{3/2} [1 + \pi^2/8\gamma_1^2]. \tag{127}$$

Recalling that $\gamma_1 \gg 1$, the first approximation to γ_1 from (127) is

$$\gamma_1 = \left(\frac{3N}{4\pi\tau} \right)^{2/3} \frac{h^2}{2mkT}. \tag{128}$$

The second approximation proves to be

$$\gamma_1 = \left(\frac{3N}{4\pi\tau} \right)^{2/3} \cdot \frac{h^2}{2mkT} \left[1 - \left(\frac{3N}{4\pi\tau} \right)^{-4/3} \cdot \frac{(2\pi mkT)^2}{12h^4} \right]. \tag{129}$$

The total energy is given by eq. (81) with $a = 1$. In terms of the general integral $U'(\rho, \gamma_1)$ in (114) it is given by

$$E = \frac{2\pi\tau}{h^3} \cdot kT \cdot (2mkT)^{3/2} U'(3/2, \gamma_1). \tag{130}$$

To the same order of approximation as that used in eq. (127) the result is

$$E = \frac{4\pi\tau kT}{5h^3} (2mkT)^{3/2} \gamma_1^{5/2} [1 + 5\pi^2/8\gamma_1^2]. \tag{131}$$

On dividing (131) by (127) and using the second approximation for γ_1, i.e., (129), the energy may be expressed in the form

$$E = \frac{3}{10} \frac{Nh^2}{m} \left(\frac{3N}{4\pi\tau} \right)^{2/3} \left[1 + \frac{5\pi^2 m^2 k^2}{3h^4} \left(\frac{3N}{4\pi\tau} \right)^{-4/3} T^2 + \cdots \right]. \tag{132}$$

The interesting difference between this result and that for an ideal gas on classical statistics is at once apparent. In the latter case we have simply $E = 3/2 \cdot NkT$, and as T approaches zero, E also approaches zero. For a strongly degenerate gas, on the other hand, the energy approaches a non-vanishing value at the absolute zero. This is known as the *zero-point energy* of the gas. Its value is

$$E_0 = \frac{3}{10} \frac{Nh^2}{m} \left(\frac{3N}{4\pi\tau}\right)^{\frac{2}{3}}.$$ (133)

The form of E in its dependence on T in (132) is also very different from that for a weakly degenerate gas, given in eq. (87). Of course, we cannot let $T \to 0$ in (87) because the approximation which enables us to write (87) no longer holds for very small T.

The existence of the zero-point energy is of sufficient importance for us to look upon it from another point of view. Of all the cells in the phase space associated with the gas only one can correspond to the energy value zero. On the Fermi-Dirac statistics there can not be more than one particle in this cell, if it is a particle without a spin. As we have seen in the discussion at the end of Sec. 4, there may be two electrons of opposite spin in each cell. For the moment, however, we confine our attention to ordinary gas molecules. Now at the absolute zero of temperature we should expect to find all the particles in the lowest energy states, i.e., all cells filled up to a certain maximum energy value. Consequently the total energy in this situation cannot vanish. This crowding of the particles into the lower energy states at $T = 0$ is another physical interpretation of the degeneracy of the gas. At $T = 0$ the degeneracy is complete. As the temperature rises some of the particles leave the lower energy states and are transferred to higher states; the degeneracy decreases. When the distribution of particles with respect to energy has become Maxwellian the degeneracy has effectively disappeared and the gas is classical.

The ideas of the previous paragraph can be used to give an alternative calculation of the zero-point energy. We recall from Sec. 4, eq. (65) that the number of energy values for an aggregate of free particles lying between E_j and $E_j + dE_j$ is

$$\frac{2\pi\tau}{h^3} (2m)^{\frac{3}{2}} \sqrt{E_j}\, dE_j.$$

If *all* energy levels from zero to some upper limit E_{max} are each occupied by a single particle and the total number of particles is N, the maximum energy value is given by

$$\frac{2\pi\tau}{h^3} (2m)^{\frac{3}{2}} \int_0^{E_{max}} \sqrt{E}\, dE = N.$$ (134)

The integration yields

$$E_{max} = \frac{h^2}{2m}\left(\frac{3N}{4\pi\tau}\right)^{2/3}.$$ (135)

The *total* energy of the whole degenerate assembly then becomes

$$E_0 = \frac{2\pi\tau}{h^3}(2m)^{3/2}\int_0^{E_{max}} E^{3/2}dE$$

$$= \frac{3}{10}\frac{Nh^2}{m}\left(\frac{3N}{4\pi\tau}\right)^{2/3},$$ (136)

in precise agreement with the value given in (133) and computed from (132).

We can also calculate the entropy for a degenerate Fermi-Dirac gas. We have already noted that eq. (91) is general and does not depend on the degree of degeneracy. Substitution of γ_1 from (129) and E from (132) into (91) yields

$$S = \frac{\pi^2 k^2 NmT}{h^2}\left(\frac{3N}{4\pi\tau}\right)^{-2/3} + \text{ terms involving higher powers of } T. \quad (137)$$

As $T \to 0$, it follows that $S \to 0$ and the entropy of a strongly degenerate gas vanishes at absolute zero.

The remarks immediately above about the physical interpretation of statistical degeneracy gain even more significance from a plot of N_j/n_j as a function of velocity magnitude. For the non-degenerate

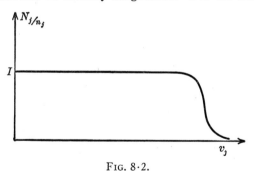

FIG. 8·2.

gas (eq. 48) this, of course, is just the probability curve already shown in Fig. 2·1 of Chapter II. The corresponding plot for a strongly degenerate Fermi-Dirac gas is given in Fig. 8·2. For a very considerable range of values of the velocity v_j from zero up, N_j/n_j remains practically constant at the value unity, indicating that all the lowest energy cells are occupied, each with its single allowed particle. As the higher velocities are approached, however, N_j/n_j drops more or less rapidly to zero, the rate of fall depending on the actual value of γ_1 and therefore largely on the temperature. In this part of the curve the classical Maxwellian distribution is simulated to a certain extent. The value of the velocity at which $N_j/n_j = \frac{1}{2}$, i.e., half the cells are occupied on the average, is

$$v_0 = \sqrt{\frac{2kT\gamma_1}{m}}, \tag{138}$$

wherein we must use the value of γ_1 given in (128) or (129). The result of the substitution from (128) is

$$v_0 = \frac{h}{m}\left(\frac{3N}{4\pi\tau}\right)^{\frac{1}{3}}. \tag{139}$$

The *average* energy per particle at $T = 0$ is, from (136),

$$\frac{E_0}{N} = \frac{3}{10} \cdot \frac{h^2}{m}\left(\frac{3N}{4\pi\tau}\right)^{\frac{2}{3}}. \tag{140}$$

This leads to a root-mean-square velocity at absolute zero of

$$v_m = \sqrt{\tfrac{3}{5}}\, v_0. \tag{141}$$

8. FERMI-DIRAC STATISTICS OF A DEGENERATE ELECTRON GAS

In the preceding sections we have not specialized the assembly of free particles to which the quantum statistical distribution formulas have been applied, save in so far as we have assumed them to be particles without spin. In the present section we shall consider specifically an electron gas in which the mutual interactions are neglected. To make the problem more specific we shall assume that the number of electrons per cm^3 is of the same order of magnitude as the Loschmidt number for an ideal gas. For example the gas might consist of the (hypothetical) free electrons in a metal in which on the average at room temperature there is one free electron per metallic atom. This will indeed form an interesting and important application of the theory of this section. The first thing we must note in the present discussion is that N_j in eq. (66) must now be multiplied by 2 in order to take account of the electron spin. This factor will follow through all the significant formulas. The easiest way to take care of its introduction is to replace τ by 2τ wherever it occurs.

The next question to settle is this: Is the assembly of electrons degenerate or non-degenerate at room temperature? Going back to eq. (77), we recall that if $e^{-\alpha} = e^{\gamma_1}$ (b is equal to unity, of course) is very small compared with unity, the degeneracy is extremely weak. This is true for actual gases over a wide range of temperatures. For the electron gas, however, such as we might expect to find in the metal silver with one free electron per atom, substitution of $m = 9 \times 10^{-28}$ gram, $N/\tau = 5.9 \times 10^{22}$, $T = 300°$ K, into

$$e^{-\alpha} = \frac{h^3 N}{2\tau(2\pi mkT)^{\frac{3}{2}}},$$

gives $e^{-\alpha}$ of the order of 2,330, which is far from being small. Evidently for such an assembly even at very *high* temperatures $e^{-\alpha}$ will still be much greater than unity, indicating that below temperatures of the order of 10,000° K, an electron gas of the kind considered will be strongly degenerate and must be treated by the appropriate form of the Fermi-Dirac statistics. The formulas (129) and (132) are the ones we must apply.

It is interesting to calculate the specific heat of such a degenerate electron gas. The specific heat per electron at constant volume is from (132)

$$\frac{1}{N}\frac{dE}{dT} = \frac{\pi^2 mk^2}{h^2}\left(\frac{3N}{8\pi\tau}\right)^{-\frac{2}{3}} T. \tag{142}$$

Per gram atom we have for the heat capacity

$$C_v = \frac{L\pi^2 mk^2}{h^2}\left(\frac{3N}{8\pi\tau}\right)^{-\frac{2}{3}} T = \frac{R\pi^2 mk}{h^2}\left(\frac{3N}{8\pi\tau}\right)^{-\frac{2}{3}} T, \tag{143}$$

where L is the Avogadro number and R the gas constant per gram atom. If now we compute the right-hand side of (143) for $T = 300°$ K for the case of silver, already mentioned, we get approximately

$$C_v = 2.4 \times 10^{-2} R.$$

The interesting thing about this result is that the classical equipartition principle when applied to an electron gas gives $C_v = 3R/2$, independently of the temperature, which is a much larger value than that above at room temperature. If we are considering an electron gas in a metal with approximately one free electron per metal atom, the contribution of the free electrons to the specific heat of the metal at room temperature is therefore relatively very small. Practically all the observed specific heat is due to the atoms themselves. This solves a fundamental difficulty that has always plagued the classical electron theory of metals. This difficulty was the one of allowing enough free electrons to account for the observed electrical properties of metals and at the same time keeping the specific heat down to the experimentally observed value which at ordinary temperatures is given very closely by $C_v = 3R$ (law of Dulong and Petit. Cf. Chapter IX, Sec. 3). In the classical theory the two requirements seemed quite irreconcilable. Quantum statistics appears to solve the problem very nicely.

9. BOSE-EINSTEIN STATISTICS OF A STRONGLY DEGENERATE GAS

We have discussed weak degeneracy from the standpoint of both types of quantum statistics and strong degeneracy from the standpoint of the Fermi-Dirac statistics. What constitutes strong degeneracy in the Bose-Einstein statistics? The fundamental distribution formula for the latter type is

$$N_j = \frac{4\pi m\tau / h^3 \cdot \sqrt{2mE_j}\, dE_j}{e^{-\gamma_1} e^{E_j/kT} - 1}. \tag{144}$$

For weak degeneracy γ_1 is negative so that $e^{-\gamma_1} > 1$ and the first term in the denominator outweighs the unity even for small values of E_j. For strong degeneracy in the Fermi-Dirac statistics $e^{-\gamma_1} \ll 1$. Evidently such a situation is meaningless in the Bose-Einstein case as it would lead to negative values of N_j for a considerable range of values of E_j. Consequently we are led to the conclusion that the strongest degeneracy, i.e., the greatest deviation from classical statistics, possible for a Bose-Einstein gas corresponds to $e^{-\gamma_1} = 1$ or $\gamma_1 = 0$. This has some interesting consequences. In the first place, the total number of particles in such a strongly degenerate Bose-Einstein gas is, from eq. (76)

$$N = \frac{\tau}{h^3} (2\pi mkT)^{3/2} \cdot \sum_{n=1}^{\infty} \frac{1}{n^{3/2}} = \frac{2.61\tau}{h^3} (2\pi mkT)^{3/2}, \tag{145}$$

where the factor 2.61 is an approximation to the summation indicated. For a given volume of such a gas with a given number of particles, eq. (145) prescribes the temperature at which complete degeneracy is attained. A glance at (76) shows that if the gas were slightly less degenerate, i.e., $e^{-\alpha} < 1$ slightly, N would become smaller. By no change can it become larger than the value given in (145). Consequently we can make the statement that for a degenerate Bose-

Einstein gas the number of particles per unit volume has an *upper* limit which at temperature T is

$$\frac{N}{\tau} = \frac{2.61}{h^3} (2\pi m k T)^{3/2}. \qquad (146)$$

This corresponds to a maximum equilibrium density for any particular temperature, a situation very different from that holding for an ideal gas. Any larger density than that given by (146) will necessarily correspond to a non-equilibrium state.

We can evaluate the energy for the case of complete degeneracy by reverting to eq. (81) and computing E for $\gamma_1 = 0$. The result is given by (82) with $\alpha = 0$ and the choice of the lower sign throughout. Thus

$$E = \frac{3\tau}{2h^3} \cdot (2\pi m)^{3/2} (kT)^{5/2} \cdot \sum_{n=1}^{\infty} \frac{1}{n^{5/2}}. \qquad (147)$$

Since $\sum_{n=1}^{\infty} 1/n^{5/2} = 1.34$ approximately, the expression for E takes the approximate form

$$E = \frac{2.01\tau}{h^3} \cdot (2\pi m)^{3/2} (kT)^{5/2}. \qquad (147')$$

The equation of state in the completely degenerate condition can now be found at once from eq. (94). It is

$$p = 1.34 \frac{(2\pi m)^{3/2}}{h^3} (kT)^{5/2}. \qquad (148)$$

In other words, the pressure is dependent on the temperature alone. This is, however, the situation one encounters in the pressure of saturated vapor and suggests that the strongly degenerate Bose-Einstein gas behaves like a gas below its critical point, so that when the temperature is reduced to a low enough value a certain kind of "condensation" takes place, removing from the higher energy states a certain number of particles and transferring them to the *lowest* energy state where they make no contribution to the pressure of the gas, a possible effect in the Bose-Einstein statistics that is of course not present in the Fermi-Dirac statistics. This "condensation" phenomenon has been studied in detail by F. London [13] and possible applications discussed, particularly to the interesting properties of liquid helium near its transition point at 2.19° K.

[13] F. London, *Phys. Rev.* **54**, 947 (1938).

Equation (147') cannot be used to derive the expression for the specific heat at constant volume. For this purpose we must use the closed form expressions (72) and (81). From (81) we have

$$\left(\frac{\partial E}{\partial T}\right)_\tau = \frac{5}{2} \cdot \frac{E}{T} + \frac{2\pi\tau}{h^3} (2\pi m)^{3/2}(kT)^{5/2}\left(\frac{\partial \gamma_1}{\partial T}\right)_\tau \cdot \int_0^\infty \frac{u^{3/2}e^{u-\gamma_1}}{(e^{-\gamma_1+u}-1)^2}\,du \quad (149)$$

where the integral certainly remains finite as $\gamma_1 \to 0$. The factor $\left(\frac{\partial \gamma_1}{\partial T}\right)_\tau$ can be evaluated by differentiating eq. (72) (with $a = -1$) with respect to T. We obtain after conducting a partial integration

$$\left(\frac{\partial \gamma_1}{\partial T}\right)_\tau = -\frac{3N/2T}{\dfrac{\pi\tau}{h^3}(2mkT)^{3/2}\displaystyle\int_0^\infty \frac{u^{-1/2}}{e^{u-\gamma_1}-1}\,du} \cdot \quad (150)$$

However, as $\gamma_1 \to 0$ the integral in the denominator approaches infinity and hence in the completely degenerate state the specific heat is given by

$$C_v = \left(\frac{\partial E}{\partial T}\right)_\tau = \frac{5}{2}\frac{E}{T}. \quad (151)$$

From (146) combined with (147') we then obtain the approximate result

$$C_v = 1.9R. \quad (152)$$

10. STATISTICS OF A PHOTON GAS. RADIATION LAW

Perhaps the most interesting application of the Bose-Einstein statistics of a strongly degenerate gas lies in the field of radiation. Let us consider a radiation field in physical volume τ to be equivalent to a collection of light particles or photons corresponding to a wide range of frequencies. With a photon of frequency v is associated energy hv and momentum hv/c, where c is the velocity of light in free space. We desire the distribution formula for the photons with respect to frequency, i.e., for a radiation field in the equilibrium state corresponding to temperature T, the average number of photons with frequency lying in the range from v to $v + dv$. We shall assume that the photon gas is effectively a collection of free particles obeying the Bose-Einstein statistics and in a state of strong degeneracy at all temperatures.

Obviously we cannot apply directly the distribution formula (144) with $\gamma_1 = 0$, since there is no meaning attached to the mass of a photon.

However, we can rewrite (144) in terms of the momentum p_j in place of energy in the numerator and so get rid of m. For a free particle we have at once

$$E_j = \frac{p_j^2}{2m}.$$

Consequently the distribution with respect to momentum (with $\gamma_1 = 0$) [14] becomes

$$N_j = \frac{4\pi\tau}{h^3} \cdot \frac{p_j^2 dp_j}{e^{E_j/kT} - 1}. \tag{153}$$

If now we set $p_j = h\nu_j/c$ and $E_j = h\nu_j$, the above expression becomes

$$N_j = \frac{4\pi\tau}{c^3} \cdot \frac{\nu_j^2 d\nu_j}{e^{h\nu_j/kT} - 1}. \tag{154}$$

Let us make the further assumption that the photons, like electrons, possess a spin. This effectively doubles the number N_j (cf. the corresponding situation in the case of electrons which we take account of by multiplying τ by 2 wherever it occurs). When we leave off sub-subscripts and denote by dN the number of photons in the frequency range from ν to $\nu + d\nu$, we have for the average number of photons per unit physical volume in the range mentioned

$$\frac{dN}{\tau} = \frac{8\pi\nu^2 d\nu}{c^3(e^{h\nu/kT} - 1)}. \tag{155}$$

Since each of these photons has energy $h\nu$, the average energy density in the radiation field for frequency ν becomes

$$dE_\nu = \frac{8\pi h\nu^3 d\nu}{c^3(e^{h\nu/kT} - 1)}. \tag{156}$$

This is the radiation law of Planck which has been found to be in substantial agreement with experimental observations. Its derivation confirms that a photon gas may be considered to behave like a strongly degenerate Bose-Einstein gas.

For very low frequencies or high temperatures (156) can be very accurately approximated by

$$dE_\nu = \frac{8\pi kT\nu^2 d\nu}{c^3} \tag{157}$$

[14] It should be stated that in the case of a photon gas $\gamma_1 = 0$ follows at once from the simple fact that the number of particles is not fixed and hence the condition $\Sigma\delta N_j = 0$ has no longer a meaning. The parameter γ_1 then really does not enter the problem.

or in terms of wavelength interval ($\lambda = c/\nu$)

$$dE_\lambda = \frac{8\pi kT d\lambda}{\lambda^4}. \tag{158}$$

Equations (157–158) are equivalent to the Rayleigh-Jeans law, which describes the distribution of energy in a radiation field rather accurately for long wavelengths. On the other hand for high frequencies or low temperatures (156) takes the approximate form

$$dE_\nu = \frac{8\pi h\nu^3}{c^3} \cdot e^{-h\nu/kT} d\nu, \tag{159}$$

the well-known distribution formula of Wien.

From the historical point of view it is interesting to recall that Bose's original deduction of Planck's radiation law was the starting point of quantum statistics. This is reason enough for reviewing Bose's method [15] here, even though it is, of course, somewhat off the track of the systematic development of this chapter.

In considering the distribution of objects in boxes or cells let us for the moment focus our attention on the cells rather than the objects. Thus of a total of Q cells we let Q_0 be the number which contain zero objects; Q_1, the number containing one object; $\cdots$ Q_j, the number with j objects, etc., with

$$\sum_{j=0}^{N} Q_j = Q, \tag{160}$$

where N is the maximum number of objects per cell. The number of ways of selecting the Q cells so that Q_0 contain no objects, Q_1 one object, etc., is

$$\Pi = \frac{Q!}{Q_0! Q_1! \cdots Q_N!}. \tag{161}$$

We now proceed to make Π a maximum subject to the conditions that

$$\sum_{j=0}^{N} E_j Q_j = E = \text{total energy} = \text{constant},$$

$$\sum_{j=0}^{N} Q_j = Q = \text{total number of cells} = \text{constant}. \tag{162}$$

Here E_j must now mean the energy associated with the cell which contains j particles. Proceeding as usual in the case of a canonical

[15] Z. Physik, **26**, 178 (1924); **27**, 384 (1924).

distribution (Sec. 2, Chapter IV) and calling the parameter $\Theta = kT$, we find

$$Q_j = \frac{Qe^{-E_j/kT}}{\sum\limits_{j=0}^{N} e^{-E_j/kT}}. \tag{163}$$

The average energy per cell appears as

$$\overline{E} = \frac{E}{Q} = \frac{\sum\limits_{j=0}^{N} E_j Q_j}{\sum\limits_{j=0}^{N} Q_j}. \tag{164}$$

Now if the particles being distributed in the cells are photons we must assume that

$$E_j = jh\nu. \tag{165}$$

Hence

$$\overline{E} = \frac{\sum\limits_{j=0}^{N} jh\nu e^{-jh\nu/kT}}{\sum\limits_{j=0}^{N} e^{-jh\nu/kT}}. \tag{166}$$

But

$$\sum\limits_{j=0}^{\infty} e^{-jh\nu/kT} = \frac{1}{1 - e^{-h\nu/kT}}, \tag{167}$$

and if the maximum number of photons per cell is large, as we have reason to suppose will be the case, we can replace the finite sum in the denominator of (166) by the infinite sum in (167). If we differentiate (167) with respect to T, the result is

$$\frac{1}{kT^2} \cdot \sum\limits_{j=0}^{\infty} jh\nu e^{-jh\nu/kT} = -\frac{h\nu/kT^2 \cdot e^{-h\nu/kT}}{(1 - e^{-h\nu/kT})^2}$$

from which (166) can be written in the form

$$\overline{E} = \frac{h\nu}{e^{h\nu/kT} - 1}. \tag{168}$$

If the photons are considered to form a gas of free particles in a volume τ with momentum values $h\nu/c$, the average number of them in the energy interval $h\nu$ to $h\nu + d(h\nu)$ will be, from Sec. 4,

$$\frac{8\pi\tau\nu^2 d\nu}{c^3}. \tag{169}$$

We have here assigned *two* photons to each energy value. Since the average energy per photon in this range is given by (168) it follows that the average energy density of the radiation in the frequency range from ν to $\nu + d\nu$ is given by (156), i.e., the Planck law again.

11. APPLICATION OF QUANTUM STATISTICS TO ATOMIC STRUCTURE

One of the most striking applications of quantum statistics is the determination of the average distribution of charge in an atom. It will be recalled that in the nuclear atom model an atom is assumed to consist of a nucleus with a positive charge and most of the mass of the atom surrounded by an aggregate of electrons equal in number (for the neutral atom) to the charge on the nucleus. It is the problem of atomic structure to determine the possible energy values of such a system as well as the average distribution of charge considered as effectively continuous. The solution also provides the potential field in the neighborhood of the atom, which is important in many applications of atomic structure. The complete formal solution is indeed possible only occasionally, i.e., when there is but a single electron, e.g., hydrogen, ionized helium. Various approximation methods have been devised to solve the problem for polyelectronic atoms. One of the most interesting of these was proposed by Fermi,[16] and independently by Thomas.[17] Their assumption is, in effect, that the electrons in a polyelectronic atom behave as a degenerate gas obeying the Fermi-Dirac statistics. If we assume that the electrons in an atom occupy a sphere of radius approximately 10^{-8} cm, the density of the electron distribution will vary from 10^{24} to 10^{26} per cm^3. From the considerations of Sec. 8 of this chapter, we see that such a gas will indeed be degenerate for all ordinary temperatures.

The problem now in question differs from that previously discussed in Secs. 7 and 8 in one important respect, namely that whereas there we considered the electrons in the gas as being free and therefore possessing only kinetic energy or at most existing in a field of constant potential, we must now think of them as moving in a variable field and for this reason as possessing, in addition to kinetic energy, potential energy varying from point to point. It will be seen, however, that the only effect of this is to make the velocity distribution a function of position in space. In fact we can use the ordinary Fermi distribution law (eq. 47) with $a = + 1$ merely by incorporating with the energy E_j the added potential energy $-eV$, where V is the potential of the field

---

[16] *Z. Physik*, **48**, 73 (1928); **49**, 550 (1928).
[17] *Proc. Cambridge Phil. Soc.* **23**, 542 (1927).

and a function of x, y, z. Thus we can now write for the number of electrons having total momentum lying in the interval $(p, p + dp)$ at the point (x, y, z)

$$dN = \frac{8\pi\tau}{h^3} \cdot \frac{p^2 dp}{1 + e^{-\gamma_1 - eV/kT} e^{p^2/2mkT}}. \tag{170}$$

This follows readily from eq. (66) with the appropriate representation of E_j in terms of momentum. Strictly speaking it is necessary to generalize the derivation of n_j in Sec. 4 to include the constant potential energy term. When this is done, eq. (170) follows. The total number of electrons per unit volume at (x, y, z) then becomes (using the first approximation for N in eq. (127) with τ replaced by 2τ to take care of the spin and γ_1 replaced by $\gamma_1 + eV/kT$)

$$n = \frac{N}{\tau} = \frac{8}{3\sqrt{\pi} h^3}(2\pi mkT)^{3/2}\left(\gamma_1 + \frac{eV}{kT}\right)^{3/2}. \tag{171}$$

It is now found convenient to set

$$v = V + \frac{kT\gamma_1}{e}, \tag{172}$$

where v thus appears as the potential of the atomic field expressed to an arbitrary additive constant $kT\gamma_1/e$. Equation (171) then becomes

$$n = \frac{8}{3\sqrt{\pi} h^3} \cdot (2\pi me)^{3/2} v^{3/2}. \tag{173}$$

The equivalent charge density, which we shall designate by ρ, is equal to $-ne$. If we treat this as a continuous static distribution, it must satisfy Poisson's equation, viz.,

$$\nabla^2 v = -4\pi\rho = \frac{32\sqrt{\pi}}{3h^3}(2\pi me)^{3/2} ev^{3/2}. \tag{174}$$

As a first approximation we shall take the distribution to be spherically symmetrical, so that v is a function of r only, where r is the distance from the nucleus. Then

$$\nabla^2 v = \frac{d^2 v}{dr^2} + \frac{2}{r}\frac{dv}{dr} = Cv^{3/2}, \tag{175}$$

with

$$C = \frac{32\sqrt{\pi}}{3h^3}(2\pi m)^{3/2} e^{5/2}.$$

The solution of (175) must be found subject to the boundary conditions

$$\lim_{r \to 0} rv = Ze; \quad \int n d\tau = Z, \tag{176}$$

where Z is the number of positive charges on the nucleus, i.e., the atomic number, and the integration is to be extended over all space. The first of the above conditions expresses the fact that when an electron is very close to the nucleus its potential is practically that due to the nucleus alone. The second condition expresses the fact that the total charge in the distribution corresponds to Z electrons, for the neutral atom. This will obviously not hold for an ionized atom, but the necessary alteration is fairly obvious and introduces no fundamental change in principle.

Equation (175) may be considerably simplified by the substitutions $x = r/(Ze)^{-\frac{1}{3}}C^{-\frac{2}{3}}$ and $\xi = v/(Ze)^{\frac{4}{3}}C^{\frac{2}{3}}$. The equation then becomes

$$\frac{d^2\xi}{dx^2} + \frac{2}{x}\frac{d\xi}{dx} = \xi^{\frac{3}{2}},$$ (177)

subject to the boundary conditions

$$\lim_{x \to 0} x\xi = 1, \quad \int_0^\infty \xi^{\frac{3}{2}}x^2 dx = 1.$$ (178)

Finally we set $\phi(x) = x\xi$ and reduce (177) to an equation without the first order term, viz.,

$$\frac{d^2\phi}{dx^2} = \frac{\phi^{\frac{3}{2}}}{\sqrt{x}}.$$ (179)

The boundary conditions (178) take the final form

$$\lim_{x \to 0} \phi(x) = 1, \quad \lim_{x \to \infty} \phi(x) = 0, \quad \int_0^\infty \sqrt{x}\,\phi^{\frac{3}{2}}dx = 1.$$ (180)

Eq. (179) has been solved numerically by Fermi and the solution is tabulated in the accompanying table.

TABLE OF VALUES OF $\phi(x)$ IN (179)

x	$\phi(x)$	x	$\phi(x)$	x	$\phi(x)$
0.0	1.000	1.5	0.315	10.0	0.024
0.1	0.882	2.0	0.244	11.0	0.020
0.2	0.793	2.5	0.194	12.0	0.017
0.3	0.721	3.0	0.157	13.0	0.014
0.4	0.660	3.5	0.130	14.0	0.012
0.5	0.607	4.0	0.108	15.0	0.011
0.6	0.562	5.0	0.079	16.0	0.009
0.7	0.521	6.0	0.059	17.0	0.008
0.8	0.485	7.0	0.046	18.0	0.007
0.9	0.453	8.0	0.037	19.0	0.006
1.0	0.425	9.0	0.029	20.0	0.005

We can use this solution to obtain the potential v and the charge density ρ. Thus

$$v = Ze/r \cdot \phi \left[\frac{r}{(Ze)^{-\frac{1}{3}} C^{-\frac{2}{3}}} \right], \tag{181}$$

and

$$\rho = ne = \frac{C}{4} \cdot \frac{(Ze)^{\frac{3}{2}}}{r^{\frac{3}{2}}} \cdot \phi^{\frac{3}{2}}. \tag{182}$$

This solves the problem of the statistical charge distribution in the atom. We should expect the resulting potential field to be a fair approximation to the actual field, and indeed one which improves as the number of electrons increases. As a matter of fact the approximation is found to be a very good one for all atoms, except in the outer regions of the electron distribution. It is a very useful approximation in various applications of atomic structure, particularly those encountered in the structure of metallic crystal lattices.

PROBLEMS

1. In a cube of gold, 1 cm on a side, assume that the number of free electrons is equal to the number of atoms. Calculate a few energy values for the electrons for small values of n_1, n_2, n_3 in eq. (59) and do the same for some larger values of these integers, e.g., of the order of magnitude of 10^2. Compare the spacing of successive energy levels in both cases.

2. If the free electrons of the cube of gold in Problem 1 form a degenerate gas at absolute zero with all energy levels filled, calculate the maximum kinetic energy. Also calculate the total kinetic energy of the electrons.

3. Calculate the total energy of one mole of oxygen at its critical temperature, treating it as a Bose-Einstein gas.

4. At what temperature (order of magnitude) does the electron gas in metallic gold cease to be degenerate?

5. Prove that the number of combinations of n_j objects N_j at a time with all possible repetitions allowed is equal to the number of combinations of $n_j + N_j - 1$ objects N_j at a time *without* repetitions. Hence derive the Bose-Einstein statistical probability (41'').

6. Show that the isothermal compressibility of an ideal gas is equal to the reciprocal of the pressure. Find the expressions for the isothermal compressibility of a weakly degenerate Bose-Einstein and a weakly degenerate Fermi-Dirac gas.

7. Use eq. (94) to find the approximate equation of state of a strongly degenerate Fermi-Dirac gas. Compare the isothermal compressibility with that of a weakly degenerate Fermi-Dirac gas.

8. Derive the expression for the entropy of a strongly degenerate Fermi-Dirac gas out to terms of the order T^2.

9. At what temperature does the atomic heat capacity of the strongly degenerate electron gas in metallic silver become equal to the value predicted by the classical equipartition principle?

10. Compute in tabular form the Fermi-Thomas statistical charge distribution in the neutral sodium atom in its normal state.

CHAPTER IX

SPECIFIC HEATS OF GASES AND SOLIDS

1. SPECIFIC HEATS OF AN IDEAL MONATOMIC GAS

The two specific heats at constant volume and constant pressure constitute important characteristics of a gas. In this chapter we discuss in systematic fashion their theoretical evaluation for certain types of aggregates. They have already been defined in Sec. 4, Chapter III and discussed in preliminary fashion in Sec. 2, Chapter V. If the average total energy of the aggregate is E and its total mass is M, the specific heat at constant volume is

$$c_V = \frac{1}{M}\left(\frac{\partial E}{\partial T}\right)_V,\tag{1}$$

and that at constant pressure is

$$c_p = \frac{1}{M}\left(\frac{\partial E}{\partial T}\right)_p + \frac{p}{M}\left(\frac{\partial V}{\partial T}\right)_p.\tag{2}$$

In this section we shall be concerned with an ideal monatomic gas consisting of N free mass particles of mass m and each possessing three degrees of freedom. We shall follow the Darwin-Fowler method in our discussion and use the energy expressions obtained in Chapter VII and Chapter VIII. For a classical ideal gas, we have

$$E = N\zeta \frac{\partial}{\partial \zeta} \log Z(\zeta),\tag{3}$$

where $Z(\zeta)$ is the partition function

$$Z(\zeta) = \sum_j g_j \zeta^{E_j},\tag{3'}$$

and $\zeta = e^{-1/kT}$. The E_j in the sum are the possible energy values of any particle in the aggregate. If we transform from ζ to T, (3) becomes

$$E = NkT^2 \frac{\partial}{\partial T} \log Z(T),\tag{4}$$

and the specific heat at constant volume is

$$c_V = \frac{k}{m} \frac{\partial}{\partial T} \left[T^2 \frac{\partial}{\partial T} \log Z(T) \right]_V. \tag{5}$$

From eq. (100) of Chapter VIII we can write the corresponding expression for an ideal gas obeying the Fermi-Dirac statistics as [1]

$$(c_V)_{\text{F-D}} = \frac{k}{Nm} \frac{\partial}{\partial T} \left[T^2 \frac{\partial}{\partial T} \sum_j n_j \log (1 + \mu e^{-E_j/kT}) \right]_V. \tag{6}$$

The corresponding specific heat at constant volume for a Bose-Einstein ideal gas (from 104 of Chapter VIII)

$$(c_V)_{\text{B-E}} = -\frac{k}{Nm} \frac{\partial}{\partial T} \left[T^2 \frac{\partial}{\partial T} \sum_j n_j \log (1 - \mu e^{-E_j/kT}) \right]_V. \tag{7}$$

We have already used (6) or its equivalent in evaluating the specific heat of a degenerate electron gas (Sec. 8, Chapter VIII, eq. 142). We have also seen that for an actual gas composed of neutral molecules for which the Bose-Einstein statistics is indicated, the modification due to the use of the former in place of classical statistics is so small under normal conditions as to be negligible. Consequently in what follows we shall use the classical statistical formula (5) for specific heat calculations.

The problem reduces essentially to the determination of the partition function $Z(T)$ given in the classical statistics by (3′). For an ideal gas this is given by eq. (77) of Chapter VII. We write it again for convenience,[2] expressing it as a function of T.

$$Z(T) = \frac{V}{h^3} (2\pi m k T)^{3/2}. \tag{8}$$

The application of (5) yields at once the familiar result

$$c_V = \frac{3}{2} \frac{k}{m}, \tag{9}$$

and the associated value of c_p also follows directly.

2. THE IDEAL DIATOMIC GAS

The ideal diatomic gas consists of an aggregate of freely moving molecules, each of which is composed of two similar atoms. The

---

[1] It should perhaps be stressed that in (6) and (7) only the differentiation of the bracket is to be conducted at constant volume.

[2] In this chapter we use V for volume.

determination of the allowed energy values of a diatomic molecule is a problem in quantum mechanics which we shall not work out here. We merely remind the reader that the energy of such a molecule is made up of three parts, viz., (a) energy of translation of the center of mass, (b) energy of rotation, and (c) energy of vibration. The possible energy values for translation have been worked out in Sec. 4, Chapter VIII and are

$$E_t = \frac{h^2}{8m}\left(\frac{n_1^2}{l_1^2} + \frac{n_2^2}{l_2^2} + \frac{n_3^2}{l_3^2}\right).$$

If we simplify by assuming that the molecules are confined to a cube of side l and volume $V = l^3$, the above expression becomes

$$E_t = \frac{h^2}{8m V^{\frac{2}{3}}}(n_1^2 + n_2^2 + n_3^2). \tag{10}$$

Here n_1, n_2, and n_3 can take all integral values.

The possible energy values for rotation for a two-dimensional rotator are [3]

$$E_r = \frac{j(j+1)h^2}{8\pi^2 I}, \tag{11}$$

where j takes on positive integral values and I is the moment of inertia of the molecule considered as a dumbbell. I is taken about an axis perpendicular to the line joining the atoms and passing through the center of mass. If indeed the molecule consists of two different atoms of masses m_1 and m_2 respectively separated by an equilibrium distance a, we have

$$I = \left(\frac{m_1 m_2}{m_1 + m_2}\right)a^2. \tag{12}$$

In the special case being considered in this section, $m_1 = m_2 = m$ and

$$I = \frac{ma^2}{2}. \tag{13}$$

The possible energy values for vibration are taken to be those for a simple harmonic oscillator of frequency ν, namely (cf. eq. 53, Chapter VII),

$$E_v = (j + \tfrac{1}{2})h\nu, \tag{14}$$

where j takes on positive integral values including zero.

[3] Cf. for example, Lindsay and Margenau, "Foundations of Physics," p. 435.

The total energy of the molecule will then be expressible as the sum of the energies E_t, E_r, and E_v. The writing of the partition function (3′) might appear to offer some difficulty because of the presence of the weight factors g_j. These can be omitted explicitly, however, if we incorporate them into the energy levels themselves by agreeing to repeat in the summation terms which have weight greater than unity. We then write

$$Z(T) = \Sigma e^{-(E_t + E_r + E_v)/kT}, \tag{15}$$

the sum being taken over all values for all three energy types. Because of the exponential form, simplification is possible. Thus

$$Z(T) = \Sigma e^{-E_t/kT} \cdot \Sigma e^{-E_r/kT} \cdot \Sigma e^{-E_v/kT}, \tag{16}$$

or

$$Z(T) = Z_t(T) \cdot Z_r(T) \cdot Z_v(T). \tag{17}$$

We can then determine the partition functions for translation, rotation, and vibration separately and find the total function by multiplication.

Let us first investigate the partition function $Z_r(T)$. From quantum mechanics it develops that each rotational energy state j has a weight $2j + 1$ associated with it. Hence

$$Z_r(T) = \sum_{j=0}^{\infty} (2j + 1)e^{-j(j+1)h^2/8\pi^2 IkT}. \tag{18}$$

It turns out [4] that (18) with j allowed to take all positive integral values is the partition function for rotation for diatomic molecules composed of different atoms. If, however, the atoms are identical, i.e., the molecule is that of an element, not all values of j are allowed in the summation; rather only the odd values or the even values are permitted. The reason for this is connected with nuclear spin and is adequately explained by Mayer and Mayer in the reference just given. We shall denote the partition function for which j is allowed to assume even integral values by $Z_{re}(T)$ and the one for the odd values by $Z_{ro}(T)$. The evaluation of the sum in (18) is a matter of approximation, the ease of which is determined largely by the value of $h^2/8\pi^2 IkT$, which, following Mayer and Mayer, we call σ for brevity. The values of σT for certain molecules are taken from Mayer and Mayer and presented in the accompanying table. For most diatomic molecules $\sigma \ll 1$ for room temperature and indeed $\sigma < 1$ for temperatures in the neighbor-

[4] Cf. Mayer and Mayer, "Statistical Mechanics," pp. 150, 172.

hood of the boiling points, the only exception being provided by hydrogen.

Table of σT Values for Diatomic Molecules

Molecule	σT (in degrees C)
H_2	84.97
I_2	0.053
N_2	2.85
O_2	2.06
HCl	14.95

If σ is the order of 0.5 or greater

$$Z_r(T) = 1 + 3e^{-2\sigma} + 5e^{-6\sigma} + 7e^{-12\sigma} \qquad (19)$$

is a sufficiently good approximation. For smaller values of σ, Mayer and Mayer have used the Euler-Maclaurin summation formula and have obtained the approximation, convergent for $\sigma \leq 1$

$$Z_r(T) = \frac{1}{\sigma}\left(1 + \frac{\sigma}{3} + \frac{\sigma^2}{15} + \frac{4\sigma^3}{315} + \cdots\right). \qquad (20)$$

They also find that for small σ, i.e. less than 0.2,

$$Z_{re}(T) = Z_{ro}(T) = \tfrac{1}{2}Z_r(T). \qquad (21)$$

The contribution of the rotational energy states to the specific heat can now be obtained at once from eq. (5) with the result that

$$c_V = \frac{k}{m}\left(1 + \frac{\sigma^2}{45} + \frac{16\sigma^3}{945} + \cdots\right) \qquad (22)$$

for $\sigma \leq 1.0$. This holds for small σ independently of whether the atoms of the molecule are the same or different since the derivative of the logarithm of Z_{re} or Z_{ro} is the same as that of Z_r (from 21). Equation (22) possesses considerable interest. It shows that for high temperature (for which $\sigma \to 0$), $c_V \to k/m$. As a matter of fact this limiting value is closely approached even at room temperature for nitrogen and oxygen and is reasonably well approximated even for hydrogen. For these gases under these conditions, then, the total contribution to the specific heat from translation and rotation becomes $(3/2 + 1)k/m = (5/2)\cdot k/m$. This confirms the conjecture in eq. (32), Sec. 2 of Chapter V, which is well substantiated by experimental observation. It suggests that at and above room temperature the vibrational energy states contribute little to the specific heat of a diatomic gas. We shall look into this theoretically presently. In the meantime we note that as T grows smaller, σ increases and the contribution of the rotational energy to the specific heat increases.　However with further increase of σ, i.e. beyond unity, eq. (22) ceases to hold and a new expression based on (19) is indicated, but it is unnecessary to derive this in order to see that as σ increases, ultimately Z_r approaches the constant value unity and c_V approaches zero.　We therefore expect at very low temperature little contribution to the specific heat from the rotational energy states. This agrees with the experimental observation that the specific heats of diatomic gases at constant volume decrease as the temperature decreases.

We now investigate the partition function for the vibrational energy states.　From (14) this becomes

$$Z_v(T) = \sum_{j=0}^{\infty} e^{-(j+\frac{1}{2})h\nu/kT}. \tag{23}$$

Here the elementary weights g_j all reduce to unity.　Since $e^{-h\nu/kT} < 1$, we can write

$$Z_v(T) = e^{-h\nu/2kT} \cdot \sum_{j=0}^{\infty} e^{-jh\nu/kT}$$

$$= \frac{e^{-h\nu/2kT}}{1 - e^{-h\nu/kT}}. \tag{24}$$

From this

$$\log Z_v(T) = -\frac{h\nu}{2kT} - \log(1 - e^{-h\nu/kT}), \tag{25}$$

and eq. (5) yields, after carrying out the indicated operations

$$c_V = \frac{k}{m} \cdot \left(\frac{h\nu}{kT}\right)^2 \cdot \frac{e^{h\nu/kT}}{(e^{h\nu/kT} - 1)^2}, \tag{26}$$

as the contribution of the vibrational energy states to the specific heat. At very high temperatures $h\nu/kT$ becomes considerably less than unity and inspection shows that under these conditions $c_V \to k/m$.　However at room temperature and below, $h\nu/kT > 1$, e.g., for H_2 at $300°$ K, $h\nu/kT \doteq 20$.　Under these circumstances [5]

$$c_V \to \frac{k}{m} \frac{(h\nu/kT)^2}{e^{h\nu/kT}},$$

[5] For data on values of the frequency ν for diatomic molecules, see John C. Slater, "Introduction to Chemical Physics," pp. 132, 141, McGraw-Hill, New York, 1939.

or a very small fraction of k/m. Compared with the contributions of the translational and rotational energies, that of the vibrational energy at room temperature is negligible. This of course finds confirmation in the experimental results already referred to. The increase in specific heat at very high temperatures due to the vibrational energy contribution is also borne out by experimental measurements.[6]

So far as the use of statistics is concerned the same method outlined above for the determination of the specific heats of diatomic gases is also directly applicable to polyatomic gases. The quantum mechanical problem of determining the energy states of rotation and vibration is of course much more difficult because of the greater number of degrees of freedom involved.[7]

3. SPECIFIC HEAT OF A CRYSTALLINE SOLID

A crystalline solid is an aggregate of atomic particles whose positions of stable equilibrium form a regular three dimensional array or lattice. The atoms do not remain at rest in their equilibrium positions, but move about them in vibratory motion with frequencies determined by the nature of the forces acting between them. Specifically a solid crystal consisting of N similar atoms has $3N$ degrees of freedom, and from the classical mechanics of vibrating systems it follows that such a system can oscillate in $3N$ harmonic modes. Quantum mechanically the possible energy values of the crystal are given by

$$E_n = \sum_{j=1}^{3N} (n_j + \tfrac{1}{2})h\nu_j, \qquad (27)$$

where the $3N$ values of ν_j are the frequencies corresponding to the possible modes of oscillation and n_j can take on all positive integral values for each j. Equation (27) is the generalization of (14).

The partition function for the crystal becomes

$$Z(T) = \sum_{n=0}^{\infty} e^{-E_n/kT}$$

$$= \sum_{n_j=0}^{\infty} e^{-\sum_{j=1}^{3N}(n_j + \frac{1}{2})h\nu_j/kT}. \qquad (28)$$

---

[6] Cf., for example, the data on CO quoted by Slater, *op. cit.*, p. 145.

[7] The reader will find an adequate discussion in Mayer and Mayer, *op. cit.*, pp. 179 ff.

The exponential can be written as a product and hence Z can be expressed as a product of sums. Thus

$$Z(T) = \prod_{j=1}^{3N} \sum_{n_j=0}^{\infty} e^{-(n_j+\frac{1}{2})h\nu_j/kT}$$

$$= \prod_{j=1}^{3N} \left(\frac{e^{-h\nu_j/2kT}}{1 - e^{-h\nu_j/kT}} \right), \qquad (29)$$

the second step being equivalent to that taken in (24). Further

$$\log Z(T) = -\sum_{j=1}^{3N} [h\nu_j/2kT + \log (1 - e^{-h\nu_j/kT})]. \qquad (30)$$

We now make the assumption that the same statistical method which we have applied to gases should also hold on suitable modification for the $3N$ particles of the solid crystal. Examination of the fundamental postulates in Chapter VII shows that this is a justifiable procedure. Only one slight modification is necessary. In our previous discussion of ideal gases the partition function referred to a single particle of the gas. Now the partition function in (28) refers to the whole assembly of oscillators. Consequently we must alter the fundamental formulas (3) and (4) giving the energy of the system in terms of the partition function by leaving out the factor N, since it already is included in Z. Thus we now have for our crystal in place of (4)

$$E = kT^2 \frac{\partial}{\partial T} \log Z(T). \qquad (31)$$

The corresponding specific heat expression becomes

$$c_V = \frac{k}{Nm} \frac{\partial}{\partial T} \left[T^2 \frac{\partial}{\partial T} \log Z(T) \right]_V. \qquad (32)$$

For the crystalline solid this takes the form (from 30)

$$c_V = \frac{k}{Nm} \frac{\partial}{\partial T} \left\{ T^2 \frac{\partial}{\partial T} \left[\sum_{j=1}^{3N} \left(\frac{h\nu_j}{2kT} + \log (1 - e^{-h\nu_j/kT}) \right) \right] \right\}. \qquad (33)$$

The result of the carrying out of the indicated operations is

$$c_V = \frac{k}{Nm} \sum_{j=1}^{3N} \frac{(h\nu_j/kT)^2 e^{h\nu_j/kT}}{(e^{h\nu_j/kT} - 1)^2}. \qquad (34)$$

Let us suppose that the temperature is high so that for every v_j, $hv_j/kT \ll 1$. Each term in the sum in (34) becomes practically unity and the result is

$$c_V \doteq \frac{3k}{m}. \tag{35}$$

A more accurate approximation is

$$c_V = \frac{3k}{m}\left[1 - \frac{1}{36N}\sum_{j=1}^{3N}\left(\frac{hv_j}{kT}\right)^2 + \cdots\right]. \tag{36}$$

The gram molecular heat capacity at high temperatures should thus approximate for all monatomic crystalline solids

$$C_V = 3R = 5.96 \text{ cal/degree C.} \tag{37}$$

This is the law of Dulong and Petit. For most monatomic crystalline solids it is in excellent agreement with experiment even at room temperature.

At low temperatures (34) approaches the asymptotic form

$$c_V = \frac{k}{Nm}\sum_{j=1}^{3N}(hv_j/kT)^2 e^{-hv_j/kT}, \tag{38}$$

indicating that as the temperature approaches absolute zero, the specific heat should approach zero. This is in general agreement with experiment though the precise rate of approach to zero is not in accord with the exponential law (38).

The endeavor to render the theory of the specific heat of a crystalline solid more exact necessitates the evaluation of the sum in (34) and this in turn demands a knowledge of the frequencies v_j. The most important attempt at a solution of this problem is due to Debye.[8] Debye replaces the sum in (34) by an integral over the whole frequency range from zero to a certain maximum frequency and seeks the distribution of the oscillations among the various frequencies by finding the number of possible modes of oscillation of the crystal lattice in each frequency interval.

Let us suppose that the crystal is replaced by an equivalent elastic solid medium taken in the form of a cube with side equal to l. The assumption was made by Debye that the actual lattice vibrations are

---

[8] *Ann. der Physik* **39**, 789 (1912). Cf. also the discussion of the Debye theory in Slater, *op. cit.*, pp. 222 ff. and Mayer and Mayer, "Statistical Mechanics," pp. 248 ff.

the same as the allowed modes of elastic wave vibration (stationary elastic waves) in the equivalent continuous elastic medium. The latter are solutions of the wave equation for the two types of elastic waves in a solid medium subject to the boundary conditions at the faces of the cube. The two wave equations are respectively [9]

$$\nabla^2 \delta = \left(\frac{\rho}{k + 4n/3}\right) \ddot{\delta},$$ (39)

and

$$\nabla^2 \xi = \left(\frac{\rho}{n}\right) \ddot{\xi}.$$ (40)

Here δ is the dilatation in the medium and eq. (39) represents the propagation of δ as a longitudinal wave with velocity

$$c_l = \sqrt{\frac{k + 4n/3}{\rho}},$$ (41)

where k is the bulk modulus, n the shear modulus, and ρ the density. In (40) ξ is a transverse displacement propagated with velocity

$$c_t = \sqrt{\frac{n}{\rho}}.$$ (42)

We assume that the solid cube is traversed by plane harmonic waves of both longitudinal and transverse types. Such a wave will correspond to a displacement in the form [10]

$$A e^{2\pi i \nu t} e^{-\frac{2\pi i \nu}{c}(\alpha x + \beta y + \gamma z)},$$ (43)

where A is the amplitude of the displacement and α, β, γ are the direction cosines of the normal to the plane wave front. The imposition of the boundary conditions assures that these progressive plane waves will become stationary plane waves with space part in the form

$$\sin \frac{2\pi\nu}{c} \alpha x \cdot \sin \frac{2\pi\nu}{c} \beta y \cdot \sin \frac{2\pi\nu}{c} \gamma z,$$ (44)

[9] Cf., for example, Stewart and Lindsay, "Acoustics," pp. 328 ff. D. Van Nostrand Co., New York, 1930.

[10] Cf. Slater and Frank, "Introduction to Theoretical Physics," p. 253, McGraw-Hill, New York, 1933.

where not all values of the frequency ν and the direction cosines α, β, γ are allowed, but only those which satisfy the boundary conditions, expressible in the form

$$\sin \frac{2\pi\nu}{c}\, \alpha l = \sin \frac{2\pi\nu}{c}\, \beta l = \sin \frac{2\pi\nu}{c}\, \gamma l = 0. \tag{45}$$

These are satisfied for

$$\nu\alpha = \frac{n_1 c}{2l}; \quad \nu\beta = \frac{n_2 c}{2l}; \quad \nu\gamma = \frac{n_3 c}{2l} \tag{46}$$

where n_1, n_2, n_3 are any three integers. Since $\alpha^2 + \beta^2 + \gamma^2 = 1$, (46) suffices to fix the allowed frequencies of plane stationary waves in the solid as

$$\nu_{n_1,\, n_2,\, n_3} = \frac{c}{2l}\sqrt{n_1^2 + n_2^2 + n_3^2}. \tag{47}$$

To each triplet n_1, n_2, n_3 corresponds an allowed frequency and a direction for the associated plane wave motion. The problem to be solved is to find the number of allowed frequencies in the given frequency interval ν, $\nu + d\nu$. This is mathematically identical with the problem solved in Sec. 4 of Chapter VIII and we shall not need to present the analysis but shall merely give the final result, remarking only that for each direction we shall expect to find one longitudinal wave and two transverse waves. The total number of modes of plane wave harmonic vibration of the solid for which the frequency lies in the interval mentioned then becomes (with $V = l^3 = $ volume of the cube)

$$N(\nu)d\nu = 4\pi V\nu^2 \left(\frac{2}{c_t^3} + \frac{1}{c_l^3}\right) d\nu. \tag{48}$$

We now follow Debye in the hypothesis that to a first approximation we can replace the real discrete distribution of frequencies in the actual crystal lattice by the continuous distribution (48). Since the total number of allowed frequencies is $3N$, there must be an upper limit to ν in (48). In fact we can compute this ν_{max} from the condition that

$$\int_0^{\nu_{max}} N(\nu)d\nu = 4\pi V \left(\frac{2}{c_t^3} + \frac{1}{c_l^3}\right) \int_0^{\nu_{max}} \nu^2 d\nu = 3N. \tag{49}$$

This results in

$$\nu_{max}^3 = \frac{9N}{4\pi V(2/c_t^3 + 1/c_l^3)}. \tag{50}$$

We can use (50) to express (48) in the form

$$N(\nu)d\nu = \frac{9N\nu^2}{\nu_{max}^3} \, d\nu. \qquad (51)$$

The specific heat expression in (34) can now be written in the integral form

$$c_V = \frac{9k}{m\nu_{max}^3} \int_0^{\nu_{max}} \frac{\left(\dfrac{h\nu}{kT}\right)^2 e^{h\nu/kT}}{(e^{h\nu/kT} - 1)^2} \, \nu^2 d\nu. \qquad (52)$$

Let us abbreviate by writing $w = h\nu/kT$, whereupon (52) becomes

$$c_V = \frac{9k}{m w_{max}^3} \int_0^{w_{max}} \frac{w^4 e^w}{(e^w - 1)^2} \, dw. \qquad (53)$$

It is usual to introduce the so-called Debye characteristic temperature defined by

$$\Theta_D = \frac{h\nu_{max}}{k}, \qquad (54)$$

so that

$$w_{max} = \frac{\Theta_D}{T}. \qquad (55)$$

Equation (53) expresses c_V as a function of T/Θ_D. The integration will not be undertaken. However we can get one interesting result at once by noting that

$$\int_0^\infty \frac{w^4 e^w dw}{(e^w - 1)^2} = \frac{4\pi^4}{15}. \qquad (56)$$

Hence for low temperatures where w_{max} may be expected to be large, the specific heat is given by

$$c_V \doteq \frac{12\pi^4}{5} \cdot \frac{k}{m} \cdot \frac{T^3}{\Theta_D^3}. \qquad (57)$$

This dependence of the specific heat on the third power of T for small T is well substantiated for a number of substances.

The accompanying figure (Fig. 9·1) gives a plot of c_V as a function of T/Θ_D. This should of course be the same for all crystalline solids. The distinction between various solids comes in the value of Θ_D. This characteristic temperature has been computed for several elements both from observed specific heat data and from the experimental elastic constants (by means of 50). The values obtained by the two methods agree rather well.[11] For example, the value of Θ_D for aluminum calculated from the observed specific heat variation is 398° K

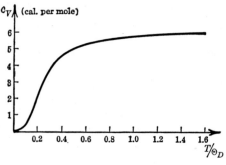

Fig. 9·1.

and that obtained from the elastic constants is 399° K. Another possibility is to obtain Θ_D by fitting the low temperature range as accurately as possible and not considering the higher temperatures. If this is done for aluminum the value is 385° K.[12]

PROBLEMS

1. Use eqs. (6) and (7) to derive the explicit expressions for the specific heat at constant volume of an ideal monatomic gas on the Fermi-Dirac and Bose-Einstein statistics respectively. Show that to a first approximation the classical formula $c_V = 3k/2m$ results. Estimate the magnitude of the correction for oxygen at its critical temperature, in the Bose-Einstein case.

2. Derive the approximation (20) for the rotational partition function for an ideal diatomic gas.

3. Prove that a plane harmonic wave of frequency ν progressing in a direction with direction cosines α, β, γ, has its displacement in the form

$$\xi = A\,e^{2\pi i[\nu t - \frac{\nu}{c}(\alpha x + \beta y + \gamma z)]}.$$

Find the expression for the displacement in the stationary waves which arise from the reflection of plane progressive waves of the above type in a cubical vessel of side l.

4. Calculate the Debye characteristic temperature for copper, silver, and aluminum from the observed elastic constants. Compare the results with the characteristic temperature for the same metals obtained from the observed specific heat values at low temperature.

[11] For details, see Slater, op. cit., p. 237.
[12] For a discussion of recent attempts to improve on Debye's theory by a more careful evaluation of the actual frequency spectrum of the crystalline solid, consult the book by Mott and Jones, "The Theory of the Properties of Metals and Alloys," pp. 6 ff., Oxford, 1936.

5. Show that the entropy of a crystalline solid can be written in the form

$$S = k \sum_{j=1}^{3N} \left[-\log (1 - e^{-h\nu_j/kT}) + \frac{h\nu_j/kT}{e^{h\nu_j/kT} - 1} \right].$$

Find the result to which this reduces if all $3N$ frequencies of the crystal are assumed to be identical and equal to ν. Find the corresponding result on the Debye theory of frequency distribution. Show that on the Debye theory at temperatures low compared with the characteristic temperature the entropy can be written approximately

$$S = 3kN \left\{ \frac{4\pi^4}{15} \left(\frac{T}{\Theta_D} \right)^3 + \cdots \right\}.$$

6. Derive the expression for the free energy of a crystalline solid on the Debye theory and show that at temperatures high compared with the characteristic temperature the value is approximately

$$\Psi = 3NkT \left[\log \left(\frac{\Theta_D}{T} \right) - \frac{1}{3} + \frac{1}{40} \left(\frac{\Theta_D}{T} \right)^2 \cdots \right].$$

CHAPTER X

QUANTUM STATISTICAL THEORY OF ELECTRICAL AND THERMAL PROPERTIES OF METALS

1. THE LORENTZ-SOMMERFELD THEORY OF ELECTRICAL AND THERMAL CONDUCTION

The most elaborate classical statistical theory of the conduction of electricity and heat in metals is due to Lorentz.[1] He attributed both effects to the motion of free electrons and treated the electron gas in the metal by the classical Maxwell-Boltzmann statistics. Sommerfeld [2] modified the Lorentz theory by the introduction of quantum statistics. We have already noted that an electron gas such as the Lorentz theory envisages in a metal with approximately one electron per metallic atom, must be strongly degenerate even at very high temperatures. The distribution law to be used will therefore be that given in eq. (47) of Chapter VIII with $a = +1$, and with γ_1 given by eq. (129) of Chapter VIII. We find it convenient to express it in terms of velocity components rather than energy. This makes it necessary to rewrite the expression for n_j in terms of the velocity components v_x, v_y, v_z in place of energy. To revert to Sec. 4, Chapter VIII we see that the possible energy values of a free particle in a closed vessel, given in eq. (59), are really equivalent to saying that the possible kinetic energy values corresponding to velocity components v_x, v_y, v_z along the three coordinate axes respectively are

$$(\tfrac{1}{2}mv_x^2)_{n_1} = \frac{n_1^2 h^2}{8ml_1^2},$$

$$(\tfrac{1}{2}mv_y^2)_{n_2} = \frac{n_2^2 h^2}{8ml_2^2},$$

$$(\tfrac{1}{2}mv_z^2)_{n_3} = \frac{n_3^2 h^2}{8ml_3^2}.$$

[1] H. A. Lorentz, "Theory of Electrons," pp. 267 ff., New York, 1916.
[2] A. Sommerfeld, Z. Physik 47, 1 (1928). See also "Handbuch der Physik," second edition, Vol. 24, p. 333. Springer, Berlin, 1933.

This should be clear from eqs. (55) and (58) of Chapter VIII. Hence the number of energy values for which v_x lies between v_x and $v_x + dv_x$ is simply

$$\frac{dn_1}{2} = \frac{m}{h} l_1 dv_x,$$

with similar expressions for the y and z directions. The total number of energy values for which v_x is in the interval v_x, $v_x + dv_x$ and similarly for v_y and v_z then becomes [3]

$$\frac{dn_1 dn_2 dn_3}{8} = \frac{m^3}{h^3} \tau dv_x dv_y dv_z. \tag{1}$$

If we assign two electrons to each energy value to take care of the spin, we have for our new n_j the expression

$$n_j = \frac{2m^3}{h^3} \tau dv_x dv_y dv_z, \tag{2}$$

and the distribution law to be used in our discussion takes the form

$$dN = \frac{2\tau m^3/h^3 \cdot dv_x dv_y dv_z}{1 + e^{-\gamma_1} e^{m(v_x^2 + v_y^2 + v_z^2)/2kT}}. \tag{3}$$

For the sake of convenience we shall mainly employ

$$f_0(x, v_x, v_y, v_z) = \frac{dN}{\tau dv_x dv_y dv_z} = \frac{2m^3}{h^3} \cdot \frac{1}{1 + e^{-\gamma_1} e^{m(v_x^2 + v_y^2 + v_z^2)/2kT}}. \tag{4}$$

The function f_0 is written as a function of x as well as v_x, v_y, v_z since we are assuming that the metal in question is in the form of a rod directed along the x axis. We wish to express the fact that the rod may not be homogeneous, whence γ_1 will depend on x. Moreover if a temperature gradient exists, T will be a function of x. Hence the distribution function will in general depend on x.

If the metal is subjected to no external influences the distribution function f_0 will remain unchanged at any particular place in the metal. We must indeed expect the electrons to suffer energy changes by collision with the metallic atoms, but on the average as many electrons will be expected to gain as to lose energy and the f_0 should not be altered by this effect. However, the situation will be different when an electric field $\mathscr{E}(x)$ is applied to the metal.

[3] We revert to the use of τ for physical volume.

Consider the electrons at a given instant t in a small volume $d\tau$ of the metal at the point x, y, z and with their velocity components in the interval v_x, $v_x + dv_x$, etc.   At the time $t + dt$, if there were no collisions, these electrons would be displaced to the same volume around the point $(x + v_x dt, y + v_y dt, z + v_z dt)$ and their velocity components would become $v_x + e\mathscr{E}/m \cdot dt$, v_y, v_z.   Note that we are assuming that the applied field acts only along the x axis.   Now because of collisions with the atoms of the metal a certain number of electrons having velocity components in the interval in question at time t will have passed out of this interval by $t + dt$.   Let this number per second be denoted by

$$a d\tau dv_x dv_y dv_z.$$

Similarly we shall assume that

$$b d\tau dv_x dv_y dv_z$$

have their velocity components brought *into* the interval per second. If there were no external field acting, equilibrium would be maintained by

$$a = b.$$

However in general we shall have when a steady state is established

$$f(x + v_x dt, \; y + v_y dt, \; z + v_z dt, \; v_x + \frac{e\mathscr{E}}{m} dt, \; v_y, \; v_z)$$

$$= f(x, y, z, v_x, v_y, v_z) + (b - a)dt, \tag{5}$$

where f is the generalized distribution function in the presence of the external field.   When the field vanishes f reduces to f_0.   Equation (5) leads to

$$b - a = v_x \frac{\partial f}{\partial x} + \frac{e\mathscr{E}}{m} \frac{\partial f}{\partial v_x}. \tag{6}$$

Because f is a function of x alone, $\dfrac{\partial f}{\partial y}$ and $\dfrac{\partial f}{\partial z}$ are absent in (6). In order to utilize this equation it is necessary to obtain an expression for $b - a$.   This involves a study of the collisions of electrons with atoms.   Let us assume that the atoms are elastic spheres of radius R and that their number per unit volume is equal to n.   The collisions of the electrons with the atoms are then elastic.   In Fig. 10·1 we have indicated such an atom with center at O.   Construct the solid angle $d\omega$ at O subtending the surface element $dS = R^2 d\omega$ at the surface of the atom. Consider the electrons with velocity $\mathbf{v}$ in the velocity interval v_x, $v_x + dv_x$, etc. The number of these which strike dS per second is the number in a cylinder of length v and base area $dS \cdot \cos \beta$,

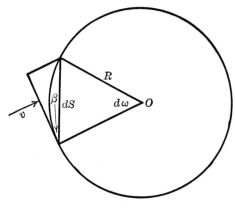

FIG. 10·1.

where β is the angle between $\mathbf{v}$ and the inward drawn normal to dS. Consequently the number is

$$nR^2 d\omega \cos \beta \, v \, f(x, y, z, v_x, v_y, v_z) dv_x dv_y dv_z.$$

Hence the average number of collisions per unit volume per second suffered by the electrons in the given velocity interval would appear to be

$$dv_x dv_y dv_z \int nR^2 v \cos \beta \cdot f(x, \ y, \ z, \ v_x, \ v_y, \ v_z) d\omega. \tag{7}$$

This assumes that all the collisions are possible, but this is true only if the gas is one obeying the classical Maxwell-Boltzmann statistics. In the Fermi-Dirac gas, which we are considering here, only those collisions are possible for which the final state was originally empty. Consequently we must correct (7) by writing it in the form

$$dv_x dv_y dv_z [1 - f(x, y, z, v_x', v_y', v_z')] \int nR^2 v \cos \beta \cdot f(x, y, z, v_x, v_y, v_z) d\omega \tag{7'}$$

where v_x', v_y', v_z' are the component velocities after collision. The number of collisions for which $f(x, y, z, v_x', v_y', v_z') = 1$ then becomes zero. The integral in (7') is the expression for a in (6).

Since we are assuming that the collisions are elastic we can calculate the velocity components after collision by the law of reflection on elastic impact. Thus, the velocity after impact being $\mathbf{v}'$ with components v'_x, v'_y, v'_z (where $|\mathbf{v}'| = |\mathbf{v}|$) the projection of $\mathbf{v}' - \mathbf{v}$ on the normal to the surface element dS is $2v \cos \beta$, and hence if the direction cosines of the normal are λ, μ, ν, we have

$$v_x - v'_x = 2v \cos \beta \cdot \lambda$$
$$v_y - v'_y = 2v \cos \beta \cdot \mu \tag{8}$$
$$v_z - v'_z = 2v \cos \beta \cdot \nu.$$

This assumes, of course, that the atoms of the metal are stationary. Since they are so much more massive than the electrons, this assumption is reasonable. Similarly if the original velocity components are v'_x, v'_y, v'_z the final ones after impact will be v_x, v_y, v_z as given in (8). Hence the expression for b in (6) is simply the integral

$$[1 - f(x, y, z, v_x, v_y, v_z)] \int nR^2 v \cos \beta \cdot f(x, y, z, v'_x, v'_y, v'_z)d\omega, \tag{9}$$

where the coefficient $[1 - f(x, y, z, v_x, v_y, v_z)]$ is inserted for the same reason as in (7'). Let us now assume that the distribution function as altered by the field can be expressed in terms of the original distribution function f_0 by means of the relation

$$f = f_0 + v_x \cdot \chi(x, v_x, v_y, v_z), \tag{10}$$

where χ, like f_0, is assumed to be a function of the velocity components through the magnitude $\sqrt{v_x^2 + v_y^2 + v_z^2}$ only. This assumption is rendered plausible by the recollection that the field is directed along the x axis and hence should be expected to change f principally through v_x. Equation (6) now takes the form

$$v_x \left(\frac{\partial f_0}{\partial x} + v_x \frac{\partial \chi}{\partial x} \right) + \frac{e\mathcal{E}}{m} \left(\frac{\partial f_0}{\partial v_x} + \chi + v_x \frac{\partial \chi}{\partial v_x} \right)$$
$$= nR^2 v \chi(x, v) \int (v'_x - v_x) \cos \beta \, d\omega, \tag{11}$$

if we assume that $\chi(x, v'_x, v'_y, v'_z) = \chi(x, v_x, v_y, v_z)$, i.e., the total energy of the electron remains unchanged by the collision. If we consider χ as a sort of correction function it will be proper to neglect $v_x \dfrac{\partial \chi}{\partial x}$ compared with $\dfrac{\partial f_0}{\partial x}$ and $\chi + v_x \dfrac{\partial \chi}{\partial v_x}$ compared with $\dfrac{\partial f_0}{\partial v_x}$. Moreover we shall write

$\dfrac{\partial f_0}{\partial v_x} = \dfrac{v_x}{v}\dfrac{\partial f_0}{\partial v}$.   Finally we use the first equation in (8).   Then eq. (11) becomes

$$v_x \frac{\partial f_0}{\partial x} + \frac{e\mathscr{E}v_x}{mv}\frac{\partial f_0}{\partial v} = - \, 2nR^2v^2\chi(x, v) \int \lambda \cos^2 \beta \, d\omega. \qquad (12)$$

We must now evaluate the integral on the right side.   Let α be the angle between the normal to the atomic surface at dS and the x axis. Thus $\lambda = \cos \alpha$.   We now take the velocity v as the polar axis of a system of spherical coordinates in which β is the co-latitude angle and ϕ is, as usual, the longitude.   By the application of the usual rule for the cosine of the angle between two lines we have

$$\lambda = \cos \alpha = \frac{v_x}{v}\cos \beta + \frac{\sqrt{v_y^2 + v_z^2}}{v}\sin \beta \cos \phi.$$

Then

$$d\omega = \frac{dS}{R^2} = \sin \beta \, d\beta \, d\phi.$$

Consequently the integral in (12) becomes

$$\int \lambda \cos^2 \beta \, d\omega = \int_0^{\pi/2} \sin \beta \cos^2 \beta \, d\beta.$$

$$\int_0^{2\pi} \left(\frac{v_x}{v}\cos \beta + \frac{\sqrt{v_y^2 + v_z^2}}{v}\sin \beta \cos \phi \right) d\phi,$$

where the upper limit of the β integration is $\pi/2$ instead of π since we are clearly entitled to count in our calculation the solid angle for a hemisphere only.   The term involving $\sqrt{v_y^2 + v_z^2}$ goes out in the integration and we are finally left with

$$\int \lambda \cos^2 \beta \, d\omega = \frac{\pi v_x}{2v}.$$

The resulting differential equation for f_0 then becomes

$$\frac{\partial f_0}{\partial x} + \frac{e\mathscr{E}}{mv}\frac{\partial f_0}{\partial v} = - \, \pi nR^2 v\chi. \qquad (13)$$

In line with our classical kinetic theory discussion in Sec. 3 of Chapter V, it is plausible to *define* the effective *mean free path* of the electrons, as far as collisions with the atoms of the metal are concerned, as

$$l = \frac{1}{\pi nR^2}. \qquad (14)$$

With this definition we can write (13) in the form

$$\chi = -\frac{l}{v}\left(\frac{\partial f_0}{\partial x} + \frac{e\mathscr{E}}{mv}\frac{\partial f_0}{\partial v}\right). \tag{15}$$

It should be pointed out that it is unnecessary to take the definition (14) too seriously. We could carry the quantity $1/\pi nR^2$ through our analysis without giving it a special name if we chose. As a matter of fact, the theory being presented here is a formal one in the sense that we shall not attempt to calculate l in a precise manner. The quantity $1/\pi nR^2$ has the dimensions of length and indeed if we insert reasonable values of n and R, e.g., for silver, $n = 5.9 \times 10^{22}$, $R \sim 10^{-8}$ cm, l comes out of the order of 5×10^{-8} cm, which is not unreasonable. It will later prove possible to deduce formulas from which l disappears by cancellation. We shall naturally be able to attach greater significance to such equations as tests of the theory.

We are now ready to evaluate the electric and thermal current densities in the direction of the x axis. The electric current density or rate of flow of charge per unit area per second is by definition

$$J = e \int\!\!\!\int\!\!\!\int_{-\infty}^{+\infty} v_x f \, dv_x \, dv_y \, dv_z. \tag{16}$$

The thermal current density or the total rate of transfer of kinetic energy per unit area per second is

$$C = \frac{m}{2} \int\!\!\!\int\!\!\!\int_{-\infty}^{+\infty} v^2 \, v_x f \, dv_x \, dv_y \, dv_z. \tag{17}$$

Substituting $f = f_0 + v_x \chi$ and recalling that f_0 is an even function of v_x, v_y, v_z, we get

$$J = e \int\!\!\!\int\!\!\!\int_{-\infty}^{+\infty} v_x^2 \chi \, dv_x \, dv_y \, dv_z. \tag{18}$$

Similarly

$$C = \frac{m}{2} \int\!\!\!\int\!\!\!\int_{-\infty}^{+\infty} v_x^2 \chi v^2 \, dv_x \, dv_y \, dv_z. \tag{19}$$

When we proceed now to spherical coordinates, we replace $dv_x \, dv_y \, dv_z$ by $v^2 \sin\theta \, dv \, d\theta \, d\phi$, with $v^2 = v_x^2 + v_y^2 + v_z^2$, θ the angle v makes with the v_z

axis and ϕ the angle its projection on the $v_x v_y$ plane makes with the v_x axis.   Integrating out the θ and ϕ parts gives

$$J = \frac{4\pi e}{3} \int_0^\infty v^4 \chi \, dv, \tag{20}$$

and

$$C = \frac{2\pi m}{3} \int_0^\infty v^6 \chi \, dv. \tag{21}$$

The next step is to substitute χ from (15) into these expressions.   The result is

$$J = -\frac{4\pi e}{3} \left[\int_0^\infty lv^3 \frac{\partial f_0}{\partial x} \, dv + \frac{e\mathscr{E}}{m} \int_0^\infty lv^2 \frac{\partial f_0}{\partial v} \, dv \right], \tag{22}$$

$$C = -\frac{2\pi m}{3} \left[\int_0^\infty lv^5 \frac{\partial f_0}{\partial x} \, dv + \frac{e\mathscr{E}}{m} \int_0^\infty lv^4 \frac{\partial f_0}{\partial v} \, dv \right]. \tag{23}$$

An integration by parts performed on the second integral in each expression yields

$$J = \frac{4\pi e}{3} \left[\frac{e\mathscr{E}}{m} \int_0^\infty f_0 \frac{\partial}{\partial v}(lv^2) \, dv - \int_0^\infty lv^3 \frac{\partial f_0}{\partial x} \, dv \right], \tag{24}$$

$$C = \frac{2\pi m}{3} \left[\frac{e\mathscr{E}}{m} \int_0^\infty f_0 \frac{\partial(lv^4)}{\partial v} \, dv - \int_0^\infty lv^5 \frac{\partial f_0}{\partial x} \, dv \right]. \tag{25}$$

It is convenient at this point to introduce the change in variable, $mv^2/2kT = u$.   Then the operator $\dfrac{\partial}{\partial v}$ becomes

$$\frac{\partial}{\partial v} = \frac{mv}{kT} \frac{\partial}{\partial u},$$

while

$$dv \frac{\partial}{\partial v} = du \frac{\partial}{\partial u}.$$

Now for convenience let $lv^2 = L$, whence $lv^3 \, dv = \dfrac{kT}{m} L \, du$.   Moreover $lv^4 = v^2 L = \dfrac{2kT}{m} uL$, etc., so that the expressions (24) and (25) now appear as

$$J = \frac{4\pi e}{3} \left[\frac{e\mathscr{E}}{m} \int_0^\infty f_0 \frac{\partial L}{\partial u} \, du - \frac{kT}{m} \int_0^\infty \frac{\partial f_0}{\partial x} L \, du \right], \tag{26}$$

$$C = \frac{2\pi m}{3} \left[\frac{e\mathscr{E}}{m} \cdot \frac{2kT}{m} \int_0^\infty f_0 \frac{\partial(uL)}{\partial u} \, du - \frac{1}{2}\left(\frac{2kT}{m}\right)^2 \int_0^\infty \frac{\partial f_0}{\partial x} uL \, du \right] \tag{27}$$

f_0 given in eq. (4) takes the form

$$f_0 = \frac{2m^3}{h^3} \cdot \frac{1}{1 + e^{-\eta_1 + u}}.$$

Hence on the assumption that in general both γ_1 and T vary with x

$$\frac{\partial f_0}{\partial x} = -\frac{\partial f_0}{\partial u} \cdot \left(\frac{\partial \gamma_1}{\partial x} + \frac{u}{T} \frac{\partial T}{\partial x} \right). \tag{28}$$

We can integrate $\int_0^\infty \frac{\partial f_0}{\partial u} L du$ by parts and find it equal to
$-\int_0^\infty f_0 \frac{\partial L}{\partial u} du$, since the integrated part vanishes at both limits.
Similarly

$$\int_0^\infty \frac{\partial f_0}{\partial u} u L du = -\int_0^\infty f_0 \frac{\partial}{\partial u} (uL) du.$$

Finally, if we abbreviate by setting

$$\int_0^\infty f_0 \frac{\partial L}{\partial u} du = A_1, \quad \int_0^\infty f_0 \frac{\partial (uL)}{\partial u} du = A_2,$$

$$\int_0^\infty f_0 \frac{\partial (u^2 L)}{\partial u} du = A_3 \tag{29}$$

the two current densities become

$$J = \frac{4\pi e}{3m} A_1 \left[e\mathscr{E} - kT \frac{\partial \gamma_1}{\partial x} - k \frac{\partial T}{\partial x} \frac{A_2}{A_1} \right]. \tag{30}$$

$$C = \frac{4\pi kT}{3m} A_2 \left[e\mathscr{E} - kT \frac{\partial \gamma_1}{\partial x} - k \frac{\partial T}{\partial x} \frac{A_3}{A_2} \right]. \tag{31}$$

We are now ready to apply the formulas (30) and (31). If the medium is homogeneous and there exists no temperature gradient, (30) reduces to

$$J = \frac{4\pi e^2 \mathscr{E} A_1}{3m}. \tag{32}$$

The electrical conductivity is defined as the reciprocal of the specific resistance, which is the ratio of the electric field intensity to the current density. Hence for the conductivity, σ, we have

$$\sigma = \frac{J}{\mathscr{E}} = \frac{4\pi e^2 A_1}{3m}. \tag{33}$$

From (29)

$$A_1 = \frac{2kT}{m} \int_0^\infty f_0 \frac{\partial (lu)}{\partial u}\, du. \tag{34}$$

We must assume that l is a function of u, though we do not know the precise dependence. Let us expand $ul(u)$ in a power series:

$$ul = \sum_{j=0}^\infty B_j u^{j+1}, \tag{35}$$

and

$$\frac{d(ul)}{du} = \sum_{j=0}^\infty (j+1)B_j u^j.$$

Substitution into (34) yields

$$A_1 = \frac{2kT}{m} \sum_{j=0}^\infty (j+1)B_j \int_0^\infty f_0 u^j du. \tag{36}$$

We recognize $h^3/2m^3 \cdot \int_0^\infty f_0 u^j du$ as identical with $U'(j, \gamma_1)$ in eq. (122) of Chapter VIII. The first approximation yields

$$A_1 = \frac{2kT}{m} \cdot \frac{2m^3}{h^3} \sum_{j=0}^\infty (j+1)B_j \frac{\gamma_1^{j+1}}{(j+1)},$$

which from (35) becomes

$$A_1 = \frac{2kT}{m} \cdot \frac{2m^3}{h^3} \gamma_1 l(\gamma_1), \tag{37}$$

where $l(\gamma_1)$ means the value of $l(u)$ with γ_1 inserted for u. The conductivity to the first approximation takes the form

$$\sigma = \frac{16\pi m e^2 kT}{3h^3} \gamma_1 l(\gamma_1). \tag{38}$$

Note from eq. (138) of Chapter VIII that $l(\gamma_1)$ is the value of the mean free path corresponding to the velocity v_0. The utility of this formula for electrical conductivity is severely restricted by our ignorance of the dependence of l on the velocity. By using the first approximation to the degenerate form of γ_1 from (128) of Chapter VIII with 2τ in place of τ we can rewrite (38) in the form

$$\sigma = \frac{8\pi e^2}{3h} \left(\frac{3N}{8\pi\tau}\right)^{2/3} l(\gamma_1). \tag{39}$$

In this formula the temperature no longer enters explicitly. The temperature variation of conductivity must therefore be sought in that of N/τ and of the mean free path $l(\gamma_1)$. Since the change of N/τ with temperature is a matter of thermal expansion only, it is extremely slight and scarcely competent to account for the change in σ. Hence the burden is laid on $l(\gamma_1)$. Calculations based on (39) using the experimental values of σ indicate that for copper, for example, on the assumption of one free electron per atom l will vary from about 7×10^{-7} cm at $1000°$ C to about 4×10^{-5} cm at $-200°$ C. These figures are larger than the value 5×10^{-8} cm computed from the simple formula

$$l = \frac{1}{\pi n R^2}$$

with 10^{-8} cm for R. This is an indication of the formal character of the theory developed in this section. The assumption that the atoms are perfectly elastic spheres is clearly not a particularly good one, unless we are willing to assign to the radius of such spheres a smaller value than 10^{-8} cm. This is, of course, a possibility; the effective radius of an atom for a collision may be much smaller than the dimensions of the core of the atom from the quantum mechanical standpoint. The variation of l with temperature is another matter untouched by the formal theory.

Let us next proceed to the thermal conductivity. In eq. (30), suppose that $J = 0$, i.e., zero electric current flow. The result shows that there must still exist an electric field intensity as long as a temperature gradient exists or the metal is non-homogeneous. Its value is given by

$$e\mathscr{E} = kT\frac{\partial \gamma_1}{\partial x} + k\frac{\partial T}{\partial x}\frac{A_2}{A_1}. \tag{40}$$

We substitute this into the expression for the heat flow (31) and obtain

$$C = \frac{4\pi kT}{3m} A_2 k \frac{\partial T}{\partial x}\left[\frac{A_2}{A_1} - \frac{A_3}{A_2}\right]. \tag{41}$$

The thermal conductivity κ, which by definition is the ratio of C to the negative temperature gradient, becomes

$$\kappa = -\frac{4\pi k^2 T}{3m} A_2 \left[\frac{A_2}{A_1} - \frac{A_3}{A_2}\right]. \tag{42}$$

To evaluate this we must compute A_2 and A_3. From (29) we have

$$A_2 = \frac{2kT}{m} \int_0^\infty \left[f_0 u \frac{d(lu)}{du} + f_0 lu \right] du. \tag{43}$$

We now fall back on the expansion (35) for ul. By the use of this, (43) becomes

$$A_2 = \frac{2kT}{m} \int_0^\infty \left[f_0 \sum_{j=0}^\infty (j+2) B_j u^{j+1} \right] du. \tag{44}$$

We now revert to the expression for U' in eq. (122) of Chapter VIII, and can write to the second approximation

$$A_2 = \frac{2kT}{m} \cdot \frac{2m^3}{h^3} \left[\gamma_1^2 l(\gamma_1) + 2c_2 \left(\frac{d^2(u^2 l)}{du^2} \right)_{\gamma_1} \right]$$

$$= \frac{2kT}{m} \cdot \frac{2m^3}{h^3} \left[\gamma_1^2 l(\gamma_1) + 2c_2 \left(2l(\gamma_1) + 4\gamma_1 \left(\frac{dl}{du} \right)_{\gamma_1} + \gamma_1^2 \left(\frac{d^2 l}{du^2} \right)_{\gamma_1} \right) \right]. \tag{45}$$

Next we must get A_3 as

$$A_3 = \frac{2kT}{m} \int_0^\infty f_0 \cdot \left(2u^2 l + u^2 \frac{d(ul)}{du} \right) du.$$

By proceeding as before, we have to the second approximation

$$A_3 = \frac{2kT}{m} \int_0^\infty \left[f_0 \sum_{j=0}^\infty (j+3) B_j u^{j+2} \right] du$$

$$= \frac{2kT}{m} \cdot \frac{2m^3}{h^3} \left[\gamma_1^3 l(\gamma_1) + 2c_2 \left(\frac{d^2(u^3 l)}{du^2} \right)_{\gamma_1} \right]$$

$$= \frac{2kT}{m} \cdot \frac{2m^3}{h^3} \left[\gamma_1^3 l(\gamma_1) + 2c_2 \left(6\gamma_1 l(\gamma_1) + 6\gamma_1^2 \left(\frac{dl}{du} \right)_{\gamma_1} + \gamma_1^3 \left(\frac{d^2 l}{du^2} \right)_{\gamma_1} \right) \right]. \tag{46}$$

We are now ready to evaluate κ. In the ratio A_2/A_1 we need to consider only the first approximation to A_1, namely, that given in (37), since simple inspection shows that the terms in the next approximation involve derivatives of l only, which we shall neglect throughout. However, in A_2 and A_3 we must consider that part of the second approximation which does not involve the derivatives. We finally obtain

$$\frac{A_2}{A_1} \doteq \frac{\gamma_1^2 l(\gamma_1) + 4c_2 l(\gamma_1)}{\gamma_1 l(\gamma_1)} = \gamma_1 + \frac{4c_2}{\gamma_1}$$

and

$$\frac{A_3}{A_2} \doteq \frac{\gamma_1^3 l(\gamma_1) + 12c_2\gamma_1 l(\gamma_1)}{\gamma_1^2 l(\gamma_1) + 4c_2 l(\gamma_1)} = \gamma_1 + \frac{8c_2}{\gamma_1}.$$

Consequently the heat conductivity becomes (with $\pi^2/12$ for c_2)

$$\kappa = \frac{16\pi k^3 T^2 m}{3h^3} \gamma_1^2 l(\gamma_1) \frac{4c_2}{\gamma_1} = \frac{16\pi^3 k^3 T^2 m}{9h^3} \gamma_1 l(\gamma_1). \qquad (47)$$

Let us now take the ratio of κ to σT. The result is

$$\frac{\kappa}{\sigma T} = \frac{16\pi^3 k^3 T^2 m}{9h^3} \cdot \frac{3h^3}{16\pi m e^2 k T^2} = \frac{\pi^2}{3} \frac{k^2}{e^2}. \qquad (48)$$

We have thus derived the well-known Wiedemann-Franz law connecting the electrical and thermal conductivities of metallic conductors. If we use the electromagnetic unit of charge for e, the value of the constant on the right side of (48) turns out to be approximately

$$\frac{\pi^2}{3} \frac{k^2}{e^2} = 2.44 \times 10^8 \frac{\text{ergs}^2}{(\text{degree C})^2 (\text{emu})^2}. \qquad (49)$$

At room temperature (293° K) we have

$$\frac{\kappa}{\sigma} = 7.15 \times 10^{10}$$

in absolute units. This agrees rather well with the mean of the experimental values for such metals as Al, Cu, Ag, Ni, Zn, Cd, Pb, Sn, Pt, Pd, Fe. The following table (taken from H. Fröhlich, "Elektronen Theorie der Metalle," Springer, Berlin, 1936) shows the nature of the agreement. It gives the experimental values of $\kappa/\sigma T$ for two different temperatures.

	Metal	Cu	Ag	Au	Zn	Cd	Pb	Fe
$\frac{\kappa}{\sigma T} \times 10^{-8}$	291°	2.28	2.36	2.43	2.31	2.42	2.45	2.88
	373°	2.32	2.37	2.45	2.33	2.43	2.51	3.00

Of these metals, iron is the only one to deviate notably from the theoretical value (49). In general the values for various steels show considerable increase with temperature. There are indeed more notable exceptions to the law. The constant for rhodium, for example, is only 1.33. In general, however, the law may be taken to be well established.

It should be pointed out that though the classical statistical theory of Lorentz also leads to a law of the form (48), the value of the constant comes out to be $2k^2/e^2$ in place of $\pi^2/3 \cdot k^2/e^2$. This is in definite disagreement with the experimental values for most metals measured and constitutes a serious objection to the Lorentz theory. The reader may show that, as might be expected, the Lorentz result can be obtained from the quantum statistical theory above outlined if one assumes a *non-degenerate* gas. This makes clear the essential failure of the Lorentz theory from the standpoint of quantum statistics.

At the same time it must be emphasized that the Sommerfeld application of the Fermi-Dirac statistics is by no means a complete picture. It dodges entirely the fundamental question of the mean free path of the electrons and treats the interaction between the electrons and the atoms of the metal in a purely superficial fashion. Only a thoroughgoing application of quantum mechanics can overcome these defects. As a first approximation, at any rate, the Sommerfeld theory must be viewed as a successful application of quantum statistics.

2. HEAT PRODUCTION IN A CONDUCTOR. THE THOMSON EFFECT

The work done per second by the electric field $\mathscr{E}$ when an electric current I flows through the length dx of a conductor is $\mathscr{E}I\,dx = \mathscr{E}JS\,dx$, where S is the area of cross-section. The power expended per unit volume is therefore $J\mathscr{E}$. Denoting, as usual, by C the rate of flow of heat per second per unit area, the rate of increase in heat content per unit volume is $-\dfrac{\partial C}{\partial x}$. Hence the net rate of heat production per unit volume is

$$Q = J\mathscr{E} - \frac{\partial C}{\partial x}. \tag{50}$$

From eq. (30) we can solve for $\mathscr{E}$ in terms of J, etc. Thus substituting for A_1 in terms of the electrical conductivity σ from eq. (33), we have

$$\mathscr{E} = J/\sigma + \frac{k}{e}\frac{\partial T}{\partial x}\frac{A_2}{A_1} + \frac{kT}{e}\frac{\partial \gamma_1}{\partial x}. \tag{51}$$

The next step is to substitute this expression for $\mathscr{E}$ in that for C (eq. 31). The result is

$$C = \frac{4\pi kT}{3m}A_2\left[\frac{eJ}{\sigma} - k\frac{\partial T}{\partial x}\left(\frac{A_3}{A_2} - \frac{A_2}{A_1}\right)\right]. \tag{52}$$

From eq. (42) we can solve for $\left(\dfrac{A_3}{A_2} - \dfrac{A_2}{A_1}\right)$ in terms of κ and get

$$\left(\frac{A_3}{A_2} - \frac{A_2}{A_1}\right) = \frac{3m\kappa}{4\pi k^2 TA_2},\tag{53}$$

whence eq. (52) can be written

$$C = \frac{4\pi k TeJA_2}{3m\sigma} - \kappa\frac{\partial T}{\partial x}.\tag{54}$$

The quantity Q therefore becomes

$$Q = J\mathscr{E} + \frac{\partial}{\partial x}\left(\kappa\frac{\partial T}{\partial x}\right) - \frac{4\pi ekJ}{3m}\frac{\partial}{\partial x}\left(\frac{TA_2}{\sigma}\right),\tag{55}$$

or, using (51) again,

$$Q = \frac{J^2}{\sigma} + \frac{\partial}{\partial x}\left(\kappa\frac{\partial T}{\partial x}\right) + \frac{JkT}{e}\frac{\partial}{\partial x}\left(\gamma_1 - \frac{A_2}{A_1}\right).\tag{56}$$

This is a very interesting expression. We recognize at once the term J^2/σ as the Joule heat production rate per unit volume. The second term, $\dfrac{\partial}{\partial x}\left(\kappa\dfrac{\partial T}{\partial x}\right)$, is the rate of heat production per unit volume due to heat conduction. It is clear that we must attribute the last term in (56) to the thermoelectric effects. Let us review these briefly.

We consider first the *Thomson effect*. If a current flows in the conductor in the direction of the positive x axis and if a temperature gradient $\partial T/\partial x$ is maintained in the conductor, it is found that for certain metals in the part of the conductor in which the temperature gradient is positive, heat is absorbed by the metal, while in the part where the temperature gradient is negative, heat is evolved by the metal. This is true, for example, in the case of copper, which is said to exhibit a positive Thomson effect. On the other hand, there are metals in which positive $\partial T/\partial x$ is accompanied by the evolution of heat and negative $\partial T/\partial x$ by absorption of heat. Iron is an example of this, and the effect is known as the negative Thomson effect. In lead the effect is so small that it is generally considered negligible. The Thomson heat, unlike the Joule heat, is reversible.

Lord Kelvin (for whom the effect is named) discovered by experiment that the thermoelectric heat energy evolved or absorbed per second per unit volume of the conductor, i.e., the heat additional to the Joule heat, is directly proportional to the product of the current density and the temperature gradient. The coefficient will be denoted by μ and called the Thomson *thermoelectric coefficient*. Thus if we denote the Thomson heat by Q_T, we have [1]

$$Q_T = \mu J \frac{\partial T}{\partial x}. \tag{57}$$

From eq. (56) it follows that for a homogeneous metal

$$\mu = \frac{kT}{e} \frac{\partial}{\partial T} (\gamma_1 - A_2/A_1). \tag{58}$$

Substituting the value for A_2/A_1 given just after eq. (46), we obtain

$$\mu = -\frac{kT}{e} \frac{\partial}{\partial T} \left(\frac{4c_2}{\gamma_1} \right). \tag{59}$$

We must now insert the value of γ_1 for a degenerate electron gas given in eq. (128) of Chapter VIII (the first approximation being sufficient). We replace τ by 2τ, as usual. Carrying out the differentiation yields

$$|\mu| = \frac{2\pi^2 mk^2 T}{3eh^2} \left(\frac{8\pi\tau}{3N} \right)^{2/3}. \tag{60}$$

The slight variation of τ/N with temperature is here neglected. We now discuss the comparison with experiment. If we substitute into (60) the value of $N/\tau = 5.9 \times 10^{22}$ appropriate for silver and take $T = 300°$ K, etc., we get approximately $\mu = 1.5$ microvolts/$°$ C (equivalent to 150 ergs/emu degree C). The experimental value of the Thomson coefficient for silver is 1.2 microvolts/$°$ C, and in general the experimental values run between 1 and 10 microvolts/$°$ C. Hence there is general order of magnitude agreement with experiment. This is interesting since the original Lorentz theory, which is equivalent to the present theory for the non-degenerate or very weakly degenerate case, gives much higher values, indeed of the order of 100 microvolts/$°$ C. In fact, the reader can show by the use of the non-degenerate forms of γ_1 and A_2/A_1 in (58) that the magnitude of μ on the classical Lorentz theory is the universal constant $\dfrac{3}{2} \dfrac{k}{e}$, which should

[1] There are many so-called Thomson coefficients, only one of which is presented here. It is the one which is ordinarily measured. For a fuller discussion, see Sommerfeld and Frank, "Statistical Theory of Thermoelectric, Galvano- and Thermomagnetic Phenomena in Metals," *Reviews of Modern Physics* 3, 1 (1931). A thorough discussion of the thermoelectric effects from the standpoint of thermodynamics will be found in P. W. Bridgman, "The Thermodynamics of Electrical Phenomena in Metals," Macmillan, 1934.

then apply to all conductors. There is one "fly in the ointment," to be sure, namely, the fact that the Sommerfeld theory in the simple form here presented is no more able than the Lorentz theory to distinguish between the positive and negative Thomson effects, i.e., we can calculate $|\mu|$ only.

3. THE PELTIER EFFECT

We next consider a non-uniform conductor maintained at uniform temperature. In eq. (56) the term in $\partial T/\partial x$ accordingly drops out and the heat production due to the flow of current through the non-homogeneous medium is given by the last term with the understanding that T remains constant while the medium changes its character with x. Let us suppose we have two different metals in "contact," which is taken to mean that they are separated by a very narrow transition layer. We shall define the heat produced per unit area of this layer per second by unit current density as the *Peltier* heat. It is denoted by π_{12}, the subscripts referring to the two metallic media. Therefore we have

$$\pi_{12} = \frac{kT}{e} \int_{x_1}^{x_2} \frac{\partial}{\partial x}\left[\gamma_1 - \frac{A_2}{A_1}\right] dx = \frac{kT}{e}\left[\gamma_1 - \frac{A_2}{A_1}\right]_{x_1}^{x_2}, \qquad (61)$$

where x_1 and x_2 refer to the boundaries of the transition layer in the two metals respectively. Utilizing the expression for the bracket already employed in eq. (59) we obtain

$$\pi_{12} = -\frac{kT\pi^2}{3e\gamma_1}\bigg]_{x_1}^{x_2} = -\frac{2\pi^2 mk^2 T^2}{3eh^2}\left(\frac{8\pi}{3}\right)^{\frac{2}{3}}\left[\left(\frac{N}{\tau}\right)_2^{-\frac{2}{3}} - \left(\frac{N}{\tau}\right)_1^{-\frac{2}{3}}\right], \qquad (62)$$

where $(N/\tau)_1$ and $(N/\tau)_2$ refer to the values for the first and second metals respectively. The calculation for the case of the copper-silver couple at $T = 300°$ K, yields approximately 100 microvolts. The agreement with experiment is not startlingly good, since the experimental value turns out to be about -30 microvolt, the minus sign signifying the evolution of heat as the current goes from Cu to Ag. Fortunately for the Sommerfeld theory, the result calculated on the old Lorentz theory is even further out of the way, being around 9,000 microvolts. It is perhaps well to emphasize that the experimental values are not too certain, rendering the comparison between theory and experiment rather precarious.

4. THERMOELECTRIC ELECTROMOTIVE FORCE.
THE SEEBECK EFFECT

We next attempt the calculation of the actual thermoelectric emf in an open circuit.

Consider two different metals 1 and 2 (Fig. 10·2) with junctions P_1 and P_2. We wish to find the potential difference between A and B, maintained at temperature T, while P_1 and P_2 are kept at temperature

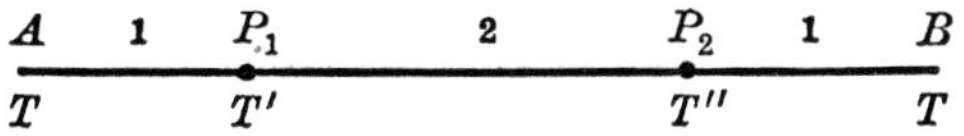

$$
\begin{array}{ccccccc}
A & 1 & P_1 & 2 & P_2 & 1 & B \\
\hline
T & & T' & & T'' & & T
\end{array}
$$

FIG. 10·2.

T' and T'' respectively. Since no current flows, eq. (40) holds for the field intensity and therefore there exists a difference in potential between A and B which has the value

$$V_{AB} = \int_A^B \mathscr{E}\,dx = \frac{k}{e}\int_A^B \frac{\partial T}{\partial x}\cdot\frac{A_2}{A_1}\,dx + \frac{k}{e}\int_A^B T\frac{\partial\gamma_1}{\partial x}\,dx. \quad (63)$$

We must evaluate this for the degenerate case and hence use $A_2/A_1 = \gamma_1 + \pi^2/3\gamma_1$. This yields

$$V_{AB} = \frac{k}{e}\int_A^B \left(\gamma_1 + \frac{\pi^2}{3\gamma_1}\right)dT + \frac{k}{e}\int_A^B T\frac{\partial\gamma_1}{\partial x}\,dx. \quad (64)$$

Integration by parts of the second integral yields $-\dfrac{k}{e}\gamma_1 dT$, whence

$$V_{AB} = \frac{\pi^2 k}{3e}\int_A^B \frac{dT}{\gamma_1} = \frac{\pi^2 k}{3e}\left[\int_T^{T'}\frac{dT}{\gamma_{11}} + \int_{T'}^{T''}\frac{dT}{\gamma_{12}} + \int_{T''}^{T}\frac{dT}{\gamma_{11}}\right], \quad (65)$$

where γ_{11} is the value of γ_1 for the first metal and γ_{12} that for the second. The use of the first approximation for γ_1 (eq. 128 of Chapter VIII) leads to

$$
\begin{aligned}
V_{AB} &= \frac{\pi^2 k}{3e}\int_{T'}^{T''}\left(\frac{1}{\gamma_{12}} - \frac{1}{\gamma_{11}}\right)dT \\
&= \frac{\pi^2 k}{3e}\cdot\frac{2mk}{h^2}\cdot\left(\frac{8\pi}{3}\right)^{\!2/3}\int_{T'}^{T''}\left[\left(\frac{\tau}{N}\right)_2^{2/3} - \left(\frac{\tau}{N}\right)_1^{2/3}\right]T\,dT. \quad (66)
\end{aligned}
$$

Furthermore if we neglect to a first approximation the dependence of τ/N on T, the approximate result is

$$V_{AB} = \frac{\pi^2 k^2 m}{3eh^2}\left(\frac{8\pi}{3}\right)^{\!2/3}\left[\left(\frac{\tau}{N}\right)_2^{2/3} - \left(\frac{\tau}{N}\right)_1^{2/3}\right](T''^2 - T'^2). \quad (67)$$

This agrees much better with experimental results than the corresponding formula for the classical Lorentz case which the reader may show is in the form

$$V_{AB}^{\text{classical}} = \frac{k}{e}\left[\log\left(\frac{N}{\tau}\right)_2 - \log\left(\frac{N}{\tau}\right)_1\right](T'' - T').\tag{68}$$

Thus for the case of a silver-sodium thermocouple substitution into (67) gives for $T'' - T' = 1$ degree C at $0°$ C

$$V_{AB} \doteq 1.0 \text{ microvolt,}$$

whereas the classical formula yields for the same couple under the same conditions 72 microvolts. The experimental value is approximately 3 microvolts. The reader should work out other cases for himself.

It may indeed be shown that (67) can be put into the form:

$$V_{AB} = 546K(t'' - t')\left[1 + \frac{1}{273}\cdot\frac{(t'' + t')}{2}\right],\tag{69}$$

where t represents centigrade temperature and K is a constant depending on the couple. This is in line with the actual *form* of the experimental observations, though the numerical values do not agree in every instance.

5. TRANSVERSE GALVANOMAGNETIC AND THERMOMAGNETIC EFFECTS

Less well known than the thermoelectric effects just discussed are those produced in a conductor through which heat or electricity is flowing by the presence of a magnetic field. The phenomena particularly studied are those in which the magnetic field is applied at right angles to the current or heat flow. Chief among them is the Hall effect in which the magnetic field applied transversely to a current-carrying rod produces a transverse potential difference at right angles to both field and current which is directly proportional to the product of the intensity of the magnetic field and the current strength and inversely proportional to the transverse width of the conductor. The proportionality constant is the so-called Hall coefficient. There are three other similar effects: (*a*) Ettingshausen effect, or the production of a transverse temperature difference by the interaction of transverse magnetic field and electric current flow, when the conductor is thermally insulated; (*b*) Nernst effect, or the production of a transverse potential difference when heat flow takes place lengthwise of the conductor; and (c) Righi-Leduc effect, or the production of a transverse temperature difference when heat flows lengthwise of a thermally insulated conductor.

All these effects constitute transport phenomena which can be treated by the theory of this chapter. The fundamental equation (10) must be generalized to take care of an additional dimension as well as the force on the electrons due to the magnetic field. The resulting transport formulas for J and C are analogous to (30) and (31) respectively but naturally rather more complicated. We shall not present the analysis or the results here [5] but merely remark that the agreement with experiment is reasonably good and of the same general character as that already encountered in the thermoelectric phenomena. One interesting byproduct of these studies is the change in effective resistance of a conductor due to the applied magnetic field.

6. MOTION OF ELECTRONS IN A CRYSTAL LATTICE.
SIMPLE TREATMENT

The Sommerfeld theory employed in the preceding sections assumes that the conduction electrons are free or at any rate move in a field of constant potential. It takes account of the interaction of the moving electrons and the atoms or ions of the metal only from the classical and formal standpoint of elastic collisions. Actually the potential field in which metallic electrons move is by no means uniform and a more thoroughgoing application of statistics to the electrical and thermal properties of metals must take account of this fact. Much recent work has been done in this field [6] but a thorough survey of it lies outside the scope of the present volume. However, a simplified special case may prove of some interest as an introduction to the modern theory of metals.

In order to employ a statistical distribution formula like eq. (47) of Chapter VIII it is essential to know the possible energy values E_j and the number of such values in any given energy interval. In our previous discussion we have used the values appropriate to a set of free electrons. We now wish to see how they are modified by the motion of the electrons in a force field. The actual field of force encountered in a crystal lattice is a complicated affair. Nevertheless if the metal is in the form of a single crystal, the regular arrangement of the atoms assures

[5] A discussion will be found in the article of Sommerfeld and Frank already cited.

[6] Cf. Mott and Jones, "The Theory of the Properties of Metals and Alloys," Oxford, 1936. Also cf. A. H. Wilson, "The Theory of Metals," Cambridge, 1936 and F. Seitz, "The Modern Theory of Solids," McGraw-Hill, 1940.

that the field will be of *periodic* character in space. We therefore examine the motion of electrons through a periodic potential field. The simplest case of this kind is the one-dimensional lattice shown schematically in the following diagram (Fig. 10·3) which plots the variation of the potential energy $V(x)$ with x. In the hollows of the

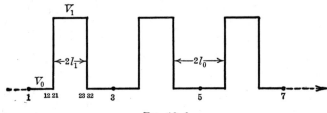

FIG. 10·3.

square saw-toothed curve the potential energy is assumed to have the constant value V_0 and in the crests the constant value V_1. For simplicity we suppose the curve extends from $-\infty$ to $+\infty$. The widths of the potential energy regions are $2l_0$ and $2l_1$ respectively. This is, of course, a highly idealized picture but it does provide a simple type of periodically varying potential energy.

The Schrödinger equations (cf. eqs. 3 and 52 of Chapter VIII) for the two regions where the potential energies are respectively V_0 and V_1 are

$$\frac{d^2\psi}{dx^2} + \frac{8\pi^2 m}{h^2}(E - V_0)\psi = 0 \quad \text{(hollow)} \tag{70}$$

$$\frac{d^2\psi}{dx^2} + \frac{8\pi^2 m}{h^2}(E - V_1)\psi = 0 \quad \text{(crest).} \tag{71}$$

If $E < V_0$ as well as $E < V_1$, it is clear that the solutions of both equations will be exponential functions with real exponents. Such functions, however, cannot correspond to genuine transmission of electrons through the structure, for the terms in which the exponents are negative will more or less quickly go to zero as x increases and hence correspond to very small probability of finding electrons very far to the right of any chosen origin, while the terms in which the exponents are positive will go to infinity as x increases, which has no meaning in quantum mechanics. We must therefore choose $E > V_0$ at least, though it will develop that we can secure transmission under certain conditions if $E < V_1$. In fact the latter situation is more interesting than $E > V_1$. Let us therefore discuss the problem for $V_1 > E > V_0$. Let

$$\frac{8\pi^2 m}{h^2}(E - V_0) = k_0^2,$$

$$\frac{8\pi^2 m}{h^2}(V_1 - E) = k_1^2. \tag{72}$$

The solutions of (70) and (71) become respectively (cf. eqs. 56 of Chapter VIII)

$$\psi = A_0 e^{ik_0 x} + B_0 e^{-ik_0 x} \quad \text{(hollow)}, \tag{73}$$

$$\psi = A_1 e^{k_1 x} + B_1 e^{-k_1 x} \quad \text{(crest)}, \tag{74}$$

where the arbitrary constants A_0, B_0, A_1, B_1 are in general complex. The transmission of electrons through the lattice is handled by setting up the boundary conditions expressing continuity in ψ and $d\psi/dx$ at each boundary surface. Differentiating and using the prime notation for differentiation with respect to x we get

$$\psi' = ik_0(A_0 e^{ik_0 x} - B_0 e^{-ik_0 x}) \quad \text{(hollow)}, \tag{75}$$

$$\psi' = k_1(A_1 e^{k_1 x} - B_1 e^{-k_1 x}) \quad \text{(crest)}. \tag{76}$$

We shall now denote the midpoints of successive hollows by 1, 3, 5 $\cdots$ and proceed to express the ψ and ψ' values at any point in a hollow in terms of their values at the midpoints denoted by the subscripts 1, 3, 5 $\cdots$. Thus we get rid of the arbitrary constants by setting

$$\psi_1 = A_0 + B_0,$$

$$\psi_1' = ik_0(A_0 - B_0),$$

whence ψ and ψ' for any point between 1 and the next boundary surface become

$$\psi = \psi_1 \cos k_0 x + \frac{\psi_1'}{k_0} \sin k_0 x,$$

$$\psi' = \psi_1' \cos k_0 x - k_0 \psi_1 \sin k_0 x. \tag{77}$$

We now denote quantities at the first boundary at the left by the subscript combination 12 (see Fig. 10·3) and at the right by the combination 21. Therefore there results

$$\psi_{12} = \psi_1 \cos k_0 l_0 + \frac{\psi_1'}{k_0} \sin k_0 l_0,$$

$$\psi_{12}' = \psi_1' \cos k_0 l_0 - k_0 \psi_1 \sin k_0 l_0. \tag{78}$$

In similar fashion the ψ and ψ' at any point in the first crest region will be given in terms of ψ_{21} and ψ'_{21} immediately at the right of the boundary by

$$\psi = \psi_{21} \cosh k_1 x + \frac{\psi'_{21}}{k_1} \sinh k_1 x,$$

$$\text{(crest)} \quad (79)$$

$$\psi' = \psi'_{21} \cosh k_1 x + k_1 \psi_{21} \sinh k_1 x.$$

Hence (to consult the diagram once more)

$$\psi_{23} = \psi_{21} \cosh 2k_1 l_1 + \frac{\psi'_{21}}{k_1} \sinh 2k_1 l_1,$$

$$(80)$$

$$\psi'_{23} = \psi'_{21} \cosh 2k_1 l_1 + k_1 \psi_{21} \sinh 2k_1 l_1.$$

Finally, we can employ (77) again to write

$$\psi_3 = \psi_{32} \cos k_0 l_0 + \frac{\psi'_{32}}{k_0} \sin k_0 l_0,$$

$$(81)$$

$$\psi'_3 = \psi'_{32} \cos k_0 l_0 - k_0 \psi_{32} \sin k_0 l_0.$$

The boundary conditions are

$$\psi_{12} = \psi_{21}; \quad \psi'_{12} = \psi'_{21}$$

$$(82)$$

$$\psi_{23} = \psi_{32}; \quad \psi'_{23} = \psi'_{32}.$$

Our task now is to use eqs. (78), (80), (81), and (82) to express ψ_3 and ψ'_3 in terms of ψ_1 and ψ'_1. The resulting equations should hold for the state functions and their gradients at *any* two successive mid-hollow points and therefore tell the general story of the electron transmission through the periodic potential field. If we utilize the boundary conditions, eqs. (80) and (81) become

$$\psi_{23} = \psi_{12} \cosh 2k_1 l_1 + \frac{\psi'_{12}}{k_1} \sinh 2k_1 l_1,$$

$$(80')$$

$$\psi'_{23} = \psi'_{12} \cosh 2k_1 l_1 + k_1 \psi_{12} \sinh 2k_1 l_1,$$

and

$$\psi_3 = \psi_{23} \cos k_0 l_0 + \frac{\psi'_{23}}{k_0} \sin k_0 l_0,$$

$$(81')$$

$$\psi'_3 = \psi'_{23} \cos k_0 l_0 - k_0 \psi_{23} \sin k_0 l_0.$$

Eliminating ψ_{12}, ψ_{12}', ψ_{23}, and ψ_{23}' from the six equations (78), (80'), and (81') yields finally

$$\psi_3 = \psi_1 \left[\cosh 2k_1l_1 \cdot \cos 2k_0l_0 + \frac{1}{2}\left(\frac{k_1}{k_0} - \frac{k_0}{k_1}\right) \sinh 2k_1l_1 \cdot \sin 2k_0l_0 \right]$$
$$+ \frac{\psi_1'}{k_0}\left[\cosh 2k_1l_1 \cdot \sin 2k_0l_0 + \sinh 2k_1l_1 \left(\frac{k_1}{k_0}\sin^2 k_0l_0 + \frac{k_0}{k_1}\cos^2 k_0l_0\right) \right]. \tag{83}$$

$$\psi_3' = \psi_1' \left[\cosh 2k_1l_1 \cdot \cos 2k_0l_0 + \frac{1}{2}\left(\frac{k_1}{k_0} - \frac{k_0}{k_1}\right) \sinh 2k_1l_1 \cdot \sin 2k_0l_0 \right]$$
$$- k_0\psi_1 \left[\cosh 2k_1l_1 \sin 2k_0l_0 - \sinh 2k_1l_1 \left(\frac{k_1}{k_0}\cos^2 k_0l_0 + \frac{k_0}{k_1}\sin^2 k_0l_0\right) \right]. \tag{84}$$

Because the structure we are considering is assumed to extend to infinity in both directions the relations (83) and (84) will hold for *any* two successive mid-hollow points and we can therefore write for any integral j

$$\psi_{j+2} = A\psi_j + \frac{B}{k_0}\psi_j', \tag{85}$$

$$\psi_{j+2}' = A\psi_j' - k_0C\psi_j, \tag{86}$$

where the A, B, C are the bracket expressions in (83) and (84).   Examination discloses that

$$A^2 + BC = 1. \tag{87}$$

Hence we may introduce the angle W such that

$$A = \cos W = \cosh 2k_1l_1 \cdot \cos 2k_0l_0 + \frac{1}{2}\left(\frac{k_1}{k_0} - \frac{k_0}{k_1}\right) \sinh 2k_1l_1 \cdot \sin 2k_0l_0. \tag{88}$$

$$B = \sqrt{\frac{B}{C}}\sin W; \quad C = \sqrt{\frac{C}{B}}\sin W. \tag{89}$$

Then (85) and (86) can be written

$$\psi_{j+2} = \psi_j \cos W + \frac{1}{k_0}\sqrt{\frac{B}{C}}\,\psi_j' \sin W, \tag{90}$$

$$\psi_{j+2}' = \psi_j' \cos W - k_0\sqrt{\frac{C}{B}}\,\psi_j \sin W. \tag{91}$$

From the symmetrical nature of the infinite structure we are able to write for every j

$$\psi_{j+2} = e^{i\theta}\psi_j, \tag{92}$$

where θ is independent of j and is a function of the energy and physical parameters of the structure only. Then

$$\psi'_{j+2} = e^{i\theta}\psi'_j. \tag{92'}$$

This means that

$$\psi'_{j+2}/\psi_{j+2} = \psi'_j/\psi_j = Z, \tag{93}$$

where Z is a constant independent of j. If we now divide (91) by (90) we obtain after a little reduction

$$Z = ik_0\sqrt{\frac{C}{B}}. \tag{94}$$

The substitution of $\psi'_j = ik_0\sqrt{\dfrac{C}{B}}\,\psi_j$ in (90) then yields

$$\psi_{j+2} = \psi_j e^{iW}, \tag{95}$$

which on comparison with (92) shows that

$$\theta = W. \tag{96}$$

If now W is a *real* angle, e^{iW} has the absolute value unity and ψ_{j+2} and ψ_j differ only in phase but not in magnitude. Here there is complete transmission of electrons through the periodic structure, since $|\psi_j|^2$ measures the average density of moving electrons at the jth mid-hollow point. On the other hand, if W is a complex angle ψ_{j+2} differs from ψ_j in magnitude as well as in phase and there is a decrease in $|\psi|^2$ as one goes from one mid-hollow point to the next. This means that when W is complex there is no transmission of electrons through the structure. Consequently we can look on cos W as a function characterizing the possibility of transmission. For cos W is real (cf. eq. 88) and hence we have transmission when

$$|\cos W| \leq 1, \tag{97}$$

and no transmission for

$$|\cos W| > 1. \tag{98}$$

If we plot cos W as a function of the energy E from eq. (88) there will be certain energy ranges for which (97) will be true and electrons of these energies will be transmitted through the metal represented by the periodic model in question; these will be separated by other energy ranges for which (98) is true and electrons of such energies will be denied transmission through the metal. In other words we can look upon the structure with the periodically varying potential field as a kind of *filter* for electrons. It is indeed analogous to electric and elastic wave filters which have been studied extensively.[7]

The energy bands for which $|\cos W| \leq 1$ give the allowed energy values for electrons which can actually move through the lattice, i.e., those electrons which are of interest for conduction of heat and electricity.

In order to plot these energy bands, let us go back to the expression for $\cos W$ in eq. (88). When $E = V_0$, $k_0 = 0$ and $k_1 = \sqrt{8\pi^2 m/h^2}$ $\sqrt{V_1 - V_0}$. Let us suppose for simplicity that $l_1 \ll l_0$ and indeed to such an extent that we can replace $\cosh 2k_1 l_1$ by $1 + 2k_1^2 l_1^2$ and $\sinh 2k_1 l_1$ by $2k_1 l_1$ to a sufficiently close approximation. Then $\cos W$ becomes

$$\cos W = (1 + 2k_1^2 l_1^2) \cos 2k_0 l_0 + \left(\frac{k_1}{k_0} - \frac{k_0}{k_1}\right) k_1 l_1 \sin 2k_0 l_0. \quad (99)$$

When $k_0 = 0$, this reduces to

$$\cos W = (1 + 2k_1^2 l_1^2) + 2k_1^2 l_1 l_0, \quad (100)$$

which is certainly greater than unity. Consequently for electrons with energy in the neighborhood of V_0 there is no transmission through the structure. On the other hand when the energy has increased sufficiently so that $2k_0 l_0 = \pi/2$, $\cos W$ becomes

$$\cos W = \left(\frac{k_1}{k_0} - \frac{k_0}{k_1}\right) k_1 l_1, \quad (101)$$

which *can* be smaller than unity in absolute value. Thus, to take an illustration in which the dimensions are reasonable for a metal crystal lattice, let $2l_0$ be of the order of 5×10^{-8} cm and $2l_1$ of order 10^{-12} cm. Let V_0 be of the order of 1 electron volt, while V_1 is of order 10 to 100 electron volts. Then $\cos W$ in (101) will be much smaller than unity and transmission is assured for the energy corresponding to $2k_0 l_0 = \pi/2$. When the energy is great enough so that $2k_0 l_0 = \pi$, $\cos W$ again becomes greater than unity, taking the form $1 + 2k_1^2 l_1^2$ as may be seen from (99). The result is that as E increases from V_0 to V_1, $\cos W$ oscil-

---

[7] For elastic wave and acoustic filters with the theory treated in mathematical analogy with the foregoing, see R. B. Lindsay, "The Filtration of Sound," Parts I and II, *Journal of Applied Physics* **9**, 612 (1938) and **10**, 680 (1939).

lates in a manner shown graphically (of course only in qualitative fashion) in Fig. 10·4. It will be seen that as E increases, $\cos W$ exceeds unity at periodic intervals given approximately by

$$2k_0l_0 = n\pi, \quad n = 0, 1, 2 \cdots. \tag{102}$$

For small energy ranges in the vicinity of the values corresponding to (102) there will be no transmission. These regions are indicated by cross-hatching in the figure. The corresponding energy values are given by

$$E - V_0 = \frac{n^2h^2}{32ml_0^2}. \tag{102'}$$

It will be noted that the forbidden regions grow progressively narrower in width as the energy increases. This can be seen on exam-

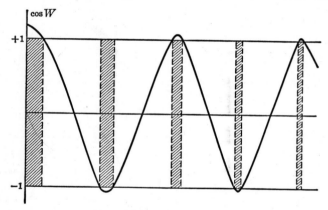

FIG. 10·4.

ination of (99). The unshaded regions in Fig. 10·4 correspond to the transmitted energy bands. The criterion (102) for the non-transmitted energy values has an interesting significance connected with the possibility of interpreting k_0 in terms of the de Broglie wavelength of the electron. For since the latter wavelength is $\lambda = h/mv$, we see from (72) that

$$k_0 = \frac{2\pi}{\lambda},$$

and hence the wavelengths not transmitted are those in the immediate vicinity of

$$\lambda = \frac{4l_0}{n}. \tag{103}$$

If we used the parlance of electrical and elastic wave filters we should call the metal lattice here being considered a *high-pass* electron filter. Of course it is also a band-pass filter as well.

The question may be raised: What happens when $E > V_1$? The solutions then become harmonic in both crests and hollows. This can be readily accommodated to the solution above by merely taking k_1 pure imaginary. Thus we set

$$k_1 = ik_1'$$

where k_1' is real and positive. Then we have

$$\cos W = \cos 2k_1'l_1 \cos 2k_0l_0 - \frac{1}{2}\left(\frac{k_1'}{k_0} + \frac{k_0}{k_1'}\right) \sin 2k_1'l_1 \sin 2k_0l_0. \quad (104)$$

If $2k_1'l_1$ is still small, however, we can use the same approximation as in the previous case with the same general consequences. Of course, as the energy increases very considerably $2k_1'l_1$ will eventually become large enough to lead to oscillations in $\cos 2k_1'l_1$ and $\sin 2k_1'l_1$ though at a slower rate than $\cos 2k_0l_0$. At the same time the ratios k_1'/k_0 and k_0/k_1' will approach unity. The result is that $\cos W$ approaches

$$\cos W = \cos 2(k_1'l_1 + k_0l_0), \quad (105)$$

with the transmission of almost *all* energies, the non-transmission bands being reduced to negligible width compared with the transmission bands.

The structure considered in this section is idealized to the extent that it extends to infinity in both directions. One might suppose that the situation would be different in a *finite* lattice which corresponds more exactly to an actual metal crystal. However the analysis indicates that the energy bands for transmission are not seriously affected by the change to the finite case.

In order to apply the ideas of this section to actual metallic lattices it is necessary to generalize them to three dimensions. This complicates the analysis considerably and we shall not embark on it here. The results are similar, however, in the sense that there are certain energy bands for which electrons are allowed to move freely through a metal crystal. This does not mean, of course, that an undisturbed metal in equilibrium will always have some current flowing through it; in equilibrium there will always be as many electrons moving on the average in any one direction as in the reverse direction. However the imposition of an electric field or a temperature gradient will upset the equilibrium and produce a net flow in a certain direction. The theory can also distinguish between good and bad conductors. In a bad conductor we have to suppose that all the lower allowed energy bands are filled with their complete quota of electrons, and that this is true even for the valency electrons which are the fastest moving electrons in the atoms composing the crystal. In order to produce a current it is necessary to transfer electrons in lower energy states to higher ones across the gap separating the allowed bands. If these gaps are sufficiently great it may take very considerable energy to cross them and the substance will then act effectively like an insulator. If on the other hand the energy bands available for the fastest moving electrons are not entirely occupied, electrons can be transferred to higher but neighboring energies without going out of the energy band and hence with effectively little change in energy and the substance behaves as a metallic conductor.

7. APPLICATION OF STATISTICS TO MAGNETISM

It is well known that an external magnetic field of intensity $\mathcal{H}$ induces in a metal a magnetic moment per unit volume, i.e., an intensity of magnetization $\mathcal{I}$, which for weak fields is directly proportional to the field intensity. We can write

$$\mathcal{I} = \chi \mathcal{H}, \tag{106}$$

where χ is known as the magnetic susceptibility. If $\chi > 0$ and is a constant independent of the field for moderate fields the metal is termed *paramagnetic*, while if $\chi < 0$, it is called *diamagnetic*. Metals possessing a finite value of $\mathcal{I}$ in the absence of a field and a susceptibility which varies with the field intensity are called *ferromagnetic*. We shall not be concerned with this type here and in fact shall concentrate our attention almost exclusively on paramagnetism.

When a magnetic field of intensity $\mathcal{H}$ changes the intensity of magnetization of a metal by $d\mathcal{I}$, the amount of energy required per unit volume is the scalar product

$$dU = \mathcal{H} \cdot d\mathcal{I}. \tag{107}$$

When the field changes from 0 to $\mathcal{H}$ the change in energy density is then (assuming (106))

$$U_{\mathcal{H}} - U_0 = -\tfrac{1}{2}\chi \mathcal{H}^2. \tag{108}$$

This represents a gain or loss in energy of the metallic electrons which are responsible for the magnetism. For paramagnetic substances, there is a loss in energy in the field, the electrons tending to line up their

magnetic moments parallel to and in the direction of the field. Dia-
magnetism is associated with the effect of a magnetic field on electrons
moving in closed orbits in which the magnetic moments induced by the
field are antiparallel to the field.

In quantum mechanics [8] it is shown that the magnetic moment of
the spinning electron is

$$\mu = \frac{eh}{4\pi mc}, \tag{109}$$

where e is the charge on the electron in esu and c is the velocity of light
in cm/sec. Strictly speaking to get the total magnetic moment of an
electron in an atom one must add to (109) the magnetic moment due
to the orbital motion of the electron. The valence electrons of metallic atoms, however, may be considered free to a first approximation and
hence their whole magnetic moment may be taken to be that due to
spin. We shall confine our attention to these free electrons.

If an external magnetic field is imposed on a metal, it is assumed
that the free electron spins are oriented either parallel or antiparallel
to the field. Hence if E is the energy of an electron in the absence of the
field, then its energy will be $E - \mu\mathcal{H}$ if it lines up parallel to the field
and $E + \mu\mathcal{H}$ if it lines up antiparallel to the field.

The number of electrons in the energy range $(E, E + dE)$ in the
absence of the field is taken to be the usual Fermi-Dirac distribution,
viz., [9]

$$N(E)dE = \frac{8\pi\tau/h^3 \cdot m^{3/2}\sqrt{2E}\,dE}{1 + e^{-\gamma_1}e^{E/kT}}. \tag{110}$$

This follows from eq. (66) of Chapter VIII with 2τ in place of τ and
$a = 1$. The notation otherwise remains the same as in Chapter VIII.
We shall find it simpler to write

$$N(E)dE = D(E)f(E)dE, \tag{111}$$

with

$$D(E) = \frac{8\pi\tau m^{3/2}\sqrt{2E}}{h^3}; \quad f(E) = \frac{1}{1 + e^{-\gamma_1}e^{E/kT}}. \tag{112}$$

On the average in the absence of a magnetic field half of these electrons

[8] Cf., for example, Lindsay and Margenau, "Foundations of Physics," p. 480.
[9] The treatment here follows in the main Fröhlich: "Elektronen Theorie der
Metalle," pp. 145 ff. Berlin, 1936.

have one type of spin and half the other. Hence when the field is applied the number of electrons with parallel spin is

$$N_p dE = \frac{D(E)}{2} f(E - \mu \mathcal{H}) dE, \tag{113}$$

while the number with antiparallel spin is

$$N_a dE = \frac{D(E)}{2} f(E + \mu \mathcal{H}) dE. \tag{114}$$

In these formulas the $D(E)$ is left unaltered, since $D(E)dE$ is the number of energy values lying between E and $E + dE$ and is unaffected by the field.

Now at $T = 0$, all states with energy less than the maximum value ϕ, which is equal to $h^2/8m \cdot (3N/\pi\tau)^{\frac{2}{3}}$ (eq. 135 of Chapter VIII with 2τ replacing τ as usual for electrons), are occupied, while all states with energy greater than ϕ are empty. If we agree to denote the maximum kinetic energy of electrons with spin parallel to the field by E_p and the maximum kinetic energy of electrons with antiparallel spin by E_a, we have

$$E_p = \phi + \mu \mathcal{H}; \quad E_a = \phi - \mu \mathcal{H}. \tag{115}$$

It is clear that there is an excess of electrons with parallel spin. In fact we can compute the excess as (note that for $T = 0$, $f(E) = 1$) $E < \phi$

$$X = \int_{\phi - \mu \mathcal{H}}^{\phi + \mu \mathcal{H}} \frac{D(E)dE}{2} = \frac{8\pi\tau m^{\frac{3}{2}}}{2h^3} \int_{\phi - \mu \mathcal{H}}^{\phi + \mu \mathcal{H}} \sqrt{2E} \, dE. \tag{116}$$

Since $\phi \gg \mu \mathcal{H}$ for magnetic field intensities less than 0.5×10^6 gauss we evaluate the integral to a high degree of approximation as

$$X = \mu \mathcal{H} D(\phi). \tag{117}$$

Associated with the excess electrons is a magnetic moment per unit of volume of magnitude

$$\mathcal{I} = \frac{\mu}{\tau} \cdot \mu \mathcal{H} D(\phi). \tag{118}$$

Consequently in so far as the magnetic properties of metals can be considered as due to free electrons, all metals should be paramagnetic and possess at $T = 0$ a susceptibility

$$\chi = \mu^2 D(\phi)/\tau. \tag{119}$$

Actually this is not the case for many metals are diamagnetic. Nevertheless there are some metals, e.g., the alkalies, for which the above assumption appears justified and which permit a comparison with experiment. The values are not given, of course, at $T = 0$, but an extension of the analysis given above shows that at low temperature there is very little variation of χ with temperature and consequently (119) should apply fairly accurately even when $T \neq 0$. In utilizing (112) we have

$$D(\phi) = \frac{8\pi\tau m^{3/2}\sqrt{2\phi}}{h^3}. \tag{120}$$

The substitution of $\phi = h^2/2m \cdot \left(\dfrac{3N}{8\pi\tau}\right)^{2/3}$ yields finally for the susceptibility

$$\chi = \frac{4\pi \hbar\iota\mu^2}{h^2} \cdot \left(\frac{3N}{\pi\tau}\right)^{1/3}. \tag{121}$$

This can be further simplified by the introduction of the value of μ from (109), whence

$$\chi = 1.9 \times 10^{-6} \left(\frac{\rho n_0}{A}\right)^{1/3}, \tag{122}$$

where ρ is the density, A the atomic weight and n_0 the number of electrons per atom. The following table gives the comparison between the experimental values for the alkali metals and those computed from (122). It should be noted that the values in the table are mass susceptibilities and are obtained by dividing χ in (122) by the density. The values quoted are in multiples of 10^{-6}.

TABLE OF SUSCEPTIBILITIES OF THE ALKALIES

(Taken from Mott and Jones, "Properties of Metals and Alloys," 1936.)

	Li	Na	K	Rb	Cs	
χ (computed)	1.5	0.68	0.60	0.32	0.24	
χ (observed)	0.5	0.51	0.40	0.07	−0.10	Honda and Owen (1912)
χ (observed)	—	0.65	0.54	0.21	0.22	Lane (1930)

The calculation of the diamagnetic susceptibility involves a consideration of the effect of the magnetic field on the orbital motion of the atomic electrons. The analysis is beyond the scope of the present volume.[10]

[10] Reference may be made to Mott and Jones, op. cit., pp. 201 ff.

PROBLEMS

1. Calculate values of the electron mean free path for sodium, copper, silver and gold from eq. (39) by using experimental values for the electrical conductivity at the temperatures $-200°$ C, $-100°$ C, $0°$ C, $100°$ C, and $200°$ C.

2. Calculate values of the electron mean free path for the metals listed in Problem 1 from eq. (47) by using experimental values for the thermal conductivity.

3. Derive the expressions for the thermal and electrical conductivities using the classical Maxwell-Boltzmann distribution function for f_0. Show that the Wiedemann-Franz ratio in this case is $2k^2/e^2$.

4. Derive the expression for the Thomson coefficient μ on the basis of the classical Lorentz theory. Evaluate it for the case of silver.

5. Verify eq. (69) and carry through the calculation for the thermoelectric emf of a copper-iron couple with junction temperatures $0°$ C and $100°$ C respectively.

6. Verify eq. (87).

7. Show that if the saw-tooth potential curve in Fig. 10·3 is replaced by one in which the variation in potential from one region to the next is continuous and very gradual the corresponding infinite linear lattice passes electrons of all energies. (Cf. the acoustical analogy in R. B. Lindsay, *J. Acous. Soc. Am.*, **12**, 378 [1941].)

8. Prove that the amount of energy per unit volume associated with the change of the intensity of magnetization of a metal by amount $d\mathscr{I}$ by a field of intensity $\mathscr{H}$ is

$$dU = \mathscr{H} \cdot d\mathscr{I}.$$

CHAPTER XI

EMISSION OF ELECTRONS FROM SURFACES

1. SIMPLE STATISTICAL THEORY OF THERMIONIC EMISSION

The emission of electrons from hot bodies, the so-called thermionic effect, is so well known and its importance in industry so well realized that it is unnecessary here to give a detailed description of the experimental facts. A good review of these will be found in the article by S. Dushman in "Reviews of Modern Physics," **2**, 381 (1930). The aim of the present discussion is the statistical derivation of the Richardson equation giving the thermionic current as a function of the temperature of the emitting metal. The method used is closely allied to that employed in Chapter X for the study of electrical conduction in metals and it is assumed that the emitted electrons form in the metal a degenerate gas obeying the Fermi-Dirac statistics.

The emitting metal is assumed to be in a vacuum with the emitting surface plane and perpendicular to the x axis. We further suppose that only those electrons are able to leave the metal for which the velocities in the x direction exceed the critical value v_{xo}. This corresponds to the kinetic energy $\frac{1}{2} m v_{xo}^2$, which we shall designate as E_c. It presumably will be a characteristic constant for the metal. Its physical significance will be discussed later. The thermionic current density will then be given by an expression like eq. (16) of Chapter X, except that in the integration only the velocity components in the y and z directions are allowed to run from $-\infty$ to $+\infty$, whereas v_x has the lower limit v_{xo}. Moreover the general distribution function f is replaced by f_o, since no external field is applied. The expression for the thermionic current density therefore is

$$ J = \frac{2m^3 e}{h^3} \int_{-\infty}^{+\infty} \int_{-\infty}^{+\infty} \int_{v_{xo}}^{\infty} \frac{v_x}{1 + e^{-\gamma_1 + E/kT}} \, dv_x \, dv_y \, dv_z. \qquad (1) $$

The evaluation of the integral is materially simplified by the fact that E in the integrand can no longer take on the value zero as in eq. (16) in Chapter X. In fact the minimum value of E is E_c. It develops that for temperatures actually employed in thermionic emission $E_c/kT -$

$\gamma_1 \gg 1$.   Consequently the unity in the denominator of the integrand can safely be neglected compared with $e^{-\gamma_1 + E/kT}$ and J becomes

$$ J = \frac{2m^3 e}{h^3} \, e^{\gamma_1} \int_{-\infty}^{+\infty} \int_{-\infty}^{+\infty} \int_{v_{xo}}^{+\infty} v_x e^{-E/kT} \, dv_x \, dv_y \, dv_z. \qquad (2) $$

The integration over v_y and v_z is immediate from the well-known integral $\int_{-\infty}^{+\infty} e^{-au^2} \, du = \sqrt{\pi/a}$.   The result is

$$ J = \frac{4\pi e m^2 kT}{h^3} \, e^{\gamma_1} \int_{v_{xo}}^{+\infty} v_x \, e^{-mv_x^2/2kT} \, dv_x, \qquad (3) $$

or on performing the final integration

$$ J = \frac{4\pi e m k^2 T^2}{h^3} \, e^{\gamma_1 - E_c/kT}. \qquad (4) $$

If we were to use the non-degenerate form for γ_1 (eq. 68 of Chapter VIII with 2τ in place of τ since we are dealing with electrons), the result would show the thermionic current density as

$$ J = \frac{Ne}{\tau} \sqrt{\frac{kT}{2\pi m}} \, e^{-E_c/kT}. \qquad (5) $$

On the other hand the more reasonable assumption of the degenerate form for γ_1 (cf. the first approximation in 128 of Chapter VIII with 2τ in place of τ, as usual) yields simply

$$ J = \frac{4\pi m e k^2 T^2}{h^3} \, e^{(\phi - E_c)/kT}, \qquad (6) $$

where for convenience we have set

$$ \phi = \gamma_1 kT = \frac{h^2}{2m} \left(\frac{3N}{8\pi\tau} \right)^{2/3}. \qquad (7) $$

Both eqs. (5–6) were set forth by Richardson,[1] who made the first elaborate studies of the phenomenon.   It proved rather difficult to decide between the two experimentally, since the temperature dependence enters much more critically through the exponential term than in the multiplicative coefficient.   Nevertheless (6) is the form which has come to be considered the better representation of the effect.

We must, however, make clear the significance of the quantity ϕ.   At first its presence might seem rather anomalous since E_c has

[1] O. W. Richardson, "The Emission of Electricity from Hot Bodies," Longmans (1921).

already been defined as the minimum kinetic energy for which electrons are able to leave the metal. The experimental interpretation of the exponent of e in the emission formula is that it represents (when its sign is changed and it is multiplied by kT) the *work function* or energy necessary to get an electron out of the metal. Now clearly E_c would actually represent this quantity only if all the emitted electrons were originally at rest. However it is most natural to assume that the electrons which get out are those with greatest kinetic energy and the work to get one of them out will be the difference between E_c and this maximum kinetic energy. We have already shown (eq. 135 of Chapter VIII, with 2τ in place of τ) that the maximum kinetic energy in a degenerate electron gas is

$$E_{\max} = \left(\frac{3N}{8\pi\tau}\right)^{\frac{2}{3}} \frac{h^2}{2m}. \tag{7'}$$

But the comparison between (7) and (7') shows us that $\phi = E_{\max}$ and our assumption then appears to be justified. The exponent $-(E_c - \phi) \cdot 1/kT$ in the emission law is consistent with the hypothesis that it is the fastest moving electrons which leave at any given temperature.

In the derivation leading to (6) we have assumed that $(E_c - \phi)/kT$ is large compared with unity. It is now necessary to justify this. We have just seen that $E_c - \phi$ represents the work necessary to get one of the fastest moving electrons out of the metal, i.e., it is the work function. Measurement indicates that in ordinary metals this is of the order of magnitude of several electron volts, but $kT = 1.37 \times 10^{-16} T$ ergs and, even for T around $1000°$ K, is a small fraction of an electron volt. Consequently our assumption is validated. Since $\frac{1}{2}mv_{xo}^2 > \phi$, it follows that $v_{xo} > v_0$ where $v_0 = h/m \cdot (3N/8\pi\tau)^{\frac{1}{3}}$ (cf. 139 of Chapter VIII) is the velocity at which the distribution function f_0 drops to the value $\frac{1}{2}$. Consequently v_{xo} is farther along on the distribution curve (Fig. 8·2) than v_0 and corresponds to a part of the curve where the latter is approximately exponential. For this reason we see that the distribution for those electrons which are concerned in thermionic emission is approximately Maxwellian.

When we consider the exact experimental verification of (6) we meet an interesting situation. Evaluation of the coefficient $4\pi emk^2/h^3$ in formula (6) gives 120.4 amperes/cm^2 (degree C)^2 approximately. This is just about double the experimental value for a number of pure metals, namely Ca, Mo, Ta, Th, and W. This discrepancy can be accounted for by assuming that at the surface of the metal there exists a potential barrier at which a certain percentage of electrons will be reflected even when their kinetic energy is greater than the potential energy associated with the barrier. Such a situation is not possible in classical mechanics but proves to be realizable in quantum mechanics. To calculate the reflection coefficient it is necessary to review the quantum mechanical theory of the transmission of electrons through a potential barrier.

2. TRANSMISSION OF ELECTRONS THROUGH A POTENTIAL BARRIER AND APPLICATION TO THERMIONIC EMISSION

We shall assume as before that the plane emitting surface of the metal is perpendicular to the x axis. The Schrödinger equation (cf. 3 and 52 of Chapter VIII) for an electron with three degrees of freedom moving in a field of force which is a function of x only and is characterized by a potential energy function $V(x)$ is

$$\nabla^2 \psi + \frac{8\pi^2 m}{h^2} (E - V(x))\psi = 0. \tag{8}$$

We try a solution in the form

$$\psi(x, y, z) = \psi(x)e^{-i(yk_y + zk_z)}, \tag{9}$$

where

$$k_y^2 = \frac{8\pi^2 m E_y}{h^2}; \quad k_z^2 = \frac{8\pi^2 m E_z}{h^2}. \tag{10}$$

Here we have set

$$E = E_x + E_y + E_z, \tag{11}$$

and think of E_x as the kinetic energy associated with the x component velocity, etc. If we substitute (9) into (8) the result is

$$\frac{d^2\psi(x)}{dx^2} + \frac{8\pi^2 m}{h^2} (E_x - V(x))\psi(x) = 0 \tag{12}$$

for the determination of $\psi(x)$.

The question now arises: How are we to represent the function

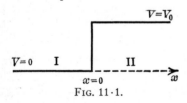

FIG. 11·1.

$V(x)$? Since we do not know the precise variation in potential at the boundary of the metal we make the simplifying assumption that $V(x) = 0$ inside the metal, while $V(x) = V_0$ everywhere outside the metal. This corresponds to the discontinuous jump in potential energy schematically sketched in Fig. 11·1. The region I to the left of the origin corresponds to the metal and the region II to the right of the origin corresponds to the vacuum outside the metal. The boundary is chosen at $x = 0$. The Schrödinger equations for regions I and II then become respectively

$$\frac{d^2\psi(x)}{dx^2} + \frac{8\pi^2 m}{h^2} E_x\psi = 0, \quad \text{(I)} \tag{13}$$

$$\frac{d^2\psi(x)}{dx^2} + \frac{8\pi^2 m}{h^2} (E_x - V_0)\psi = 0, \quad \text{(II)} \tag{14}$$

where E_x is of course positive. The general solution of (13) is (cf. eqs. 55 and 56 of Chapter VIII)

$$\psi_1 = A_1 e^{-ik_1 x} + B_1 e^{ik_1 x}, \tag{15}$$

with $k_1^2 = 8\pi^2 m E_x/h^2$. If ψ_1 is assumed to be a harmonic function of the time we can interpret $A_1 e^{-ik_1 x}$ as a plane harmonic wave progressing from left to right while $B_1 e^{ik_1 x}$ corresponds to a similar wave in the opposite direction. This interpretation makes for greater picturesqueness in the discussion. The solution of (14) depends on the relation between E_x and V_0. Let us first assume that $E_x > V_0$. The general solution of (14) then becomes

$$\psi_2 = A_2 e^{-ik_2 x} + B_2 e^{ik_2 x}, \tag{16}$$

with $k_2^2 = 8\pi^2 m(E_x - V_0)/h^2$, where we shall employ the wave interpretation as in (15). The functions ψ_1 and ψ_2 must satisfy the boundary conditions

$$\psi_1(0) = \psi_2(0), \tag{17}$$

$$\left(\frac{d\psi_1(x)}{dx}\right)_0 = \left(\frac{d\psi_2(x)}{dx}\right)_0. \tag{18}$$

In other words there must be continuity in both the ψ function and its gradient in crossing the boundary. The use of (15) and (16) in (17) and (18) yields

$$A_1 + B_1 = A_2 + B_2 \tag{19}$$

$$A_1 - B_1 = \frac{k_2}{k_1} \cdot (A_2 - B_2). \tag{20}$$

If we assume that the region II extends indefinitely to the right there will be no ψ wave function corresponding to motion in the negative x direction in II. We must therefore take $B_2 = 0$. With this choice the solution of (19) and (20) leads to the ratio of reflected to incident charge density (cf. the physical meaning of the ψ function, Sec. 1, Chapter VIII)

$$\frac{|\psi_r|^2}{|\psi_i|^2} = \frac{|B_1|^2}{|A_1|^2} = \frac{(k_1 - k_2)^2}{(k_1 + k_2)^2}, \qquad (21)$$

while the corresponding ratio of transmitted to incident density is

$$\frac{|\psi_t|^2}{|\psi_i|^2} = \frac{|A_2|^2}{|A_1|^2} = \frac{4k_1^2}{(k_1 + k_2)^2}. \qquad (22)$$

To get the relative average rates of flow of charge we must multiply the charge density in each case by the electron velocity. To the left of the boundary this is

$$v_1 = \sqrt{\frac{2E_x}{m}} = \frac{k_1 h}{2\pi m}, \qquad (23)$$

whereas to the right of the boundary

$$v_2 = \sqrt{\frac{2(E_x - V_0)}{m}} = \frac{k_2 h}{2\pi m}. \qquad (24)$$

If we define the transmission coefficient D as the ratio of the average rate of flow of charge away from the boundary in II to the average rate of flow up to the boundary in I, we obtain

$$D = \frac{4k_1 k_2}{(k_1 + k_2)^2}. \qquad (25)$$

Similarly the reflection coefficient R is

$$R = \frac{(k_1 - k_2)^2}{(k_1 + k_2)^2}. \qquad (26)$$

We see that $R + D = 1$, as should be expected. It will be observed that unless $k_1 = k_2$, i.e., $V_0 = 0$, there is *always* some reflection, which increases in amount as V_0 increases. In fact as $V_0 \to E$, $k_2 \to 0$ and $R \to 1$. The distinction between classical theory and quantum mechanics is well illustrated by the fact that whereas on classical mechanics all electrons with energy larger than V_0 should be able to climb to the V_0 level or plateau, quantum mechanics predicts some reflection even in this case, a reflection that, to be sure, decreases as rapidly as $E - V_0$ increases.

It is left as a problem to the reader to solve the transmission problem for $E < V_0$ and to show that

$$\frac{|\psi_t|^2}{|\psi_i|^2} = \frac{4k_1^2}{k_1^2 + k_2^2}. \tag{27}$$

However, the velocity in II now becomes imaginary and hence there can be no average flow of charge through II. Indeed the wave function in II is an exponential function of x with a negative exponent.

We are now ready to apply the theory of this section to thermionic emission. The fundamental eq. (1) must be rewritten to take account of the transmission coefficient which is a function of v_x. The thermionic current density now becomes

$$J = \frac{2m^3 e}{h^3} \int_{-\infty}^{+\infty} \int_{-\infty}^{+\infty} \int_{v_{xo}}^{+\infty} \frac{v_x D(v_x)}{1 + e^{-\gamma_1 + E/kT}} \, dv_x \, dv_y \, dv_z \tag{28}$$

where $D(v_x)$ is given by eq. (25). If we employ the same type of approximation used in the first part of the section, J becomes

$$J = \frac{4\pi m e kT}{h^3} e^{\gamma_1} \int_{E_c}^{\infty} D(E_x) e^{-E_x/kT} \, dE_x. \tag{29}$$

The transformation $u = (E_x - E_c)/kT$ changes this to

$$J = \frac{4\pi m e k^2 T^2}{h^3} e^{(\phi - E_c)/kT} \cdot \int_0^{\infty} D(u) e^{-u} du. \tag{30}$$

Now if $V_0 = E_c$, eq. (25) yields

$$D(u) = \frac{4\sqrt{ukT} \ \sqrt{E_c + ukT}}{[\sqrt{ukT} + \sqrt{E_c + ukT}]^2}. \tag{31}$$

From what has been said previously $kT/E_c \ll 1$. For values of $u > E_c/kT$ we get very little contribution to the integral in (30) because of the exponential factor e^{-u}. Therefore the evaluation can best proceed by expanding in powers of $\sqrt{ukT/E_c}$. We have

$$\int_0^{\infty} D(u) e^{-u} du = 4 \int_0^{\infty} \frac{e^{-u} \ \sqrt{ukT} \, [1 + ukT/2E_c + \cdots] \, du}{\sqrt{E_c} \ [\sqrt{ukT/E_c} + \sqrt{1 + ukT/E_c}]^2}. \tag{32}$$

After a little reduction this becomes

$$\int_0^{\infty} D(u) e^{-u} du = 4\sqrt{\frac{kT}{E_c}} \int_0^{\infty} e^{-u} \sqrt{u} \left(1 - 2\sqrt{\frac{ukT}{E_c}} - \frac{3}{2}\frac{ukT}{E_c} + \cdots \right) du.$$

Utilizing the fact that $\int_0^\infty \sqrt{u}\, e^{-u}du = \sqrt{\pi}/2$, $\int_0^\infty ue^{-u}du = 1$ and $\int_0^\infty u^{3/2}e^{-u}du = 3\sqrt{\pi}/4$, we can finally write to the indicated approximation from (30)

$$J = \frac{4\pi emk^2T^2}{h^3}\, e^{(\phi - E_c)/kT} \cdot 4\sqrt{kT/E_c}$$

$$\cdot \left[\sqrt{\pi}/2 - 2\sqrt{kT/E_c} - \frac{9}{8}\sqrt{\pi} \cdot \frac{kT}{E_c} + \cdots \right]. \quad (33)$$

The factor $4\sqrt{kT/E_c} \cdot [\sqrt{\pi}/2 - 2\sqrt{kT/E_c} \cdots]$ can be considered as an effective *average* transmission coefficient and denoted by $\overline{D}(u)$. If the temperature is 1000° K, kT is approximately 0.1 electron-volt and if $E_c = 10$ electron-volts, $kT/E_c = 0.01$. Substitution indicates that here $\overline{D}(u) = 0.27$ approximately. While this is not equal to the 0.50 apparently demanded in order to make the theoretical J agree with experiment for a number of metals, the order of magnitude agreement is sufficient to indicate that the method of explanation is at any rate on the right track. It is very unlikely that the abrupt potential barrier visualized in Fig. 11·1 is actually realized in fact. It is much more likely that the situation is that depicted in Fig. 11·2 where the transi-

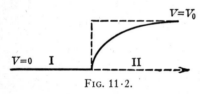

FIG. 11·2.

tion from $V = 0$ to $V = V_0$ takes place more or less gradually. This will decrease the reflection for given excess energy, i.e., $E_x - E_c$, and hence increase $\overline{D}(u)$. However, the analysis will in general be rather complicated. Moreover the exact

shape of the transition curve in Fig. 11·2 is unknown anyway. However, the value of the amplitude term in the thermionic current varies very widely and values higher than 60 amperes/cm² (degree C)² are not uncommon.

In the preceding discussion we have neglected a force whose influence is to round off the course of the potential energy function as indicated in Fig. 11·2. This is the so-called *image* force from electrostatics. It corresponds to an attraction of magnitude $e^2/4x^2$ when the electron is at distance x from the interface of the two media. Associated with this is a potential energy function $V = -e^2/4x$. We shall consider its use in Sec. 4.

3. TRANSMISSION OF ELECTRONS THROUGH A POTENTIAL HILL AND APPLICATION TO THERMIONIC EMISSION

It is conceivable that if the surface of a metal is coated with a film of some foreign substance the nature of the potential barrier will be materially altered from that shown in Figs. 11·1 or 11·2. Indeed it may look rather like Fig. 11·3, where the potential rises at the surface of the metal to $V = V_0$ and after the thickness l is traversed, falls to the value $V = V_1$. Let us compute the electron transmission through such a hump. We shall assume that $E_x > V_1$ though it need not be

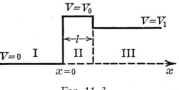

FIG. 11·3.

greater than V_0, as will be seen. The solutions of the one-dimensional Schrödinger equation for the regions I, II, and III are respectively, with $E_x > V_0 > V_1$

$$\psi_1 = A_1 e^{-ik_1 x} + B_1 e^{ik_1 x},$$
$$\psi_2 = A_2 e^{-ik_2 x} + B_2 e^{ik_2 x}, \tag{34}$$
$$\psi_3 = A_3 e^{-ik_3(x-l)},$$

where $k_1^2 = \dfrac{8\pi^2 m E_x}{h^2}$, $k_2^2 = \dfrac{8\pi^2 m}{h^2}(E_x - V_0)$, and $k_3^2 = \dfrac{8\pi^2 m}{h^2}(E_x - V_1)$, and k_1, k_2, and k_3 are all real. The term $B_3 e^{ik_3 x}$ has been omitted for the usual reason. The factor $(x - l)$ is used in place of x in ψ_3 merely for convenience. The boundary conditions at $x = 0$ are

$$A_1 + B_1 = A_2 + B_2,$$
$$A_1 - B_1 = \frac{k_2}{k_1} \cdot (A_2 - B_2), \tag{35}$$

and at $x = l$,

$$A_2 e^{-ik_2 l} + B_2 e^{ik_2 l} = A_3,$$
$$A_2 e^{-ik_2 l} - B_2 e^{ik_2 l} = \frac{k_3}{k_2} \cdot A_3. \tag{36}$$

The problem is to eliminate B_1, A_2, and B_2 between (35) and (36) and obtain A_3 in terms of A_1. We shall find it convenient to set $k_2/k_1 = k_{21}$ and $k_3/k_2 = k_{32}$. Eliminating B_1 between the two equations (35), we get A_1 in terms of A_3 and B_2. We can solve (36) for A_2 and B_2 in terms of A_3. The result is

$$A_3 = \frac{4A_1}{(1 + k_{21})(1 + k_{32})e^{ik_2 l} + (1 - k_{21})(1 - k_{32})e^{-ik_2 l}}. \tag{37}$$

On expansion this can be written

$$A_3 = \frac{2A_1}{(1 + k_{21}k_{32}) \cos k_2 l + i(k_{21} + k_{32}) \sin k_2 l}. \tag{38}$$

Therefore

$$\frac{|A_3|^2}{|A_1|^2} = \frac{4}{(k_{21} + k_{32})^2 + (k_{21}^2 - 1)(k_{32}^2 - 1) \cos^2 k_2 l}. \tag{39}$$

To get the transmission coefficient we must introduce the electron velocities in regions I and III namely

$$v_1 = \frac{k_1 h}{2\pi m}, \quad v_3 = \frac{k_3 h}{2\pi m}.$$

Proceeding as in Sec. 2, and setting $k_3/k_1 = k_{31}$ gives for the transmission coefficient

$$D_1 = \frac{4k_{31}}{(k_{21} + k_{32})^2 + (k_{21}^2 - 1)(k_{32}^2 - 1) \cos^2 k_2 l}. \tag{40}$$

Before considering D_1 further, let us examine the case in which $V_0 > E_x > V_1$. Then since k_2 is now pure imaginary, we find it convenient to set $k_2 = ik_2^*$, $k_{21} = ik_{21}^*$, and $k_{32} = - ik_{32}^*$ where k_2^*, $k_{21}^* = k_2^*/k_1$, and $k_{32}^* = k_3/k_2^*$ are all real and positive. Substitution into eq. (37) gives after rearrangement of terms

$$A_3 = \frac{2A_1}{(1 + k_{21}^* k_{32}^*) \cosh k_2^* l - i(k_{21}^* - k_{32}^*) \sinh k_2^* l}. \tag{41}$$

This leads to

$$\frac{|A_3|^2}{|A_1|^2} = \frac{4}{(1 + k_{21}^{*2})(1 + k_{32}^{*2}) \cosh^2 k_2^* l - (k_{21}^* - k_{32}^*)^2}. \tag{42}$$

The interesting thing about this result is that in spite of the fact that $E_x < V_0$, there is still transmission through the potential barrier. Indeed the transmission coefficient is

$$D_2 = \frac{4k_{32}^* k_{21}^*}{(1 + k_{21}^{*2})(1 + k_{32}^{*2}) \cosh^2 k_2^* l - (k_{21}^* - k_{32}^*)^2}. \tag{43}$$

If we resubstitute in terms of the actual energies, the result is

$$D_2 = \frac{4\sqrt{(E_x - V_1)/E_x}}{\dfrac{V_0}{E_x} \cdot \dfrac{(V_0 - V_1)}{(V_0 - E_x)} \cdot \cosh^2 k_2^* l - \left[\sqrt{\dfrac{E_x - V_1}{V_0 - E_x}} - \sqrt{\dfrac{V_0 - E_x}{E_x}}\right]^2}. \tag{44}$$

The transmission vanishes for $E_x < V_1 < V_0$, as is evident from the remarks made immediately following eq. (27). However (44) indicates that the transmission coefficient rises from zero to a definite value as E_x goes from V_1 to V_0 and thereafter increases as E_x increases. A rough plot of the behavior of D as a function of E_x is shown in Fig.

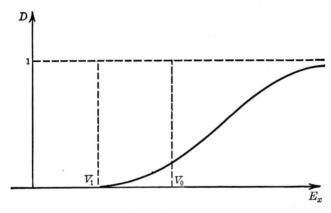

FIG. 11·4.

11·4. This is, of course, a composite of D_2 (from V_1 to V_0) and D_1 from V_0 on.

The thermionic current in this example will be evaluated from eq. (30) on substitution of the appropriate value of D. Thus we seek (placing $E_c = V_1$)

$$\overline{D}(u) = \int_0^\infty D(ukT + V_1)e^{-u}\,du. \tag{45}$$

This can at once be split up as follows

$$\overline{D}(u) = \int_0^{(V_0-V_1)/kT} D_2 e^{-u}\,du + \int_{(V_0-V_1)/kT}^\infty D_1 e^{-u}\,du \tag{46}$$

with

$$D_1 = \frac{4\sqrt{ukT/(ukT+V_1)}}{\left[\sqrt{\dfrac{V_1-V_0+ukT}{ukT+V_1}}+\sqrt{\dfrac{ukT}{V_1-V_0+ukT}}\right]^2 + \dfrac{V_0(V_1-V_0)\cos^2 k_2 l}{(ukT+V_1)(ukT+V_1-V_0)}} \tag{47}$$

while

$$D_2 =$$

$$\frac{4}{V_0(V_0-V_1)} \cdot \frac{1}{\left[1+\dfrac{\cosh 2l\sqrt{V_0-V_1-ukT}\cdot\sqrt{8\pi^2m/h^2}}{2(V_0-V_1-ukT)} - \dfrac{(ukT+V_1)}{V_0(V_0-V_1)}\cdot\left[\sqrt{\dfrac{ukT}{V_0-V_1-ukT}}-\sqrt{\dfrac{V_0-V_1-ukT}{ukT+V_1}}\right]^2 \right]}.$$

$$\text{(48)}$$

Now in the evaluation of the second integral in (46) $u > (V_0 - V_1)/kT$ or $V_1 + ukT > V_0$. Hence for most of the way from $u = (V_0 - V_1)$ $1/kT$ to ∞, D_1 will approximate unity. Therefore the second integral becomes of the order of $e^{-(V_0-V_1)/kT}$. Keeping this in mind we examine the first integral. By a slight rearrangement and expansion of the square bracket in the denominator of (48) we have

$$D_2 = \frac{16}{V_0(V_0 - V_1)} \cdot \frac{\sqrt{ukT}\sqrt{ukT + V_1}(V_0 - V_1 - ukT)}{D}, \quad \text{(49)}$$

where

$$D = 2 + e^{2l\sqrt{V_0-V_1-ukT}\cdot\sqrt{8\pi^2m/h^2}} + e^{-2l\sqrt{V_0-V_1-ukT}\cdot\sqrt{8\pi^2m/h^2}}$$

$$- \frac{\left\{ 4ukT(ukT+V_1)+2(V_0-V_1-ukT)^2 - 8\sqrt{ukT}\sqrt{ukT+V_1}(V_0-V_1-ukT) \right\}}{V_0(V_0-V_1)}.$$

Evidently the dominant term in D in the range of u involved in the first integral is the second. If we neglect the rest we obtain

$$\int_0^{(V_0-V_1)/kT} D_2 e^{-u}\, du$$

$$= \frac{16}{V_0(V_0 - V_1)} \int_0^{(V_1-V_0)/kT} e^{-u}\sqrt{(ukT)(ukT+V_1)}$$

$$\cdot (V_0 - V_1 - ukT)e^{-2l\sqrt{V_0-V_1-ukT}\cdot\sqrt{8\pi^2m/h^2}}\, du. \quad \text{(50)}$$

After some expansions based on the smallness of ukT/V_1, etc., we finally arrive at the approximate result that the above integral is

$$\frac{\sqrt{\pi}}{2} \cdot \sqrt{V_1 kT}\cdot(V_0 - V_1)e^{-2l\sqrt{V_0-V_1}\cdot\sqrt{8\pi^2m/h^2}}. \quad \text{(51)}$$

This leads to

$$\bar{D}(u) = \frac{8\sqrt{\pi}\sqrt{V_1 kT}}{V_0} e^{-2l\sqrt{V_0-V_1}\cdot\sqrt{8\pi^2 m/h^2}} + \text{a term of order}$$
$$e^{-(V_0-V_1)/kT}. \tag{52}$$

Now for much of the thermionic range we may neglect the second term compared with the first. The thermionic current density can then be put into the form

$$J = AT^2 e^{-b_0/T}, \tag{53}$$

with

$$A = \frac{8\sqrt{\pi}}{V_0} \sqrt{V_1 kT} \, e^{-2l\sqrt{V_0-V_1}\cdot\sqrt{8\pi^2 m/h^2}} \cdot \frac{4\pi m e k^2}{h^3} \tag{54}$$

and

$$b_0 = \frac{E_c - \phi}{k}. \tag{55}$$

In a general way (53) agrees with experiment. For details the reader should consult Dushman's article on *Thermionic Emission* previously referred to, particularly pp. 468 ff.

4. EFFECT OF STRONG FIELDS ON EMISSION

In our discussion of thermionic emission we have neglected the effect of the electric field actually used to get the electrons away from the surface, assuming with apparent success that its influence is very small. However, as the external field strength is increased it becomes a significant factor. Suppose the intensity of the applied field is F (assumed uniform), corresponding to a negative potential energy $-eFx$. Taking the boundary at $x = 0$, as usual, and including the image force potential energy (already mentioned at the end of Sec. 2), the total potential energy in the neighborhood of the boundary may be written in the form

$$V = V_0 - \frac{e^2}{4x} - eFx. \tag{56}$$

Here V_0 is the asymptotic height of the potential wall outside the metal in the absence of an external field.[2] The effect of the external field is to lower the potential below this asymptotic level, as indicated

---

[2] The formula (56) obviously cannot apply right at the boundary, $x = 0$. We shall assume that it holds to within 10Å or so of the boundary.

in Fig. 11·5. The first effect is to reduce the effective jump in potential across the boundary. The maximum value of V in (56) occurs at $x_1 = \sqrt{e/4F}$ and is equal to $V_{\max} = V_0 - e^{3/2}\sqrt{F}$. If we could assume that

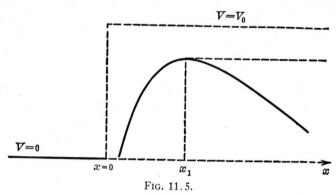

$V=V_0$

$V=0$

$x=0 \qquad x_1 \qquad x$

Fig. 11.5.

the principal effect of the field really is to lower the effective V by the amount $e^{3/2}\sqrt{F}$, i.e., neglect the portion of the V curve beyond x_1, the sole correction to the emission formula (33) would be multiplication by the factor $e^{\sqrt{F}e^{3/2}/kT}$. Thus (33) would become

$$J = \frac{4\pi e m k^2 T^2}{h^3}\, \overline{D}(u) e^{(\phi - E_c)/kT} e^{\sqrt{F}e^{3/2}/kT}, \tag{57}$$

corresponding to increased transmission with increasing field intensity. The experiments of de Bruyne [3] agree rather well with (57).

As the value of F is increased to about 10^6 volts/cm, the dip of the

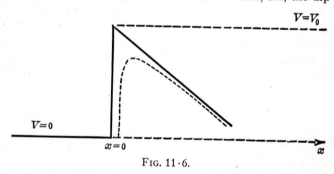

$V=V_0$

$V=0$

$x=0 \qquad x$

Fig. 11·6.

potential curve near the maximum becomes so great that the above approximation no longer holds. The situation is approximately depicted in Fig. 11·6 in which the effect of the image force, leading to

[3] *Proc. Roy. Soc.* **120**, 423 (1928).

the rounded off dotted curve, may be neglected and for the sake of simplicity the potential course may be represented by the heavy curve. This is intended to approximate the situation at absolute zero.   To the left of the barrier the Schrödinger equation for the x dependent part of the function is

$$\frac{d^2\psi}{dx^2} + \frac{8\pi^2 m}{h^2} E_x \psi = 0, \qquad (58)$$

and to the right of the barrier

$$\frac{d^2\psi}{dx^2} + \frac{8\pi^2 m}{h^2} (E_x - V_0 + eFx)\psi = 0. \qquad (59)$$

The complete solution of the transmission problem has been given by Fowler and Nordheim [4] and we shall merely quote the result for the transmission coefficient (NOTE: $E_x < V_0$), which is

$$D(E_x) = \frac{4\sqrt{E_x(V_0 - E_x)}}{V_0} e^{-[4 \cdot \sqrt{8\pi^2 m/h^2}(V_0 - E_x)^{3/2}]/3F}. \qquad (60)$$

By referring to eqs. (28, 29, and 30) we can now write for the electron current density

$$J = \frac{4\pi m e k T}{h^3} \int_0^\phi D(E_x) \int_0^\infty \frac{d\eta}{e^{\eta + (E_x - \phi)/kT} + 1} \cdot dE_x, \qquad (61)$$

where our previous formulas are modified to a certain extent since the energy of the electrons cannot exceed the maximum energy $\phi = \gamma_1 kT$, corresponding to low temperatures.   In spite of this limitation (61) indicates that a non-vanishing current exists.   It should be pointed out that in (61) $\eta = m(v_y^2 + v_z^2)/2kT$.   The evaluation of J depends first on the integral

$$\int_0^\infty \frac{d\eta}{e^{\eta + (E_x - \phi)/kT} + 1}.$$

Since $E_x < \phi$, $(E_x - \phi)/kT$ is large negatively.   Consequently we may evaluate the integral from (114) of Chapter VIII using $\rho = 0$.   It will be sufficient to take only the first term in the result (eq. 122 of Chapter VIII) and write

$$\int_0^\infty \frac{d\eta}{e^{\eta + (E_x - \phi)/kT} + 1} \sim \left(\frac{\phi - E_x}{kT}\right). \qquad (62)$$

[4] *Proc. Roy. Soc.* **119**, 173 (1928).

Substitution into (61) with the use of (60) yields

$$J = \frac{16\pi m e}{V_0 h^3} \int_0^\phi \sqrt{E_x(V_0 - E_x)}(\phi - E_x)e^{-[4\cdot\sqrt{8\pi^2 m/h^2}(V_0 - E_x)^{3/2}]/3F}dE_x. \quad (63)$$

To evaluate the integral, let $\phi - E_x = \xi$ and expand $(V_0 - \phi + \xi)^{3/2}$ in powers of ξ. For convenience represent $\sqrt{8\pi^2 m/h^2}$ by μ. The integral then becomes

$$e^{-4\mu(V_0-\phi)^{3/2}/3F} \cdot \int_0^\phi \xi\sqrt{(\phi - \xi)(V_0 - \phi + \xi)} \cdot e^{-2\mu(V_0-\phi)^{1/2}\xi/F}d\xi.$$

We expand the radical in powers of ξ. The resulting integration is simple and the final result becomes

$$J = \frac{e}{2\pi h V_0} \cdot \sqrt{\frac{\phi}{V_0 - \phi}}\, F^2 e^{-4/3\cdot\mu(V_0-\phi)^{3/2}/F}. \quad (64)$$

The experimentally observed emission agrees in general with (64) being indeed of the form

$$J = KF^2 e^{-a/F}, \quad (65)$$

where K and a are constants. The exponential dependence on F is particularly well substantiated by experiment.[5]

5. THE PHOTOELECTRIC EFFECT

An electron emission problem closely allied to thermionic emission is the photoelectric effect. When light falls on a cold metal surface, electrons are emitted if the frequency of the light exceeds a certain threshold frequency ν_0. We can understand this situation in terms of the preceding sections of this chapter, since when the metal is at a temperature near absolute zero the maximum kinetic energy of the electrons is about equal to ϕ (Sec. 1). Consequently in order that an electron with energy E less than ϕ shall get over the barrier $E_c = V_0$ it must get from the incident light quantum the energy $h\nu$ such that

$$h\nu + E = E_c. \quad (66)$$

The least frequency which will satisfy this condition is therefore ν_0, where $h\nu_0 + \phi = E_c$ or

$$\nu_0 = (E_c - \phi)/h. \quad (67)$$

---

[5] See Fowler, "Statistical Mechanics," second edition, p. 357 and accompanying references.

The photoelectric threshold thus proves to be vitally related to the thermionic *work function*. This relation is well substantiated by the experimental values for many metals as the accompanying table shows. In considering the comparison we must, of course, recall that the threshold is not usually measured at $T = 0$ and there is bound to be some temperature effect.

TABLE OF THERMIONIC WORK FUNCTIONS AND PHOTOELECTRIC THRESHOLDS

(From Fowler, " Statistical Mechanics ")

The values are in electron volts

Metal	Cs	Ta	Mo	W	Ni	Pd
$h\nu_0$	1.9	4.11	4.15	4.54	5.01	4.97
$(E_c - \phi)$	1.81	4.12	4.15	4.54	5.03	4.99

We shall give an elementary analysis of the emission based on the assumption that the photoelectric current density per unit light intensity is simply proportional to the number of electrons incident per second normally on the surface of the metal for which

$$E_x + h\nu > E_c,$$

where E_x is the kinetic energy associated with the direction normal to the metal surface taken as the x axis. Now the number of electrons with x component velocity lying between v_x and $v_x + dv_x$ striking unit area of surface per second is (from Sec. 1, eq. 1)

$$dJ = \frac{2m^3 e}{h^3} v_x dv_x \int_{-\infty}^{+\infty} \int_{-\infty}^{+\infty} \frac{dv_y\, dv_z}{1 + e^{-\gamma_1 + E/kT}}. \tag{68}$$

There is a certain advantage in transforming from v_x, v_y, v_z to cylindrical coordinates v_x, ρ and ϕ, where

$$\rho^2 = v_y^2 + v_z^2; \quad dv_y\, dv_z = \rho\, d\rho\, d\phi. \tag{69}$$

Then (68) becomes

$$dJ = \frac{4\pi m^3 e}{h^3} v_x dv_x \int_0^\infty \frac{\rho\, d\rho}{1 + e^{-\gamma_1 + mv_x^2/2kT + m\rho^2/2kT}}. \tag{70}$$

The integration yields

$$dJ = \frac{4\pi m^2 ekT}{h^3} v_x \log\left(1 + e^{\gamma_1 - mv_x^2/2kT}\right) dv_x. \tag{71}$$

The photoelectric current density per unit light intensity is then

$$I = K \cdot \frac{4\pi m e k T}{h^3} \int_{E_c - h\nu}^{\infty} \log\left(1 + e^{(\phi - E_x)/kT}\right) dE_x, \qquad (72)$$

where K is a constant proportionality factor. Introduce the transformation $w = e^{(\phi - E_x)/kT}$ and call $e^{[\phi - (E_c - h\nu)]/kT} = w_0$. The current density takes the form

$$I = \frac{K \cdot 4\pi m e k^2 T^2}{h^3} \int_0^{w_0} \frac{\log(1 + w)}{w} dw. \qquad (73)$$

The integral is a well-known one. We distinguish between two cases, i.e., (a) $\nu \le \nu_0$ for which $w_0 \le 1$, and (b) $\nu > \nu_0$, for which $w_0 > 1$. For (a) we have, setting $\dfrac{h\nu_0 - h\nu}{kT} = \alpha$,

$$I = K \cdot \frac{4\pi m e k^2 T^2}{h^3} \left[e^{-\alpha} - \frac{e^{-2\alpha}}{2^2} + \frac{e^{-3\alpha}}{3^2} \cdots \right]. \qquad (74)$$

For (b) we write

$$\int_0^{w_0} \frac{\log(1 + w)}{w} dw = \int_0^1 \frac{\log(1 + w)}{w} dw + \int_1^{w_0} \frac{\log(1 + w)}{w} dw$$

$$= 2\left(1 - \frac{1}{2^2} + \frac{1}{3^2} \cdots\right) + \frac{1}{2}[\log w_0]^2 - \frac{1}{w_0} + \frac{1}{2^2 w_0^2} + \cdots,$$

whence for $\nu > \nu_0$

$$I = K \cdot \frac{4\pi m e k^2 T^2}{h^3} \left[\frac{\alpha^2}{2} + \frac{\pi^2}{6} - \left(e^{\alpha} - \frac{e^{2\alpha}}{2^2} + \frac{e^{3\alpha}}{3^2} \cdots \right) \right]. \qquad (75)$$

We thus see that the photoelectric current density I is given in the general form

$$\frac{I}{T^2} = Af(\alpha) \qquad (76)$$

where A is the constant $K \cdot 4\pi m e k^2/h^3$ and $f(\alpha)$ is a function to be evaluated from the previous equations (74) and (75). We note at once the interesting fact that if $\nu = 0$, so that $\alpha = h\nu_0/kT = (E_c - \phi)/kT$, the equation (76) reduces to a close approximation to

$$I = AT^2 e^{-(E_c - \phi)/kT}, \qquad (77)$$

which is just the thermionic emission equation (6) with the exception of the multiplicative factor K. The higher terms in the expansion (74) i.e., $e^{-2\alpha}$, $e^{-3\alpha}$, etc., are all negligible compared with $e^{-\alpha}$ in this case.

Following DuBridge [6] we examine the form of eq. (76) when the surface of the metal is at $T = 0$. Here the argument of the function f is $+\infty$ or $-\infty$ according as $\nu < \nu_0$ or $\nu > \nu_0$. Consequently we get the alternative results

$$(I)_{T=0} = 0 \text{ for } \nu \leq \nu_0 \tag{78}$$

$$(I)_{T=0} = \frac{K \cdot 2\pi m e}{h^3} (h\nu - h\nu_0)^2 \text{ for } \nu \geq \nu_0.$$

If then we plot the photoelectric current density as a function of frequency, we find *no* emission out to the threshold frequency ν_0; thereafter the emission is a quadratic function of the frequency. The curve is indeed a parabola with vertex at $\nu = \nu_0$ as indicated in the accompanying figure (Fig. 11·7). For $T > 0$, the plot of (76) using (74)

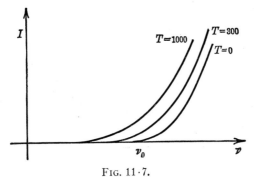

FIG. 11·7.

and (75) yields curves of somewhat similar shape which, however, do not touch the axis at precisely ν_0. It is clear that the threshold frequency has a precise meaning only at absolute zero. At higher temperatures there is no absolutely sharp threshold, as the current-frequency curves approach the axis more gradually. Nevertheless it is convenient to continue to look upon $\nu_0 = (E_c - \phi)/h$ as the threshold, as it actually would be if we could lower the temperature of the surface to $0°$ K without altering E_c and ϕ. We are justified in looking upon ν_0 as an important characteristic of the surface.

Let us go back to eq. (76) and again setting $(h\nu_0 - h\nu)/kT = \alpha$,

[6] L. A. DuBridge, "New Theories of the Photoelectric Effect," Actualités Scientifique, 268, Paris, 1935.

take the logarithm of both sides (base 10 is usually the more convenient). Thus

$$\log_{10}(I/T^2) = B + \Phi(\alpha) \tag{79}$$

where $B = \log_{10}A$ (a constant independent of ν and T) and $\Phi(\alpha) = \log_{10}f(\alpha)$. If $\log_{10}(I/T^2)$ is plotted against α, the resulting curve will be independent of the metal and the temperature except for an additive constant. In other words the curve should be superposable on the curve obtained by plotting $\Phi(\alpha)$ against α by a shift along the ordinate axis of amount B. The form of $\Phi(\alpha)$ is shown approximately in Fig.

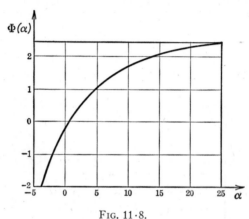

FIG. 11·8.

11·8.   Unfortunately α is known for given frequency only when ν_0 is known and this depends on the metal. Fowler therefore suggested the plotting of the experimental values of log (I/T^2) against $h\nu/kT$. This curve should agree with the theoretical curve (79) by a backward shift along the axis of amount $h\nu_0/kT$ and a vertical shift of B. By ascertaining the horizontal shift, Fowler was able to obtain theoretically good values of ν_0. For more complete discussion of the agreement with experiment DuBridge's paper should be consulted.

We next consider the energy distribution of the emitted photoelectrons and examine the case of those electrons which emerge normally to the metallic surface. Experimentally the distribution is measured by applying a retarding potential between the emitting surface and the collecting electrode and then measuring the photoelectric current as a function of this potential. The number of photoelectrons emerging per second normally from the surface against a retarding potential V may be obtained by a slight modification of eq. (72). Thus we divide by the charge e and in the lower limit of the integral employ $E_c + Ve$ in place of E_c. The number in question as a function of V becomes

$$N(V) = \frac{K \cdot 4\pi mkT}{h^3} \int_{E_c + Ve - h\nu}^{\infty} \log\left(1 + e^{(\phi - E_x)/kT}\right) dE_x. \qquad (80)$$

If we call the integrand $n(E)$, i.e.,

$$n(E_x) = \frac{K \cdot 4\pi mkT}{h^3} \log\left(1 + e^{(\phi - E_x)/kT}\right),$$

it follows that

$$n(E_c - h\nu + Ve) = \frac{K \cdot 4\pi mkT}{h^3} \log\left(1 + e^{-Ve/kT} \cdot e^{h(\nu - \nu_0)/kT}\right), \qquad (81)$$

and this is the number of photoelectrons emitted per second by light of frequency ν per unit energy interval with the energy $E = Ve - h(\nu - \nu_0) + \phi = Ve + E_c - h\nu$. It is called the "normal" energy distribution function. At $T = 0$, it reduces to

$$n_0(E_c - h\nu + Ve) = \frac{K \cdot 4\pi m}{h^3} [h(\nu - \nu_0) - Ve]. \qquad (82)$$

When plotted as a function of $Ve - h(\nu - \nu_0)$, n_0 is a straight line as in Fig. 11·9, intersecting the axis of abscissas at $h(\nu - \nu_0) = Ve$. When $T \neq 0$, the curve tails off as shown by the dotted line in Fig. 11·9. The general agreement with experiment is not too good, probably because

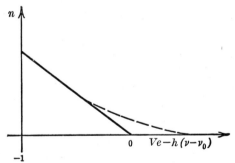

FIG. 11·9.

of the neglect to take account of a transmission coefficient as we did in the treatment of thermionic emission. For a complete analysis of the experimental data, consult DuBridge. The result is that in the vicinity of the energy $h(\nu - \nu_0)$, the experiments check the theory rather well.

Further investigation of the photoelectric effect would take us too far afield. The reader who is interested in the total energy distribution of the photoelectrons, i.e., the distribution taking account of all the velocity components, will find a thorough discussion in DuBridge's article.

6. CONTACT POTENTIAL

In the immediate neighborhood of the surface of a metal in a vacuum there will be at every temperature an atmosphere of electrons in equilibrium with the metal. The electrostatic potential of the field produced by this electron gas will be equal to that at the surface of the metal; but the latter is a function of the metal. Consequently we expect that when two different metals are very close together in a

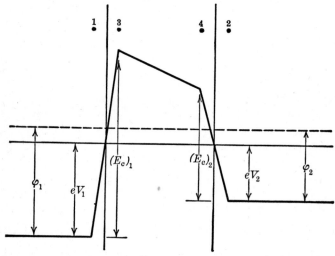

FIG. 11·10.

vacuum, a potential difference will be set up between them. This is the so-called *contact potential*. We can obtain an interesting relation between the contact potential and the thermionic work functions for the metals by the following simple considerations.

In Fig. 11·10 we represent schematically the two metals 1 and 2 separated by a vacuum. The temperature is kept constant at the value T. The average number of free electrons per unit volume of metal 1 at the surface is given by eq. (171) of Chapter VIII

$$n_1 = \frac{8}{3\sqrt{\pi}h^3}(2\pi mkT)^{3/2}\left(\gamma_1 + \frac{eV_1}{kT}\right)^{3/2} \tag{83}$$

where V_1 is the electrical potential just inside the surface and $-eV_1$ is the potential energy of the electrons at this place. (We are here, of course, treating e as a positive quantity.) Similarly in metal 2 the average density of free electrons is

$$n_2 = \frac{8}{3\sqrt{\pi}h^3} (2\pi mkT)^{3/2} \left(\gamma_1 + \frac{eV_2}{kT}\right)^{3/2}. \tag{84}$$

But from our study of thermionic emission we know that

$$\gamma_1 + \frac{eV_1}{kT} = \frac{\phi_1}{kT} \tag{85}$$

and

$$\gamma_1 + \frac{eV_2}{kT} = \frac{\phi_2}{kT} \tag{86}$$

where ϕ_1 and ϕ_2 are the maximum kinetic energies of the electrons in the two metals respectively. In Sec. 1 of this chapter we used $\phi = \gamma_1 kT$ to denote the maximum kinetic energy of the free electrons of the metal. However if the electrons are in a force field and possess potential energy also, an extension of the analysis of Sec. 7 of Chapter VIII shows that it is $\gamma_1 kT + eV_1$ which corresponds to the maximum kinetic energy. Hence (85) and (86) are justified. ϕ_1 and ϕ_2 are sometimes referred to as the *inner* work functions. From (85) and (86), we have

$$e(V_1 - V_2) = (\phi_1 - \phi_2). \tag{87}$$

Now $V_1 - V_2$ can be written in the form

$$V_1 - V_2 = V_1 - V_3 + V_3 - V_4 + V_4 - V_2, \tag{88}$$

where V_3 is the electrical potential in the vacuum at the point 3 just outside the metal 1, while V_4 is the potential in the vacuum at the point 4 just outside the metal 2. The quantity $-e(V_3 - V_1)$ is the minimum kinetic energy for those electrons in 1 which are able to cross the surface. If we use the notation of Sec. 1 we should call this $(E_c)_1$. Similarly

$$-e(V_4 - V_2) = (E_c)_2.$$

Consequently

$$\phi_1 - \phi_2 = (E_c)_1 - (E_c)_2 + (V_3 - V_4)e$$

or slightly rewritten

$$e(V_3 - V_4) = [(E_c)_2 - \phi_2] - [(E_c)_1 - \phi_1]. \tag{89}$$

Now $(E_c)_1 - \phi_1$ is the thermionic work function for the first metal and $(E_c)_2 - \phi_2$ that for the second, while $(V_3 - V_4)$ is the difference in electrical potential between two points just outside each metallic surface respectively. It is by definition the contact potential. The relation (89) connects the contact potential between two metals with their thermionic work functions. It has been verified experimentally for a number of cases, though exact measurements of contact potentials are difficult to carry out. For a discussion of the experimental agreement Fowler's "Statistical Mechanics," p. 364, may be consulted.

PROBLEMS

1. Evaluate the thermionic current density for molybdenum at $T = 1,000°$ K, $1,500°$ K, and $2,000°$ K using both forms of the Richardson equation, i.e., (5) and (6). Take $E_c - \phi = 4.08$ electron volts. Compare the results with those obtained using the experimental data listed in S. Dushman, *Rev. Modern Phys.*, **2**, 381, 1930, p. 394.

2. Discuss the transmission of electrons through a boundary barrier in which the potential rises from $V = 0$ to $V = V_0$ continuously and very slowly with a continuous gradient. Show that in this case there is complete transmission for all energies. (Cf. the elastic wave analogy in R. B. Lindsay, *J. Acous. Soc. Am.*, **12**, 378 [1941].)

3. Solve the transmission problem of Sec. 2 for $E < V_0$ and show that eq. (27) results.

4. Find the value of E_c which makes the effective average transmission coefficient $\overline{D}(u) = 0.50$ for $T = 1,000°$ K.

5. An image force potential barrier may be represented by the equations

$$V = - V_0 \qquad , \quad x \leq 0$$

$$V = - \frac{e^2}{4x + e^2/V_0}, \quad x \geq 0$$

where $x = 0$ represents the boundary. Find the expression for the average transmission coefficient in this case.

6. For a monatomic layer of thorium on tungsten assume that $V_0 = 10.3$ electron volts and $V_1 = 8.4$ electron volts. Take $l = 2.85 \times 10^{-8}$ cm. Compute the effective average transmission coefficient.

7. Plot the photoelectric current density per unit light intensity (divided by the constant K; cf. Sec. 5) for the metals tungsten and nickel at $T = 500°$ K and $1,000°$ K respectively.

8. Plot the normal energy distribution function of the photoelectrons from potassium at $20°$ C, i.e., eq. (81).

INDEX

301